THE IRWIN SERIES IN ECONOMICS

CONSULTING EDITOR

LLOYD G. REYNOLDS
YALE UNIVERSITY

BOOKS IN THE IRWIN SERIES IN ECONOMICS

52/6

PROBABILITY AND PROFIT

A Study of Economic Behavior along Bayesian Lines

PROBABILITY

AND PROFIT

A Study of Economic Behavior
along Bayesian Lines

by WILLIAM FELLNER

Sterling Professor of Economics

Yale University

1965

RICHARD D. IRWIN, INC.

HOMEWOOD, ILLINOIS

ACKNOWLEDGMENTS

Mr. Irving LaValle of the Harvard Business School kindly agreed to go over a preliminary draft of the manuscript of this volume. His help was invaluable because he not only discussed all sections of the draft with me in great detail but also gave me an opportunity to benefit from his ideas about the problem at large to which this book relates. Subsequently I revised most parts of the manuscript. Mr. LaValle is responsible for many improvements, as compared to the preliminary draft, but for none of the shortcomings of the final product. Of these shortcomings I am conscious, all the more because one would have to be a specialist in several fields at the same time to write a book of this kind as well as it would deserve to be written. But I feel convinced that the time is ripe for neo-Bayesian efforts in various disciplines, including economics. The results of these efforts will differ from one another in their strong and in their weak points, so all of us interested in the theme of this volume should be willing to stand up for our views.

I of course owe a substantial debt to many writers on the subject. I mean primarily the debt of the reader. But this is not all, because with some of these contributors I exchanged notes and with others I had oral discussions. I am particularly aware of having benefited from several informal conversations with Professor Francis J. Anscombe of the Yale Statistics Department. Many remarks I heard from him proved educational either on the spot, or several months later. Some will prove educational years from now, when it will be too late for this book, but I hope not for its author.

I made use, mostly in modified form, of some materials which were included in articles I published earlier. For permission to do so, I would like to thank the *Quarterly Journal of Economics* and the *Review of Economics and Statistics*.

TABLE OF CONTENTS

INTRODUCTION

Two centuries have elapsed since the time when, after the death of its author, Thomas Bayes's famous paper (4)[1] was presented to the Royal Society.[2] In this paper, Bayes formalized a method of blending probability judgments which are rooted in frequency observations—in observations creating the presumption that frequency ratios converge on definite values—with probability judgments derived from mere hunches of the decision maker or from his ignorance. Recently, an increasing number of scholars have concluded that a fruitful approach to problems of the theory of profit, and to decision theory in general, requires building on subjective-probabilistic foundations which, partly at least, are Bayesian foundations.

While the present writer favors a somewhat modified framework of this kind, and while various sections of this brief volume are devoted to an explanation of this modified framework (see particularly Chapter 6, Section 6), much of the book consists of a discussion of the subjective-probabilistic and Bayesian approach *in the usual sense*. From a technical point of view, the book limits itself to the analysis of simple problems. Thus, it may be regarded as a brief general introduction to the study of the modern theory of subjective probability, utility, and profit, even though the reader will become acquainted also with the author's specific position. The orientation of the writer is "positive" and "normative" at the same time: He feels that decision theory should develop principles according to which reasonable and well-informed individuals observably tend to behave when faced with decision problems which they take seriously and which they have properly understood.

Readers particularly interested in the postulational premises of the author's analysis will find these developed in Chapter 3, Sections 4, 5, and

---

[1] Boldface numbers in parentheses indicate references to Bibliographical Commentaries (pp. 212–35).

[2] For particulars, see n. 4, p. 26.

1

13; in Chapter 6, Section 6; and in the Appendix to Chapter 6. A comparison with L. J. Savage's axiomatic system will be found in Chapter 6, Section 9. An account of some of the author's experimental results is presented in Chapter 9, which serves as an Appendix to the volume as a whole.

Before turning to Chapter 1, a few explanatory comments will be given here. Some of these relate to the way in which the author is inclined to look at his problem at large (see the immediately following Sections 1 through 4); other explanatory comments relate to various technical terms which need to be understood clearly (see the Note appended to the four sections).

(1) *Probability as a Decision-Theoretical Concept*

In this volume, probability will be regarded as a concept of decision theory. Understanding of the behavior of reasonable decision makers requires the use of probabilistic concepts.

Decisions of direct interest to economists usually involve monetary pay-offs, and we shall be concerned largely with such decisions. These have a property which makes them relatively well suited to theoretical exploration because, on certain postulates which possess intuitive appeal, operational methods can be used to assign utilities to monetary pay-offs. Such methods are based on the observation of an individual's behavior rather than on an interpretation of his assertions about his views and feelings. There exist no similarly convincing operational methods by which utilities could be assigned to the satisfaction which a person derives from being right or helpful or being popular, or to the dissatisfaction which is caused to him by his being wrong or harmful or being unpopular.

Still, even where the pay-offs are nonmonetary, and where there exists no operational method for converting the pay-offs into monetary equivalents, any consistent decision maker should be visualized as acting in view of these nonmonetary benefits or disadvantages. If he does not care whether he is right or wrong, then he is not faced with any worthwhile problem. If he does care, then this implies that in some sense he is willing to commit himself and to feel that he has staked something on this commitment. But for reasons explained in the preceding paragraph, my analysis will be concerned in detail only with a special variety of nonmonetary consequences. These are nonmonetary (or nondirectly monetary) consequences connected with acts involving monetary pay-offs: in particular consequences developing because it matters whether, in retrospect, one's decisions (concerning acts involving monetary pay-offs) do or do not seem convincing to others and to oneself. Hence, it matters whether one's probability judgments are or are not widely shared, and whether they are firm or vague. Of this nonmonetary factor, we shall take account explicitly, even in the central sections of the formal analysis relating to situations in which the basic pay-offs are monetary.

In their own minds, readers may want to reformulate some of the problems to be discussed in the volume in such a way as to imply that the main pay-offs, too, are of nonmonetary character. Some sections of the analysis in this volume will suggest that it is possible and useful to do so. Such reformulations are subject to limitations arising from the fact that they require defining a "utility function" for these nonmonetary pay-offs. Nevertheless, readers may find it useful to engage in such reformulations for specific purposes. These possibilities are illustrated by Chapter 8, Section 2, where *desirable principles of statistical reporting* are discussed, without regard to the nature of the rewards.

(2) *Superiority of the Subjevistic View*

If a person limits himself to mathematical statements about the numerical values of the theoretical probabilities which may be computed for ideally random tosses of a perfect coin, or for analogous idealized sets of events, then he is not using probability as a tool in a decision process. He is claiming definite validity for purely logical propositions which were derived from specific axioms and are dependent only on these. On the other hand, acceptance of the proposition that a given physical coin may for all practical purposes be considered unbiased, and that specific observable tosses may for all practical purposes be considered random tosses, changes these mathematical probabilities into tools of decision making for the specific set of tosses. In the context of decision problems the probabilities become degrees of belief.

Among the decision problems to which the concept of probability is applicable, practically random tosses of a practically fair coin and similar sets of events represent merely a very special case. This is true even if the term "similar sets of events" is interpreted in a rather inclusive sense. I go along wholeheartedly with the subjectivist view that it is arbitrary and undesirable to limit the application of the concept of probability to physical processes which the decision maker interprets as reasonably good physical analogues of ideal tosses of an ideal coin. To be sure, the belief that heads and tails with a given coin are equiprobable is derived from factual observations the character of which is different from that of the observations leading a person to believe that (say) tomorrow the Dow Jones industrial average is equally likely to rise as not to rise. But in no two physical processes generating alternative types of events are the *sources* of an individual's degrees of belief identical. It is, in my opinion, not fruitful to try to draw a hard and fast line between degrees of belief that are probabilities and degrees of belief that are not probabilities according as the source of the degrees of belief happens to be a set of observations suggesting that the specific physical process is a reasonably good approximation to the ideal coin-tossing process or the source of the beliefs is something other than this.

In other words, the author of this book finds the "frequentist" position, which here will be interpreted as the "objectivist" position, unconvincing. In my view, subjective degrees of beliefs of all sorts—degrees of belief relating to events of various kinds—should be regarded as probabilities. And yet, I shall now add to this statement an explanation which in a sense qualifies the statement.

(3) A Semiprobabilistic Position

While the view which this book will take of the concept of probability is subjectivistic, the writer's views about the central problems of decision theory may be described as semiprobabilistic views. By this I mean to say that in my opinion the directly observable weights which reasonable and consistent individuals attach to specific types of prospects are not necessarily the genuine (undistorted) subjective probabilities of the prospects, although these *decision weights* of consistently acting individuals do bear an understandable relation to probabilities, i.e., to weights that do satisfy the rules of probability theory.

A good many reasonable decision makers—though by no means all—seem to act differently depending on whether they act under the influence of shaky degrees of belief, i.e., of probabilities the numerical values of which are highly unstable in their minds, or act under the guidance of firm and stable degrees of belief. Degrees of belief that are highly unstable are appreciably influenced by what a few pages further on will be defined as "elusive hypotheses." These beliefs usually also have the property of being interpersonally controversial even among the well informed and even among individuals who exchange their information. Such degrees of belief are apt to become unconvincing in retrospect, a fact of which individuals are well aware in advance. There is little observable difference between the content of the statement that many reasonable decision makers are influenced by whether their degrees of belief are or are not *shared* by groups of other individuals, and the content of the statement that these decision makers are influenced by whether their degrees of belief are or are not expected to stay *stable in their own minds.* It seems to me that both these statements make good sense.

To accept one or both of these statements implies that the directly observable decision weights (expectation weights) which these decision makers attach to alternative monetary prospects need not universally be on a par with the probabilities attached to heads-or-tails events but may in many cases be derived from such probabilities by means of a process of "slanting" or "distortion." Slanting expresses an allowance for the instability and the controversial character of some types of probability judgment; the extent of the slanting may even depend on the magnitude of the prize which is at stake when a prospect is being weighted. We shall see that an alternative way of stating this is to say that the decision weights of reasonable decision makers are always *true* (rather than slanted) probabilities but that the utility functions of reasonable individuals contain allowances for the disutility of reliance on shaky and controversial judgments. More precisely expressed, these are allowances for *differences* between the probabilistically expected nonmonetary consequences of monetary opportunity losses suffered through reliance on shaky judgments, and the analogous consequences of opportunity losses suffered through *not* acting on the basis of such judgments.

In this volume, I shall sometimes refer to that version of the theory which emphasizes the idea of slanted probabilities as Version 1, and to the version which suggests technical incorporation of nonmonetary rewards into the utility function as Version 2. In some ways, Version 2 is more pleasing—sounds less heretical—but my presentation will mostly make use of Version 1. This is because Version 2 can be developed in *operational* terms only if the behavior of the "slanting" individual can be made to disclose the values of his genuine ("corrected") probabilities; yet, in actual fact, this can be done only if special simplifying assumptions are satisfied (see particularly Chapter 6, Section 8). At the present stage of the discussion, I should not like to commit myself to any of these simplifying assumptions, although other investigators might find it fruitful to do so. In the general case the semiprobabilistic individual discloses through his behavior only *ranges* within which his true probabilities are located, and this is not enough for giving Version 2 operational content. As for the *intuitive-introspective* level of discourse—or the normative, advice-giving level—the difference between the two versions reduces to fine points which appear to be more important on first thought than on second and which it is difficult to articulate.

Say the decision maker tells us that he assigns to the prospect "Dow Jones will rise" a *true* probability of 0.75 but that he feels very uncertain indeed about this judgment and he knows he will be exposed to more reproaches from others to whom he feels responsible, and will also have more intense remorse, if he suffers an opportunity loss by betting on this stock exchange event than if he suffers an opportunity loss by not betting on it. Hence, so he tells us, he will assign the weight 0.6 rather than 0.75 to the stock exchange prospect when he places a bet on it. Now, quite aside from the operational considerations previously mentioned, it seems doubtful to me whether we help such a customer much by talking him into restating his point, and into telling himself that he is assigning the decision weight 0.75 to the prospect. Having done so, he would have to add that in estimating his expected utility, he deducts from the probabilistically weighted utility of the reward not only the probabilistically weighted disutility of the potential monetary loss but also the probabilistically weighted *net* disutility of suffering the loss on a shaky and controversial judgment ("net" because the last item should be the excess of that disutility over the disutility of the potential opportunity loss through not betting).

Or to put it more pragmatically from our point of view: Our theoretical structure will apply to a decision maker only if he satisfies *specific consistency requirements* (see Chapter 6, Section 6),[3] and it will prove simpler and more convenient to require that his observable (slanted) decision weights of Version 1 should obey these consistency requirements than that his "utility function" of Version 2 should possess certain properties. As will be seen later, the axiomatic systems which possess considerable appeal for individuals uninfluenced by what I call "semiprobabilistic" (slanting) inclinations will *at any rate* be violated by the *directly observable* preference rankings of individuals who do show these inclinations, and I find it easier to discuss the needed modifications along the lines of Version 1 than along those of Version 2. These are the reasons why Version 1 will be in the foreground of that part of our presentation which relates to our modification of the subjective-probabilistic approach (i.e., to the part of our analysis which is not straightforward

---

[3] Decision makers not satisfying the consistency requirements of Chapter 6, Section 6, will be said to act nonprobabilistically (rather than semiprobabilistically). See Appendix to Chapter 3; and Chapter 6, Section 9.

subjective-probabilistic). *But fundamentally, Version 1 may be interpreted as a "proxy" for Version 2*, where the proxy relationship expresses itself in the fact that the weighting system of the individual reflects certain utilities and disutilities which do not lend themselves well to being incorporated into "utility functions."

As was said in Section 1, above, for specific purposes the reader may want to reformulate some of the problems discussed in this volume in such a way as to imply that the prizes set on various events are nonmonetary. In such reformulations the basic nonmonetary pay-offs (those which take the place of our monetary ones) may be lumped together with the nonmonetary consequences of relying on probability judgments of alternative types—firm or shaky, uncontroversial or controversial judgments —since, in such reformulations, it is necessary at any event to define a utility function for nonmonetary pay-offs. The results of these reformulations are likely to serve a purpose which is largely normative. It would be difficult to engage in generalizations as to the precise nature of the reformulations which may prove helpful in any given situation of this sort, but I believe that in *some of these cases* the difficulty of insistence on the use of undistorted probabilities, along with utility functions such as include *all* nonmonetary rewards, is no greater than are the difficulties involved in insistence on the formulation of *any* sort of nonmonetary utility function. Hence, in such reformulations the reader may sometimes want to use Version 2 itself, rather than to use our Version 1 as a proxy for Version 2.

The term "semiprobabilistic" fits Version 1 because the directly observable decision weights of the decision makers, whose behavior is described by such analysis, should be viewed as slanted or distorted probabilities. These weights result from the slanting of genuine subjective probabilities (true probabilities) when such individuals bet on events concerning which their probability judgments are shaky and interpersonally controversial. However, even semiprobabilistic individuals will be assumed to use as their observable decision weights undistorted probabilities when facing events generated by what we shall call *standard processes*. These may be thought of as processes of the heads-or-tails or the card-drawing variety with guaranteed equipment. In Version 1 the utility-of-wealth functions of all decision makers will be derived from their betting behavior in standard processes when merely monetary pay-offs are at stake, and the semiprobabilistic individual will be said to apply in his nonstandard process bets slanted probabilities to the utilities so established. The slant expresses an allowance for a specific type of nonmonetary rewards and disadvantages. To the extent to which we base our interpretation of semiprobabilistic slanting behavior on the interpersonally controversial character of some types of probability judgments— rather than merely on their psychological instability—we are stressing the fact that practically all decisions possess some characteristics of those made for groups including many individuals. In situations involving *group decisions,* it is not a matter of indifference whether the probability judgments on which the responsible agent has based his betting behavior do or do not appear to be plausible to other members of the group. Many decisions obviously fall in the category of group decisions. But it needs to be added that a good many decisions which at first sight do not appear to possess a group aspect of this kind *do* in fact possess such an aspect, if for no other reason than because most of us have family responsibilities. Quite aside from this, it is true also that our reputations and our opportunities in life depend significantly on how reasonable our decisions appear to others, even in those cases in which we individually bear all the *direct* consequences of these decisions.

One is apt to develop somewhat different kinds of "dynamic" speculations, depending on whether the emphasis is placed primarily on the psychologically unstable or on the interpersonally controversial character of the judgments which give rise to semiprobabilistic slanting. If importance is attached primarily to the first of the two interpretations, then it seems plausible to expect that in a good many cases the semiprobabilistic slanting inclinations will diminish (though they will not disappear) as the decision maker *gets used* to being faced with some specific type of decision problem. The second interpretation, on the other hand, suggests more the dynamic hypothesis that the semiprobabilistic slanting inclinations will diminish (though they will not disappear) wherever larger groups of *like-minded* individuals are formed. Both kinds of dynamic speculation possess plausibility, and both would seem to deserve future exploration.

(4) Semiprobabilistic Slanting Distinguished from Dependence of Undistorted Probabilities on Which Way One Bets

It is essential to be aware of the fact that a phenomenon superficially reminiscent of semiprobabilistic slanting is observable also in the purely probabilistic behavior of subjects in standard processes such as tossing a coin or rolling a die with guaranteed properties. But despite the superficial resemblance, this other phenomenon—which may be observable either in standard processes or in others—must be sharply distinguished from semiprobabilistic slanting in nonstandard processes (i.e., from slanting relative to standard process probabilities). The other phenomenon—observable also in standard process behavior—can be described as follows: A subject may feel that the probability of an event depends on whether he is placing a bet on the event or on its complement (*a*) because his making the bet will induce others or himself to influence the probabilities one way or another (say, the die will have one or two aces, depending on whether he bets on an ace or on a nonace), or (*b*) because the fact that he is given an opportunity to bet on the event but not on its complement, or vice versa, gives a clue about the probabilities (say, about the characteristics of the die which will be used). These are cases in which events are supposed to depend on how a bet is placed in an experiment.

In experiments, it is possible to exclude both these factors—i.e., (*a*) and (*b*)—and in real life, there exist many situations in which neither of these two factors can affect the observed behavior of decision makers. Indeed, factor (*b*) presupposes that the individual should be given no choice between betting on an event or on its complement on terms precisely specified before the bet is made. At any rate, neither (*a*) nor (*b*) could be said to mark deviations from purely probabilistic behavior. They do not illustrate semiprobabilistic slanting. The potential importance of factor (*a*) was recently pointed out by Bruno de Finetti in a study presented to a conference on insurance problems in Italy (**17**), while the role of factor (*b*) is one of the subject matters of K. R. W. Brewer's note in the February, 1963, issue of the *Quarterly Journal of Economics*. We shall assume in this volume that probabilities are *measured* in operations in which both factor (*a*) and factor (*b*) are *avoided*.

Semiprobabilistic slanting expresses itself in the assignment of different decision weights to an event according as the decision maker bets on the event or against it, not because he believes that the genuine probabilities depend on which way he bets but because his reaction to an opportunity loss is different depending on whether this loss results from betting on shaky and controversial judgments or results from excluding acts which would have to be based on judgments of this kind.

The statements contained under the four section headings of this Introduction could not be fully explained in these few pages. But I believe that these statements and the comments which I have added to them will make the analysis that follows here more easily understandable.

At any rate, the concept of probability, as it will be interpreted in the present volume, is at the heart of the problem of decision making under uncertainty. This problem, in turn, is one of the central problems of economics. In particular, it must be regarded as the central theme of any adequate theory or profit. The extension of the scope of probability theory to the area with which modern economic theory is concerned is a new development. It will take the effort of many economists to rethink our major themes in the light of ideas which have originated in the work of mathematicians. A good deal of bridge building will be needed to accomplish this.

One of several advantages which may well result from this reorientation is that of an increasingly critical attitude toward so-called "objectivist" methods of arriving at conclusions in the social sciences and also in various other disciplines. These methods fail to articulate the subjective probability judgments and utility assignments which no decision process can circumvent. Hence the allegedly objectivist methods dispose of these elements by implication and in an arbitrary fashion: They frequently impose someone else's subjective preferences on the decision maker.

Throughout this volume, I shall refer to those authors to whom probability means a personal degree of belief as "subjectivists," and I shall regard the frequentists as "objectivists." Since brief designations of this sort are never very accurate, it will take familiarity with the analysis as a whole to see in what sense these terms nevertheless point in the right direction. At present, the terms *are* mostly used in the way in which they will be employed here. But in the past, several authors who defined probability as a personal degree of belief argued that their views possessed an essential trait of objectivism. For example, John Maynard Keynes **(27)**, and perhaps also Harold Jeffreys **(26)**, claimed this (although there is some question as to whether Keynes should not be said to have abandoned this claim in his essay on Frank Ramsey which in 1933 was included in Keynes' well-known *Essays in Biography*). The claim was based (1) on the statement that a probability is not just any degree of belief but needs to be a *reasonable* degree of belief (with this we all agree, since a probabilistic system must obviously satisfy reasonable postulates); (2) on the statement that a probability judgment always implies a given amount and kind of information (with this we also agree); and (3) on the assertion that any two reasonable individuals possessing precisely the identical information would arrive at the identical probability judgments. This assertion is vague. Furthermore, while vague assertions may sometimes be revealing and intuitively convincing, I believe this assertion to be an unrevealing and unconvincing implicit definition of equal information. Hence, I shall disregard the claim of some degree-of-belief probability theorists to objectivism in the foregoing sense. Indeed, the most important contemporary version of this kind of probability theory—the de Finetti–Savage version—makes no such claim. On the other hand, the frequentists, who have an inclination unduly to narrow the scope of probability theory, have at least this legitimate claim to objectivism: They limit their discussion to judgments about which reasonable individuals *are* very likely to agree.

NOTE ON THE USE OF THE TERMS "DECISIONS," "EVENTS," "DECISION WEIGHTS," AND "HYPOTHESES"

a) To reach a *decision* means that one is going to do something. That is to say, a decision must always be understood to lead to the choice of an *act*. An act can be defined by the consequences it has, consequences which may depend on whether this or that specified event occurs.

b) The *state of nature* existing at any time can be described by the statement that certain *events* have happened. A complete listing of these events is of course impossible; but to be useful, a description of the state of nature must include a statement concerning events that are significant for some specific purpose. The events with which probability theory is concerned are *prospective* events. Yet, some of these may be prospective only for the individual who is making a probability judgment. Others may know that the event has or has not happened, as long as the decision maker feels uncertain about this. For the present purpose, it must be assumed that the subsequent occurrence or nonoccurrence of an event can be ascertained by a procedure acceptable to all concerned.

c) The directly observable *decision weights* which an individual attaches to prospective events mean the following. If a prize is made contingent on the occurrence of an event, then a person acts as if he had been promised unconditionally an amount of utility which equals the algebraic product of the utility of the prize with a specific numerical factor. In other words, he would be willing to settle for the outright receipt of an amount of money carrying this amount of utility to him. The numerical factor in question may assume a range of values which is bounded by one and zero. This factor will be called the observable decision weight which the individual attaches to the event under consideration for some given prize.

We may observe for each bet of an individual also another decision weight, namely, the weight he attaches to an event if he bets *against* it by staking his fortunes on the complement of the event. This other decision weight for an event is obtained by deducting from the number one the decision weight attached to the complement of the event if the individual bets on the complement. In no instance is the individual assumed to bet both on an event *and* on its complement; he is assumed to disclose his decision weight for a bet on the event and his decision weight for a bet against it, and we may assume that the question whether he is going to bet one way or the other will be decided by a chance process. In purely probabilistic decision processes the two decision weights—the weight the individual attaches to a prospective event if he bets *on* it and one minus the weight he attaches to the complement of the event if he bets on the complement—coincide; both weights equal the probability which the individual assigns to the event in question. In semiprobabilistic decision processes, these two decision weights do not generally coincide. The range between the two decision weights of the semiprobabilistic individual is his observable probability range for the event, i.e., the range within which the true value of the probability or degree of belief is located. In semi-probabilistic circumstances the observable decision weights do not satisfy the rules of probability theory. The semiprobabilistic individual, whom we shall hold to specific consistency requirements, will be interpreted as *slanting* the true probability (or degree of belief) which he attaches to an event at the present moment; and he will be interpreted as obtaining his decision weights by this process of slanting in which he engages because he regards some of his degrees of belief (probabilities) as shaky judgments which will not stay stable in his mind. Indeed, the width of the range between the two decision weights may depend on the magnitude of the prize which is at stake because the degree of slanting may not be the same for all prizes.

By directly observable decision weights we shall mean the weights attached to an event if the individual bets *on* the event (except in cases in which we shall make it entirely clear that in that specific context, we mean the weight attached to an event against which the bet is made). For events generated by specific types of processes—"standard processes" —we shall postulate purely probabilistic decision making, and this will enable us to define the decision weight attached to a nonstandard process event as the probability of *that* standard process event on which the individual is equally willing to stake a prize of given magnitude as on the nonstandard process event in question.

d) A *hypothesis*, as we shall interpret the concept in this volume, is a conjecture which contributes to determining an individual's probability judgments concerning events. The decision maker feels that a hypothesis may or may not be valid and that if it is valid, then from this either direct conclusions follow with respect to the assignment of true (undistorted) probabilities to events, or conclusions follow with respect to the specific values of other parameters[4] on which the probabilities of events depend. The essential content of hypotheses can be described by what they imply, in the case of their validity, *with respect to the specific values of such parameters, and thus of true numerical probabilities.* From this, in turn, it follows that once a decision maker maintains a hypothesis with nonzero probability, this will have an effect on his probability judgments concerning events, regardless of whether he assigns a high or a low probability to the validity of the hypothesis itself. Hypotheses may be conjectures about the probabilities of other hypotheses; but on the top of such a hierarchy, there is always an *ad hoc* postulate—*not* to be regarded as a hypothesis—which says that the probabilities assigned to a set of hypotheses are right. If, *in his acts,* the decision maker is willing to commit himself to the numerical effect of a hypothesis on his probability judgments about events, then we shall call the hypothesis a *straightforward* hypothesis. A hypothesis which does not meet this requirement we shall call an *elusive* hypothesis. A decision maker maintaining an elusive hypothesis does have in his mind a judgment about what this hypothesis implies with respect to the numerical values of the true probabilities of events; but in his acts, he is unwilling to commit himself to the *ad hoc postulate* concerning the correctness of the probability *now* assigned to the hypothesis itself (and thus also to at least one other hypothesis), because he feels that his way of arriving at this *ad hoc* postulate might soon seem unconvincing. In other words, the true subjective probabilities of events in the mind of the decision maker—all his degrees of belief—result from straightforward and/or from elusive hypotheses which are weighted and which jointly exhaust the possibilities assumed to exist at any time; but if some of his hypotheses are elusive, then this creates a feeling of doubt or uncertainty in him about some of his probability judgments concerning events. These doubts—which we do not call hypotheses—may in turn induce him to "slant" his probabilities concerning events, that is, to employ decison weights which are distorted probabilities. The appropriate size of the slant—the appraisal expressing itself in the allowances for the doubts about the probability judgments

---

[4] Parameters are variables in a sufficiently *generally* formulated functional relationship, but assume specific values for subclasses of these relationships, where each subclass is defined by our assigning a specific value to a parameter (or specific values to parameters). The probabilities themselves are parameters.

which are influenced by such hypotheses—is practically always an inter-personally controversial matter. The language we are using here and in what follows is that of Version 1; but in Section 3, above, it was explained that the reader is free to interpret this version as a proxy for Version 2.

To say that one *accepts* one hypothesis and *rejects* others implies that one intends to act as if unitary probability were to be assigned to one hypothesis and zero probability to the others. There exist many cases in which the useful attitude to rival hypotheses is not to "accept" or to "reject" them but to attach positive probabilities to several alternative hypotheses and to adjust these probabilities in the light of accumulating evidence.

The validity of some hypotheses is equivalent to the occurrence of unequivocally ascertainable events, on which the probabilities of other events depend, and the decision weights attached to such hypotheses are operationally observable in the same sense as are the decision weights attached to events in general. But this is not true of all hypotheses which the decision maker needs to weight in order to obtain his observable decision weights for events. The probabilities assigned to some hypotheses are merely implicit in the probabilities assgned to ascertainable events; not for all hypotheses is it possible to define "observable" decision weights, because the validity of some hypotheses never becomes ascertainable in the sense in which events do.

e) It is revealing to make a mental note of the fact that instead of speaking of probability assignments to events and to hypotheses, we are free to speak of probability assignments to propositions. For example, there is no difference between assigning a probability to the prospect that the Dow Jones average will rise and assigning a probability to the truth of the *proposition* that that index will rise. Bernard O. Koopman's work (**30**) illustrates the use of this terminology; he calls propositions to which probabilities can be assigned *contemplated* propositions, adding that if such a proposition can be verified by experiment, then it belongs in the subclass of contemplated propositions which may be called *experimental* propositions. However, propositions, the validity of which is generally postulated, or is postulated in a specific context, are not contemplated but are *asserted* propositions. These are not subject to probability assignment. As a result of what we said about the *ad hoc postulate* which must always be placed on top of a hierarchy of hypotheses, we must conclude that probability judgments are asserted propositions of a special sort, though they relate to contemplated propositions. From our point of view, we may add also that for some decision makers the *ad hoc* postulates, which assert in a given situation the completeness of the list of contemplated propositions (hypotheses) and the acceptability of the weights attached to them, create great discomfort; and that this is what gives rise to the phenomenon of semiprobabilistic slanting. Having said this about the terminology involving propositions, we shall continue to speak of probability assignments to events and hypotheses.

Chapter 1

PROBABILISTIC BEHAVIOR AND ITS BEARING ON PROFIT THEORY: AN INFORMAL DISCUSSION

Opinions differ concerning the range of observable events to which it is reasonable to apply the Calculus of Probabilities. But there exists no essential disagreement about what it *means* to apply the Calculus of Probabilities to a set of physical events. The meaning of this is that we make our expectations concerning various events internally consistent with one another *by those specific standards of consistency which are formalized in the theory of probability.* Later in this volume, the basic rules with which probabilistic expectations must comply will be discussed in detail. Let us first consider in an informal way the nature of the agreement concerning the specific requirements of consistency for probabilistic expectations, and let us consider informally also the nature of the disagreement concerning the scope of applicability of these rules in the real world.

(1) Coins, Cards, Dice et Hoc Genus Omne

If a person says that the probability of a perfect coin's falling heads on any occasion is ½ and that the probability of its falling heads twenty times in a row is $\frac{1}{2^{20}}$, then (as we have already said) he is making a statement with which it is not legitimate to disagree, since the validity of the statement follows from the definition of the concepts used. The same is true of analogous statements about idealized coins, dice, etc., such as are not themselves perfect in the usual sense but the *bias* of which is *perfect*, so that one side of the coin or the die is favored in a precisely definable way (possibly in a way that depends on the outcome of other coin processes, etc.). Such statements are of purely logical character. They relate to imaginary processes. However, it is an observable fact that practically all reasonable people believe that imaginary results of this kind—probabilistic results established for idealized coin processes, card processes, rolls of dice—provide a very good approximation to the results obtainable in real-world experiments with good coins, with well-shuffled decks of cards, etc., and also to the results of various physical processes of great scientific importance. Any such belief concerning the practical equivalence of a physical process with an idealized probabilistic process implies a set of expectations pertaining to the outcome of the physical process, since acceptance of the analogy leads to weighting the possible outcomes of the physical process by theoretical probabilities.

There exist various ways in which a person may arrive at the conviction that the behavior of the frequency ratios in a physical process suggests close analogy to an idealized coin process possessing the definitional property that an unlimited increase in the number of tosses makes the frequency ratios *almost always* converge on some true value.[1] If the person relies exclusively on his own observations of the behavior of frequency ratios in the physical process, then it takes him a large number of trials to make the analogy practically compelling and to obtain dependable estimates concerning the behavior of frequency ratios. In probabilistically well-behaved physical processes, such estimates are almost always confirmed by subsequent experience, because extremely bad or good luck is exceedingly rare.

Consensus exists as to what the internal consistency requirements

[1] The phrase "almost always" relates to a problem which must not stay unmentioned but which may be left out of account in our decision-theoretical applications of probabilistic concepts.

The phrase is needed to make the sentence in the text precise, because, according to the mathematical theory of probability, it is not logically impossible that ideally random tosses of a perfect coin should fail to establish frequency ratios converging on the true probabilities when the number of tosses is increased further and further. This result of nonconvergence has zero probability, but the result is not logically *impossible* (just as it is true of any specific outcome of some experiment that if, when the number of trials is increased toward infinity, the outcome can occur only in a finite number of cases at wholly unpredictable points of the sequence, then the outcome in question has zero probability but is not an impossible outcome).

Richard von Mises has formulated a separate axiom by which the convergence expressed in the text, above, is postulated *generally*, i.e., without the "almost always" clause. In his presentation, too, it is logically possible that one should not find convergence in an idealized coin experiment in which the number of tosses is increased toward infinity; yet, according to Mises' axiom in question, if the number of experiments (in each of which the number of tosses is increased toward infinity) is *itself* increased toward infinity, then the number of ill-behaved experiments will assuredly tend to acquire a weight of zero. I am not aware of other modern authors on probability who would have found this special axiom convincing, and who would have dispensed with the "almost always" clause on the grounds suggested by Mises. I agree with the ruling opinion that the "almost always" clause is needed in the sentence of the text to which the present footnote is attached.

However, in decision-theoretical applications the qualifying clause in question—the "almost always" clause—may be left out of account. The reason for this is that if a person decides to regard a physical process as analogous to an idealized coin process, then this decision involves using as a frame of reference an idealized process viewed as yielding the result which it yields with unitary probability *without* allowance for the zero-probability outcome. To put it differently, it makes no sense to say that I shall assuredly interpret this physical coin as a fair one, but with allowance for the possibility that *behaviorally* it may be indistinguishable from an irregular coin!

are for any person's set of expectations about the results of a coin-flipping experiment, provided he considers the physical experiment as a practical equivalent of an idealized coin process. If he regards the coin as a practically fair one, and the tosses as random tosses, he will, for example, assign the same probability to any *ex ante specified* sequence of given length, regardless of how many heads or tails figure in that sequence (e.g., regardless of whether the specified sequence consists exclusively of heads or whether it consists of a precise alternation of heads and tails, etc.). The basic propositions of the mathematical theory of probability are generally accepted. To be sure, no one has thought his way through all significant propositions of which probability theory *now* is made up; but any intelligent person is aware of the fact that in case of doubt, he should rely on expert advice, as he would in other areas of mathematics. Here, as elsewhere, individuals must decide *ad hoc* whether they wish to interpret a process in the real world as a sufficiently good approximation to some imaginary process. But for many kinds of coins and for many well-shuffled decks of cards, there exists practical consensus about the goodness of this approximation. What is much more important, such consensus exists also about a great many processes with which fundamental research in the natural sciences is concerned and, perhaps to a somewhat lesser extent, also about various biological and social processes which serve as a basis for the institution of insurance. In these cases the practically compelling character of the analogy results from observations concerning the actual behavior of frequency ratios in a real-world process. The numerical outcome of such observations determines also the specific characteristics of the idealized process to which the physical process is regarded as strictly analogous.

The essential common property of the physical processes belonging in this area is that they generate *mass phenomena* made up of a long series of events—such as many individual coin tosses—and that for some given purpose, it is not fruitful to try to distinguish these events from one another by any *individual* characteristic, so that the different outcomes of the *individual* events stay inexplicable; yet, it *is* fruitful to interpret the relative frequencies of various classes of outcomes in terms of definite regularities. In particular, it is highly convincing to suggest for these processes that the frequency ratios they generate tend to converge in long runs of trials.

It is a *de facto* uncontroversial proposition that processes suggesting this analogy with an idealized model do exist in the physical world, and that intelligent people feel that in these processes they *should* attach to each potential outcome decision weights which obey the rules of the pure theory of probability. Of the usefulness of this prescription it is possible to convince practically all intelligent people. The general lack of intelligence of the dissenters can be established by independent criteria. Not the only criterion, but one of the criteria, is the lack of success of most of the dissenters. Operational tests for proving that an intelligent person is guided by probabilistic considerations would in some cases be unmanageable. But it frequently is possible to devise reasonably satisfactory tests.

(2) Tests of Whether a Person's Decision Weights Are "Probabilities"

Take a scientific proposition whose foundations are probabilistic. Such a proposition can often be expressed by the statement that an experimental observation (measurement) is equally likely to yield a value which is higher as to yield a value which is lower than a definite theoretical value; and often, it is possible to add that the value which the observation will yield is very likely to come out within a narrow range around the theoretical value. Many propositions with which this statement can be illustrated are of great importance in the sciences. But for the sake of simplicity, we may think of a very simple and rather trivial illustration: If a fair die is rolled n times, and n is sufficiently large, the die should be expected to fall with an *even* number up *about* $\frac{n}{2}$ times.

Once a person has accepted such a proposition, he may be expected to prove indifferent between being offered a prize of, say, $100 contingent upon an observed value's coming out *higher* and being offered the same prize contingent upon the observed value's coming out *lower* than the theoretical value (in this case, $\frac{n}{2}$). He also may be expected to show a strong *preference* for a prize contingent upon the observed value's coming out in the neighborhood of the theoretical value rather than upon its lying far away from that value. A person's behavior may thus give strong indications of his subjective acceptance of the Calculus of Probabilities. Tests of this sort are *operational* in the sense of being based on the observation of an individual's behavior in an operation.

For various reasons the method of operational testing is merely moderately satisfactory in this area of research. Indifference is not *strictly* testable, since even if a person is indifferent between two alternatives, he has to choose one of these, and thus he acts each time as if he preferred one alternative to the other. There exist methods, somewhat imperfect ones, of getting around the difficulty of testing indifference. For example, one may discover that either of the two alternatives is consistently preferred to the other as soon as a slightly higher reward is set on the alternative in question, no matter which alternative it is. This method is somewhat cruder than it might appear at first sight, because the reaction to *very small* differential advantages may be rather whimsical, and the fact that *large* premiums induce people to shift from one alternative to another does not disclose dependably that the two alternatives appear to be approximately equiprobable to them. It may be possible to use other methods based on the postulate that true indifference between two *equally* rewarded prospects should show in each prospect's being chosen with the same frequency as the other—that is, in 50 per cent of all cases—while various degrees of preference should show in various frequency ratios of choice in favor of the preferred alternative. Operational testing of indifference and of preference poses difficult problems of various sorts. Yet, if the pitfalls are watched carefully enough, operational tests can give significant indications about the way in which a person arrives at decisions.

The results may then either support or contradict the hypothesis that to each prospect the decision maker was attaching decision weights which satisfy the rules of probability. This hypothesis may lead to good or to poor predictions of his observable behavior. Our account of such operational tests implied that, other things equal, a reasonable individual prefers a gain prospect to which he attaches higher probability to one carrying lower probability, and that he is indifferent as between prospects he deems to be equiprobable. We have seen that tests of this sort can often be made strongly suggestive, even if the results are not fully conclusive.

There also exist nonoperational methods the use of which may add to the evidence. One may interrogate subjects and ask them to explain their reactions, or one may simply draw inferences from statements which they make freely on their own initiative. Needless to say, this method, too, has definite pitfalls—people are frequently unclear about the basic characteristics of their own modes of action, and in other cases they are reluctant to discuss these frankly—but some combination of operational testing and of interrogation, supplemented with introspection and common-sense observation, can throw more light on our problem than could any of these methods all by itself. One important point here is that even where operational testing through betting experiments is not used, and much reliance is placed on interviews, the investigator is likely to get more articulate and more dependable answers to questions which are formulated *as if* they were operational test questions than to questions which lack this quasi-operational character. "How would you behave, on reflection, if you had a choice between making a significant prize contingent on this or on that prospect?" is frequently a more useful question than "What do you *think* of the likelihood of this or of that event?"

In the previous pages, we considered a person's reaction to the question whether he prefers to make a prize of given magnitude contingent on one or on another risky prospect. A person's willingness to put up various amounts *of his own money at various odds* on some given prospect depends not only on his expectations concerning the prospect of gain versus that of loss but also on how much satisfaction he derives from x dollars' worth of addition to his wealth as compared to the loss of satisfaction caused by x dollars' worth of deduction from his wealth. In other words, the terms on which a person is willing to put up money of his own in a bet are significantly influenced by the shape of his utility-of-wealth function in some range around his initial position of wealth. Yet, these terms, too, disclose whether in a specfiic physical process—say, in coin flipping or die rolling—he is using probabilities as his decision weights. If in some physical process the individual appraises all prospects in accordance with the rules of probability and his decision weights are numerically known values of the various probabilities, then he will maximize his mathematical expectations of utility—i.e., his so-called *moral expectations*—on the basis of these probabilities, and his betting behavior on events generated by the process will disclose the shape of a consistent utility function. In the present chapter, this will be explained merely in a very general, nontechnical fashion.

Say that a reasonable person feels firmly convinced of a guarantee according to which a given coin is practically fair, and that his expectations concerning the outcome of a coin-flipping experiment obey the consistency rules of probability theory. About these rules he may have to consult experts, but this is a different question. Such a person will prove indifferent between making a given prize contingent on any two coin-flipping events—or on any two sequences of events—which according to the textbook have equal probabilities. For example, two heads in a row are probabilistically equivalent to "either three heads in a row will be tossed, or three tails in a row will be tossed." Subsequently, we may establish the characteristics of his utility-of-wealth function in some range surrounding his initial position by exploring the terms on which he is just barely willing to put up various amounts of his own money on a bet relating to the outcome of a further toss. One point of his utility function may, for example, be detected by the following experiment. Say that this individual is just barely willing to risk with probability ¼ a dollar's worth of loss on condition that he makes a dollar's worth of gain if an event occurs the probability of which is ¾ (such as that the coin will not fall heads twice in a row). Then a one-dollar addition to his wealth is worth to him, in terms of utility, one third of the worth of the last dollar which he already possesses. An additional dollar multiplied by ¾ expresses to him the same utility as does the last dollar now owned when this latter is multiplied by ¼. We may infer that this person's utility function shows rather sharply diminishing marginal utility. If, for example, we set the zero point of his utility scale at his initial position of wealth, and if we call the utility which the last dollar already in his possession carries to him "one utile," then we may conclude that the next dollar is worth to him one third of a utile. Thus, insistence on terms of betting which are better than the actuarially fair ones discloses diminishing marginal utility, and willingness to accept terms that are worse than the actuarially fair ones discloses rising marginal utility. A linear aggregate utility function within some range—that is, constant marginal utility within that range—expresses itself in a person's willingness to accept actuarially fair terms, but none that are worse. Once we have estimated the utility function of an individual in some range by exploring his willingness to put up specific stakes for specific potential gains at specific probabilities, we may test the probabilistic character of his behavior by discovering whether he behaves consistently when confronted with differently constructed but probabilistically equivalent terms.

In conclusion, if we surmise that a person attaches to each potential outcome of a physical process decision weights which reflect genuine (undistorted) probabilities of known numerical values, and that, by using these probabilities as his decision weights, he maximizes his probabilistic expectations of utility, then we can test the correctness of these suppositions by experimental methods that qualify as operational. He should in this case be indifferent between accepting a given prize contingent upon one or another event (or one or another sequence of events), provided these two events (or two sequences) have the same probability; and he should show an observable preference for accepting a given prize contingent on an event that has greater probability than another, and an observable preference also for a greater prize over a smaller prize whenever the events on which these prizes are made contingent are equiprobable. Generally, in betting experiments in which his decision involves prizes and stakes of varying sizes and carrying different probabilities, he should disclose a consistent utility function such as implies the maximization of his probabilistic utility expectations.

(3) The Minimum Scope of Probabilistic Behavior

There exists no view which mankind would hold unanimously. But I shall assume that practical consensus may be reached on the following propositions, which have already been stated briefly in the preceding pages. Intelligent people living in the area of the now-dominant civilization can be convinced of its being reasonable to proceed as if certain mass phenomena of the real world had the same characteristics as tosses of perfect coins (or tosses of biased coins with the definitional property of generating convergent frequency ratios the values of which may possibly depend on the outcome of other coin processes). To prospective events generated by processes of this sort, intelligent people tend to attach decision weights which are genuine (undistorted) probabilities. Not only do there exist real coins and real decks of cards that approximate their ideal counterparts closely enough to justify this attitude, but the mass phenomena generated by small physical entities (molecules, atoms, and smaller entities) doubtless lend themselves to this interpretation; and a large class of biological, technological, and social mass phenomena usually considered insurable have at least *some* essential properties in common with those just mentioned. *For any intelligent person, there exists some minimum scope of physical processes which have the following property: These processes generate events to which he feels he should apply decision weights that are the same kind of "probabilities" as those developed by mathematicians for pure models possessing the property of almost always generating frequency ratios which converge on definite values.* For a large number of conventional problems involving practically fair coins, dice, etc., these theoretical values can, of course, be looked up with great ease.

Our statement needs to be supplemented by an observation which I do not regard as legitimately controversial, although in the past its validity was occasionally denied. If a person's degrees of belief for a mass phenomenon of the real world are formed strictly in accordance with the rules of probability—say he takes it for granted that he is faced with tosses of a practically fair coin—then consistency requires that he should take a probabilistic view not only of the outcome of a *large number* of trials but also of the outcome of a *single* trial. He must be willing to judge that heads or tails on the next single toss have probability ½. This addition to our previous statement becomes logically cogent as a misleading appearance is dispelled.

A misleading appearance needs to be dispelled because it *is* possible to make a number of very essential statements about the outcome of 100 or of 1,000 tosses which have no counterpart for a single toss or for a small number of tosses. But this is not because a single toss poses a problem that would lack the probabilistic character of the 100-toss problem. On the contrary, the reason is that the *probabilistic properties* of the single-toss problem are in part different from those of the 100-toss problem. In a universe consisting of many single tosses, the outcome of each individual toss deviates very greatly from the mean, since the individual toss always results either in heads or in tails, while the mean tends to be half heads, half tails; in a universe consisting of many 100-toss units, the outcome of most of these large units deviates relatively little from the 50–50 result which tends to become the mean result for *this* universe as a whole. It follows that simply by observing the frequency ratios in a very large unit (comprising a great many tosses), one may obtain a confident estimate of the approximate probability governing the process, while the frequency ratios obtained in a unit consisting of merely a few tosses provide little evidence. Further, it follows that a person to whom the marginal utility of wealth decreases as he acquires more wealth should prefer to stake $1.00 on each of 100 tosses to staking $100 on a single toss, since to such a person the variance about the mathematical expectation of the monetary outcome is painful (he gains less utility through the pluses than he loses through the minuses). But it does *not* follow that a person who knows the numerical values of the probabilities involved in a 100-toss unit, and who in his behavior in relation to such units would be guided by these probabilities, may abandon his probabilistic attitude if he becomes faced with merely a single toss of the coin in question. If he is guided by the judgment that in very long sequences of tosses the frequency of heads tends to equality with that of tails, then he must be guided *with equal firmness* by the judgment that in a single toss the probability of heads is ½ although he should, of course, take account of the fact that some probabilistic statements which apply to long sequences can be applied only *mutatis mutandis* for short sequences or for single tosses.

The basic reason which must lead one to this conclusion is that a 100-toss unit (or a 1,000-toss unit, or a 1,000,000-toss unit) is a unique instance in the same sense as that in which a one-toss unit is a unique instance. The probabilistic features of these unique instances of various sizes are different, but it takes precisely the probabilistic approach to understand these differences. It is all very well to point out that when a fair coin is tossed 100 times, the probability of obtaining heads between 40 and 60 times is exceedingly high—to be specific, 0.9648—and that this particular statement has no counterpart for a single toss. For a single toss the result will quite clearly be either "all heads" or "all tails," while the results "all heads" and "all tails" have *negligible* probability for a 100-toss unit. It is all very well to point this out: Statements of this sort are essentially statements relating to the significant diminution of the standard error of the mean with increasing sample size. But the fact remains that belief in the probability 0.9648 expresses by definition the limit value of the relative frequency with which the outcome of 100-toss units will almost always[2] fall in this range, *when the number of 100-toss trials is made ever larger.* To use this limit value for deriving conclusions concerning the probability of the 40–60 range for a *single* 100-toss unit is logically no different from using the limit value of the frequency of heads in *many one-toss units* for deriving conclusions concerning the probability of heads in a *single toss.*

To summarize: To events generated by processes in which they see a close analogy with an ideal coin-tossing process (and the like), all reasonable individuals tend to apply decision weights that satisfy the laws of probability theory, and this implies that they tend to attach such weights also to *single* events generated by these processes. The numerical values of the probabilities in question are limit values of frequency ratios. I think no reader will object to this statement. How about the decision weights applied to events generated by processes such as do *not* appear to establish convergent frequency ratios? Do these decision weights of a reasonable person also satisfy the rules of probability?

(4) The Grand Controversy

The great founders of the mathematical theory of probability did not discuss explicitly the question with which our preceding section ends. The Bernoullis, Fermat, Bayes, Laplace, Poisson, Gauss—to mention just a few among them—developed their theories for ideal processes with the appropriate characteristics of randomness and convergence.[3] Yet, several of these masters—perhaps particularly Bayes, Laplace, and Poisson— formulated various propositions which are valid only on the postulate

---

[2] For the meaning of the "almost always" clause, see n. 1, p. 17.

[3] Strictly speaking, with the characteristics of randomness and "convergence in almost all cases"; see n. 1, p. 17.

that the decision maker should fit his guesses into a strictly probabilistic framework even if he is faced with a problem not involving convergent frequency ratios.

For example, Laplace's analysis (**31, 32**), which in this regard originated in Bayesian ideas, acquaints us with the problem of a decision maker who has been guaranteed the composition of two urns, each of which contains (say) red and black balls in specific numerical proportions, although in different proportions. The probability of the decision maker's drawing a red ball or a black ball depends not only on the guaranteed composition of the urns but also on whether during the present experiment the drawing happens to take place from the one or from the other of the two urns. About this the decision maker must make a guess which —after one, two, etc., drawings—he can improve. Bayes had developed a theory of how rational individuals should make such estimates when they are confronted with a problem very similar to the urn problem which Laplace later used in his illustration. The Bayes-Laplace theory is based on the idea that the question of a person's having become faced—by an experimenter or by nature—with *this* or with *that* urn creates essentially the same problem in probabilities as the question of his drawing one or the other color from an urn of guaranteed composition. The two phases of what in this approach is essentially regarded as *one and the same problem* should be merged and should be subjected to a unified piece of probabilistic reasoning. They should be merged even though a probability judgment about the nature of the urn with which a person is faced in an experiment—say, as the result of an experimenter's decision—is not a judgment based on converging frequency ratios.

Bayes's original illustration[4] was somewhat less easy to follow than Laplace's. We may say, however, that Bayes took it for granted, as did

---

[4] Bayes's illustration is contained in the paper which was submitted to the Royal Society by Dr. Richard Price in 1763, two years after Bayes' death. The illustration did not relate to urns but to a problem the main property of which was the following: An object had been thrown many times in such a way that it had to fall into one of two contiguous subdivisions of an area of known size; the decision maker had no prior knowledge of where the dividing line between the two subareas—say, Subareas A and B—had been drawn, i.e., what the sizes of these subareas were, and he wanted to arrive at a judgment about how probable it was that the size of (say) Subarea A lay within this or that specified numerical range. Initially, all ranges of equal width seemed equiprobable to him when guessing about the numerical ranges in which the true size of Subarea A might lie. But a posteriori, he could examine his observations about the number of times the object had fallen into Subarea A; and he could infer that if the probability of finding this observed result was *m* times as great assuming that the size of the subarea lay within some numerical range (Range One) than assuming that the size lay within a different range (Range Two), then the estimate "the size of Subarea A lies within Range One" is *m* times as likely to be correct as the estimate "the size of Subarea A lies within Range Two."

later Laplace, that complete a priori ignorance of the decision maker describes a standard situation for which it is revealing to develop the technical analysis. In terms of Laplace's urn model, this means that the decision maker assigns the identical initial (or "prior") probability to his being faced with either of the two urns and that it is *this* particular probability which should be gradually corrected as one, two, etc., drawings start giving a clue as to whether the balls are more likely to be drawn from the one or from the other of the two urns. This prior probability of ½ for each of two urns is not derived from any experience with frequency ratios suggesting convergence, for it is *not* maintained that the experimenter has flipped a coin to decide which urn should be used. What *is* maintained is that complete ignorance, on which the assignment of the initial prior probabilities is based, poses to the rational decision maker the same kind of problem as that with which a perfect coin faces him. The postulate expressing this conception is commonly called the Principle of Insufficient Reason. If I have absolutely no reason to give preference to either of the two existing possibilities (in a situation in which I know for sure that the two possbilities are exhaustive), then—so the postulate says—I should proceed as if I had to decide whether I want to stake my fortune on a perfect coin's falling heads or on its falling tails, i.e., as if I were faced with a repetitive process producing frequency ratios which in the long run tend to converge on ½. But in these cases, I am, of course, not *really* faced with converging frequency ratios; it is merely postulated that the same logic applies to the two kinds of situation.

Laplace, too, found it convincing to express the absence of prior information by the assumption that the decision maker assigns the same initial probabilities to the a priori possible cases, although he may have done a little more to keep us aware of the fact that these assumptions concerning the assignment of prior probabilities could be modified without changing the essential characteristics of the approach.[5] In the modern versions of the Bayesian approach, account is taken of the fact that in most cases the decision maker has initial hunches which make it inappro-

---

[5] On pp. x and xi of his introductory comments to *Facsimiles of Two Papers by Bayes* (**4**) Edward C. Molina of the Bell Telephone Laboratories places great stress in this connection on a passage in Laplace's *Théorie analytique des probabilités* (3d ed., 1820, p. 184; Molina says p. 182). (**31**). In this passage, Laplace says quite explicitly that the prior probabilities need not be uniformly distributed among the a priori possible hypotheses. But I think Molina makes too much of this passage because Laplace's discussion that follows the passage is concerned with situations where one of the a priori possible hypotheses becomes *cogently* excluded through an observation (for example, the possibility that an urn contains no balls of a specific color becomes excluded as soon as one ball of that color is observed). This is not really the problem of asymmetrically distributed prior hunches.

priate for him to start with *equal* prior probabilities for the possible outcomes, say, with the probabilities ½–½ for Laplace's two urns. In what sense such tentative judgments are or are not rooted in prior information is a moot question: They need not be rooted in any *articulate* information. The crude initial guesses of the individual in question may, for example, be expressed by the prior probabilities ⅚–⅙. The neo-Bayesian approach would then consider these degrees of belief the same kind of probabilities as those which are derived from, say, a die-rolling experiment when the chances of rolling a nonace must be estimated. The Bayesian decision maker with the initial hunch 5 ÷ 1 in favor of one of the two urns acts *as if* he were guaranteed that nature had selected his urn by means of such a die-rolling experiment; and it is these prior probabilities which the Bayesian decision maker is gradually correcting in the light of successive drawings from the urn, drawings that gradually provide clues about the true composition of the urn which he faces. Before any drawings have taken place, the decision maker knows, of course, that the initially conjectured probability ratio of, say, 5 ÷ 1 may be too high or too low; but his doubts in this regard are symmetrical, and by the Principle of Insufficient Reason his doubts become neutralized.

At any rate, in the eighteenth-century as well as in the modern versions of the Bayes-Laplace approach, the theorems of probability theory, originally developed for processes producing repetitive events with convergence characteristics, are extended to degrees of belief in general. The concept of probability becomes extended even to degrees of belief the origins of which are exceedingly hazy to the decision maker. It is implied that the decision weights to be attached to alternative prospects are degrees of belief satisfying the rules of probability theory—hence, that they are to be regarded as probabilities—irrespective of the source of these beliefs.

The seventeenth-, eighteenth-, and early nineteenth-century pioneers of probability theory were little concerned with the axiomatic foundations of their approaches. For example, when, in his *Essai philosophique sur les probabilités* of 1814 (**32**)—and also in his *Théorie analytique* (**31**)—Laplace built his analysis on Bayes's mid-eighteenth-century ideas, he did not explore the question of what, in terms of fundamentals, is involved in merging, under the heading of probability, degrees of belief the origins of which are quite different. It is not even clear—at least not clear to the present writer—whether this extension or merger was a break with the seventeenth- and the *early* eighteenth-century tradition because, until very recently, most statements about the philosophic foundations of probability were very casual. What *is* clear is that in the second half of the eighteenth century, Bayes suggested a systematic method of linking judgments based on frequency observations with judgments which are probabilistic *only* in the sense in which complete ignorance may be regarded as 50–50. Subsequently, Laplace approved of this, but how the earlier masters would have reacted to this suggestion is hard to guess. The methodological position of most writers of the following generations also seems to have remained unclear.

Much later, from his 1919 publication on, Richard von Mises (**36**) felt convinced that his own contribution was the first to clear up this central point of methodology thoroughly. He did indeed sharpen the issue considerably, and thereby he contributed importantly to its clarification. But Mises moved in a direction contrary to that in which the discussion seems to be moving at the present time.

Mises was a thorough-going *frequentist* (objectivist) who maintained that the concept of probability could be applied only to sets of events—collectives—which satisfy the condition of randomness and in which the tendency of frequency ratios to converge on some theoretical value is "observable." To Mises, the scope of applicability of probability theory was similar to that which we have described as the minimum scope (see Section 3). The physical collectives to which Mises *limited* the application of probability theory have the characteristic that a sufficient increase in the number of trials clearly tends to make a frequency ratio converge on some definite number, or on some number falling within a very small range; and they have the characteristic that this number, or this small range, remains the same regardless of where we start counting the trials and regardless of which trials we omit in a random fashion when observing the results. These, of course, are the physical analogues of the phenomena generated by the ideal coin, the ideal die, etc.

It seems to me that as Richard von Mises, the mathematician, represented the positive side of the strict frequentist position, F. H. Knight, the economist, may be said to have represented its negative side (**29**). While Mises was interested in what it *was* possible to achieve in the natural sciences and in the analysis of insurance problems, etc., with the aid of a probability concept based on converging frequency ratios, Knight arrived at the conclusion that entrepreneurial decisions and profits could *not* be explained by considerations which would apply also to frequency probabilities. To take a simple illustration, if someone acts on the assumption that profits on an investment are more likely to be positive than negative, he must take action without the benefit of observations relating to frequency ratios such as tend to convergence on some specific true value. The experience of businessmen includes significant classes of data which do not have the property of pointing more or less conclusively to a single, numerically correct "mean value" of the kind which is approached in the heads-or-tails illustration as the number of observed data is increased. It is more as if each time a different kind of biased coin were flipped, any kind *just once*. Such a collective is, of course, not well behaved by the criteria of the frequentists, and the strict frequentist-objectivist position does not recognize the existence of a legitimate *probabilistic* problem for decision makers concerned with such events. Mises placed the emphasis on the fact that reasonably well-behaved collectives do exist in many areas of scientific inquiry; Knight's analysis drove it home to his fellow economists that business decisions are mostly based on observations relating to collectives which by these standards are *not* well behaved. It is true that Knight called the problem of entrepreneurial judgments also one of "probabilities"—in a different sense from that of frequency probabilities—but he might just as well have denied these judgments that name: He did not suggest a general system of rules (a body of theory) within which frequency probabilities, on the one hand, and business appraisals, on the other, would have fallen in their proper places. The concept of business profits, on the one hand, and that of gains and losses in frequency-probabilistic situations, on the other, did not emerge from a unified basic theory.

In the Knightian analysis the problems to which the concept of frequency probability *was* properly applicable were termed problems of risk. The problems involving conjectures to which the concept of frequency probability was *not* applicable he called problems of uncertainty. He concluded that entrepreneurial decisions and profits belong in the theory of uncertainty, not in that of risk.

The difficulty with the Knightian reasoning is that it does not develop a *theory* of uncertainty. Knight's analysis suggests that if there does exist a useful theory of uncertainty, it must be different from the theory of probability in the sense of the frequentist-objectivists, except that there exist borderline problems which it is difficult to classify. The discussion which Knight presented was apt to leave the reader with the impression that in matters of uncertainty, to which the frequency concepts are not applicable, "anything goes." Several authorities in mathematical economics, including Kenneth J. Arrow (3), have felt (rightly, I think) that this somewhat anarchic inclination results from Knight's conviction that the field should be left completely open for the creativeness of the decision maker under uncertainty.

Yet, even if degrees of belief *in general*—not only those relating to Mises' well-behaved collectives—were subjected to the uniform rules of probability, this would merely imply that the entire set of degrees of belief which an individual develops must obey the internal consistency requirements of probability theory. The act of *developing* a set of degrees of belief without the guidance of the numerical values of textbook probabilities—that is, for universes in which converging frequency ratios are not observable—would still leave the creative faculties of the decision maker all the room these faculties can reasonably claim. A useful decision theory must be able to draw a distinction between consistent behavior, on the one hand, and erroneous or wholly whimsical behavior, on the other. In matters which all theorists regard as probabilistic (matters involving convergent frequency ratios), untutored individuals can and do make mistakes which, we all agree, need to be corrected; it is unsatisfactory to argue that in matters of decision making under uncertainty, complete lawlessness is in order. While Knight may not have intended to suggest a wholly anarchic attitude to what he regarded as the area of uncertainty, he has left many of his readers with the impression that the main difference between risk and uncertainty is that an articulate theory was applicable to the former but not to the latter.

Over the past 10 or 15 years the pendulum has been swinging the other way. We now have a well-developed school of thought that insists on the validity of probabilistic rules for degrees of belief in general, that is, on the applicability of probability theory to the whole area of rational decision making. The main pioneering achievement in the modern phase of development was that of Frank Ramsey (43), an English mathematical logician in Cambridge who died very young in January, 1930. The theory was developed further by Bruno de Finetti in Italy (19), by L. J. Savage in the United States (45), and more recently by several other important contributors. The views of the school in question are usually referred to as *subjectivistic* or *personalistic*.

According to these views, the same logical criteria should be applied to the degrees of belief relating to, say, stock prices or the outcome of elections, etc., as to experiments with practically fair coins. No one denies, of course, that an element of objectivity enters into the degrees of belief concerning the conventional coin experiments to a much greater extent than into degrees of belief concerning the stock exchange, since most intelligent people admittedly arrive at (practically) the identical degrees of belief about (practically) fair coins, while the degrees of belief relating to the stock exchange, to business investments of all sorts, to political elections, etc., are subjective not only *in principle*, but are subjective in the essential sense of reflecting very wide interpersonal differences of appraisal even among the well informed.

Yet the purely probabilistic version of the subjectivist doctrine, which expresses itself most completely in Savage's theory, maintains that in their decision processes, intelligent individuals should *in general* attach to (prospective) events weights which obey the laws of probability theory, regardless of how their degrees of belief concerning these prospects were derived. Their decision weights should obey these laws irrespective of which of their degrees of belief are interpersonally controversial and which are *de facto* uncontroversial, and also regardless of which of these beliefs are stable in the mind of the decision maker and which are of an unstable, vacillating kind. According to the purely probabilistic decision theory, the behavior of a reasonable person should, for example, not show the following two traits at the same time: (*a*) a preference for making a prize contingent on the rolling of a nonace with a fair die over making the same prize contingent on the rise of specific stock prices, and (*b*) a preference for making a specific prize contingent on the rolling of an ace with a fair die over making the same prize contingent on the prospect that the stock prices in question will not rise. If, given the identical initial circumstances, a person shows both these traits, then, according to the Ramsey–de Finetti–Savage theory, he is making a mistake. This is because the theory in question implies that in terms of *fair-die probability equivalents* the decision weights attached to the two stock exchange prospects should add up to unity (just as the probability of a die-rolling event and that of its complement add up to unity); and this condition requires that, given our individual's preference under (*a*) above, he should show the contrary preference under (*b*) above. When staking his fortunes on these events, the individual we were considering attached to the prospect "the stocks will rise" a decision weight which behaviorally is the equivalent of *less* than a die probability of $\frac{5}{6}$; and he attached to the prospect "the stocks will not rise" a weight with a die probability equivalent of *less* than $\frac{1}{6}$. According to the purely probabilistic decision theory, such a person *should* correct his behavior, just as a person who acts as if two heads in a row with a practically fair coin had some probability other than $\frac{1}{4}$ should mend his ways. The meaning of this presumably is that intelligent individuals, if properly informed about the nature of the problems we are discussing, *do* on reflection accept the Ramsey–de Finetti–Savage principles and that they then *do* tend to act according to these postulates.

Over the past 10 or 15 years, but particularly since 1954, when

Savage's *Foundations of Statistics* (**45**) was published, the purely probabilistic "subjectivist" or "personalistic" position has been gaining ground.
The work of the statistical decision theorists Robert Schlaifer (**48**) and
Howard Raiffa (**33, 48**) has been moving along these lines. The contributions of Harry Markowitz (**34**) and James Tobin (**52**) to the economic problem of portfolio selection and the work of Thomas C. Schelling (**47**) on the theory of bargaining have also been influenced by these
ideas. These are merely a few outstanding examples. As concerns the
views to be expressed in the present volume, these views are subjectivistic
or personalistic; but if judged by the standards of the purely probabilistic
position, they are somewhat heretical. The present writer wishes to make
allowances for a fact which has been recognized also in the earlier work
of N. Georgescu-Roegen (**16**) and more recently by C. A. B. Smith (**51**).
This fact is that many reasonable individuals feel more uneasy about
action based on mere hunches—on shaky and highly controversial degrees of belief—than about action motivated by well-established and
firmly held numerical appraisals. As we see it, the firm judgments usually
also have the characteristic of being interpersonally noncontroversial
(hence, in a sense, "objective"). The shaky probability judgments are
those which are appreciably influenced by "elusive hypotheses" (see Introduction). In practice, the appraisal of elusive hypotheses is invariably
a controversial matter, and the probablity judgments which are appreciably influenced by such hypotheses are frequently revised. In some
cases a person may feel eager to base an act on an unstable and controversial judgment and more reluctant to base it on a firm judgment, but
these cases would appear to be rare. What matters is that according to
the semiprobabilistic position, which I shall be presenting here, reasonable individuals are entitled to feel *differently* about relying on one or
the other of these *various types* of judgments. (I am using here Version
1 terminology, the pros and cons of which as compared to Version 2
terminology were appraised in the Introduction to the volume.)

While in the purely probabilistic framework of de Finetti, Savage,
etc., the position I am describing here is indeed heretical, I should like to
make it clear from the outset that I have no intention of reverting to the
presubjectivist state of affairs, which was one of anarchy concerning all
degrees of belief other than those derived from converging frequency
ratios. A reasonable and consistent individual is, I feel, entitled to deviate
from the de Finetti–Savage criteria of decision making, but he must do
this *in a systematic fashion*. He must satisfy the consistency requirements
of semiprobabilistic behavior. Furthermore, I shall, of course, recognize

the existence of purely probabilistic individuals who in their decision processes do tend to behave according to the de Finetti–Savage principles, that is to say, do place practically all their decision weights on a par with coin or die probabilities. This, in short, is the position I shall take.

(5) The Purely Probabilistic Subjectivist Theory Contrasted with Modified Versions

We have seen that even in the simplest cases where there is little doubt about the correct numerical value of probabilities, certain difficulties are encountered in efforts to test the probabilistic character of behavior operationally. Take tosses of a practically fair coin, the rolling of a practically fair die, or drawings from a thoroughly shuffled deck of regular French cards. Such processes we shall call *standard processes*. The subject may suspect that a trick is involved in the experiment, but let us disregard this possibility. He may find it more enjoyable to win on red than on black, or on heads than on tails; when small differences are at stake, he may act whimsically rather than as a maximizer, etc. These difficulties do exist even for standard processes. For these processes, one should be able to get around most of the difficulties; but even in these simple situations, nonoperational methods—discussion, interrogation, etc.—may serve a useful purpose *after* completion of the operational tests. Some degree of conditioning is required, at any event, to make a person behave probabilistically; but for the standard processes, some of this conditioning is achieved by the general educational processes of Western countries; and if additional conditioning is needed, this usually comes as easily as the act of convincing an intelligent person that in matters of physics or chemistry, he should trust the textbook or the expert.

The difficulties of conducting valid operational tests increase significantly if we turn to degrees of belief which are not rooted in frequency observations. This may, to some extent, be a consequence of the fact that at present only a minority of the experts would be willing to engage in the same kind of conditioning for nonstandard sets of events as for standard processes. It is a fact that the educational system *does* instill in us a conviction that once we regard a coin as unbiased, we should follow the textbook rules of probability in forming our expectations concerning the outcome of tosses, but the educational system *does not* at present make us feel foolish or whimsical if we show simultaneously the two traits described on page 32. No one knows what changes in attitudes would develop if the undiluted de Finetti–Savage position were thoroughly sold to the professions, the views of which dominate our educational processes.

Even if an effort were made to condition the population to these views, the effort might backfire, since people who were taught to disregard some of their basic inclinations will sometimes develop delayed reactions by which they subsequently deprive their teachers of influence in practically *all* respects. No one really knows how *fundamental* (in this sense) the inclination of many people is to behave differently, depending on whether they are confronted with nonstandard sets of events or with standard processes.

According to the purely probabilistic-subjectivist position, this inclination rests on erroneous reasoning, and intelligent people should tend to lose this inclination under the influence of proper tutoring. But this latter statement is much less clear-cut than some followers of Savage would like to have it, because it raises all the problems on which we have just been touching, problems connected with different degrees of conditioning and with the durability of the effect of various kinds of conditioning. At any rate, it is a fact that at present, only a minority of the profession would stand for the degree of conditioning the advocacy of which is implicit in the de Finetti–Savage position.

Let us look at this aspect of the problem more closely. Say that the behavior of a person shows both traits described on page 32. Our individual proves convinced of the fairness of a given die (that is, he is indifferent between staking his fortunes on even or on odd, and the prospect of "one or two or three" is demonstrably equally attractive to him as "four or five or six," etc.). However, our individual's behavior discloses that he consistently prefers to accept a prize contingent upon an ace rather than contingent upon a specific stock's *not* rising. Hence, when he bets on the prospect of a rise of the stock, he attaches to this prospect a decision weight which in terms of fair-die probabilities is less than $\frac{5}{6}$, and yet, when he bets on the prospect "no rise," he attaches to this prospect a decision weight which in terms of fair-die probabilities is less than $\frac{1}{6}$. We shall see that there are strong reasons to assume that an appreciable proportion of intelligent individuals behaves in this or in some similar fashion. What inference should we draw from this?

To be sure, one inference we may wish to draw is that such individuals have failed to understand their decision problems. The stock must obviously either rise or not rise. Savage's school does indeed maintain that our individual is making a mistake (or discloses a kind of imperfection from which no theory is free). The charge of confused behavior is at present not *generally* accepted. According to the present volume, the phenomenon which we are considering is too significant to be called an imperfection. Nor shall we raise the charge of confused behavior against individuals showing such behavior, provided their behavior satisfies a specific set of consistency requirements which will be discussed later in this volume. It will be seen later that these requirements of consistency include not only transitivity of preferences among bets but also ability to draw the proper inferences from randomization opportunities that *may be* available to the decision maker. Such randomization opportunities may set limits to the size of the discount at which a rational decision maker can place his stock exchange probabilities (and the like) relative to his fair-coin or fair-die probabilities. But we wish to take account of the fact that the lesser psychological stability and the interpersonally controversial character[6] of various nonstandard process probabilities may legitimately make some individuals more reluctant (and others perhaps more willing) to base acts on these judgments than on standard process probabilities. This is how some probabilities become "slanted" (are placed at a discount), i.e., are turned into decision weights which are systematically distorted probabilities. Slanting implies, of course, a difference between how disturbing it is to suffer an opportunity loss by having based an act on a flimsy hunch and how disturbing it is to suffer an opportunity loss by not having followed such a hunch. Some tentative ideas about conditions under which slanting inclinations may tend to decrease—though hardly to disappear—were expressed in Section 3 of the Introduction to this volume.

(6) The Basic Methodological Issue

As I said before, the analysis of the preceding section is concerned with a question that places us in a borderline area between normative and positive economics. After all, what criteria are available for deciding whether deviations from purely probabilistic norms which we observe on the behavior of intelligent individuals are or are not legitimate ones?

It might be possible to expose various groups of individuals to strong conditioning along the de Finetti–Savage lines—the purely probabilistic lines—and to discover whether they actually get rid of the impurity in question. Subsequently, it might be possible to expose the same persons to the argument according to which this impurity or deviation is a legitimate property of preference systems, and then to examine the question whether conversion has or has not been a one-way road. It might be possible to examine systematically also the question whether the reaction

---

[6] I mean "controversial" even if all information which it is practically possible to articulate is shared.

of various groups of subjects to these two kinds of conditioning is or is not correlated with their intelligence as gauged by independent criteria. These would be difficult experiments which so far have not been carried out in any satisfactory form. Some day, they will perhaps be performed.

Very modest experiments—faint copies of the grand experiment about which I was speculating in the preceding passage—have been undertaken on various occasions, but they have not *decided* the issue at hand. At least one author, Howard Raiffa of Harvard University, claims that his experiments point to peoples' mending their ways—to their getting rid of the impurity—when exposed to purely probabilistic conditioning. I happen to place somewhat more confidence in observations which suggest a strong inclination to persist in the deviation in circumstances where the subject has been exposed to *both* arguments before making his final decision. In the Appendix to the present volume (Chapter 9), I shall report on some such experiments. But I should like to say in advance that I consider it a much more characteristic trait of this volume that it is a volume on subjective probability than that it is somewhat heretical by the specific standards of de Finetti and Savage.

I share the belief that the subjectivistic view will continue to gain ground over the frequentist (objectivistic) view, and I expect distinct benefits from this change. In the past the dominance of the objectivist position led some scholars to exclude from the area of rational decision theory many problems of great significance which are not amenable to objectivist methods. Other investigators were led to adapting objectivist methods to the requirements set by these problems, but the adaptations which have become fashionable merely hide and obscure the role of essential subjective factors, thereby giving the wrong impression that consensus should exist about various numerical results which in reality are legitimately controversial. These are undesirable consequences of limiting the concept of probability to problems involving convergent frequency ratios. Basically, they are undesirable consequences of the objectivist orientation in probability theory. I believe that in retrospect the observable spread of the subjectivist view will be interpreted as a process of liberation.

(7) Significance of the Problem for Economic Theory

The problem which in this chapter was discussed merely in a preliminary fashion bears quite directly on the concept of profit in economics. Indirectly, it bears on practically all matters with which economic theory is concerned.

Before we get around to problems of profit theory in the conventional sense (Chapters 4, 5, and 7), quite a bit will be said about conditions under which individuals are indifferent between alternatives. Real and imaginary tests of probabilistic and of semiprobabilistic behavior involve situations of this sort.

However, in the economic theory of profit, conditions of this sort play merely the role of benchmarks. If a person is free to decide how much to bet on a prospect for which the market has set the terms, he will place himself in a situation of indifference at the margin of his betting, that is, for the last dollar which he puts up in that specific venture. This usually implies that in the intramarginal region of his betting, he makes a gain in terms of expected utility; that is to say, he acquires a utility surplus which may be of substantial size. The probabilistic view of profit leads to the conclusion that the profit-maximizing individual should be interpreted as maximizing this kind of surplus. This profit which he maximizes is always a nonnegative magnitude.

Obviously, we are talking here about an ex ante surplus. Ex post surpluses may be positive, zero, or negative. Their algebraic sign and their size depend partly on the element of luck. They depend importantly also on how skillful the probability judgments of the decision maker were. This last sentence relates to the kind of profit with which economic theory is concerned (business profit), but not to ex post profits from heads-or-tails bets, because it takes no skill to look up the probabilities for tosses of a fair coin. The difference between probabilities the numerical values of which have become well established by conventional methods and probabilities the appraisal of which requires skill and flair is of very great practical importance. Even the purely probabilistic decision theory recognizes this clearly; and in a semiprobabilistic approach, it will have to be added that as a result of this difference, it is not in general possible to reconstruct the precise numerical values of the decision maker's nonstandard process probabilities from his observable decision weights. While, for the nonstandard processes, merely probability ranges can be established by observation, it remains true that in the analysis of the present volume, as well as in the purely probabilistic theory, the concept of business profits and that of frequency-probabilistic gains emerge from the *identical* theoretical structure.

Chapter 2

A CLOSER LOOK AT THE FREQUENTIST, THE SUBJECTIVIST, AND THE BAYESIAN APPROACHES

(1) *Reminder of the Classical Origins*

While the seventeenth- and eighteenth-century pioneers had laid the foundations for the frequency theory, the most radical twentieth-century frequentist, Richard von Mises, was in some ways more critical of these masters than are the modern subjectivists. This is because the early masters were *also* the founders of the subjectivist approach. As we saw, they did not distinguish between these two views carefully at all (see Chapter 1, Section 4).

Laplace (**31**, **32**), for example, usually proceeded on the assumption that by dividing the number of *favorable* outcomes by the number of *possible* outcomes an obviously acceptable value of a probability can be obtained, regardless of whether such a frequency ratio does or does not show a tendency to converge on a definite value and, in general, regardless of the properties of the set of events for which such a ratio was observed. Indeed, Laplace defined probability as the ratio of favorable to possible outcomes, and this conception is implicit also in the earlier work of Jacques Bernoulli, Thomas Bayes, and others. From the point of view of a modern frequentist, this conception is wrong because a frequentist would argue that unless the set of events (the collective) is well behaved by his standards, no probabilities can be established for the events, while if the collective is well behaved, then the probabilities are defined by the limit values of frequency ratios. Modern subjectivists have misgivings of a different sort against the suggestion that the number of possible (i.e., of *equally* possible) outcomes is given from the outset and can serve as a basis for a general definition of probability in Laplace's fashion. According to the modern subjectivists, if a person regards n outcomes as equally possible (equiprobable), then thereby he already implies a probability judgment which others may or may not share with him. The Laplace definition falls between the frequentist definition (limit values of frequency ratios) and the subjectivistic definition (degrees of belief), as indeed many of the early masters took off from uncertain grounds and moved sometimes in one direction and sometimes in the other.

Occasionally, this had undesirable by-products. In particular, some of the subjective numerical probability judgments for which Laplace claimed general validity, and which he obtained by taking the ratio of favorable outcomes to *allegedly* equally possible outcomes, seem highly implausible to any modern reader.

But after having mentioned these slips, we shall not refer to them again. For what matters more is the fact that both the basic theorems which are of crucial importance for the frequentist approach *and* some of the basic propositions of the theory of subjective probability have their origins in the contributions of the early masters. Modern scholars are well aware of this debt, despite occasional strictures.

(2) The Frequency Theory of Richard von Mises

The first German edition of Richard von Mises' book *Probability, Statistics and Truth* was published in 1928 (36). Even in the subsequent revised editions, this work remained organized into six "Lectures."[1] In the first Lecture the author performed the following experiment: He placed 90 round discs bearing the numbers 1–90 in a bag; he drew a disc from the bag and then replaced the disc, mixing it in thoroughly with the others; he repeated this operation 100 times. Each time he registered the symbol 1 if the number was odd and the symbol 0 if the number was even. The table he obtained contained these entries:

```
1 1 0 0 0 1 1 1 0 1
0 0 1 1 0 0 1 1 1 1
0 1 0 1 0 0 1 0 0 0
0 1 0 0 1 0 0 1 1 1
0 0 1 1 0 0 0 0 1 1
0 1 1 1 1 0 1 0 1 0
1 0 1 1 1 1 0 0 1 1
0 0 1 1 0 1 1 1 0 1
0 0 1 1 0 0 1 1 0 1
0 1 1 0 0 0 1 0 0 0
```

Mises explained to his audience that from a table of this sort, one gets a very strong indication that the relative frequency with which this process produces odd and even tends to about ½ for each. The total number of odd in the 100 drawings was 51, although we find four columns and one row with as many as seven entries of odd, and one column with

[1] The latest (revised) English translation was prepared by Hilda Geiringer from the third German edition (1951 edition), and it was published by the Macmillan Co. in 1957.

as few as two. But in a set of 100 drawings the basic tendency usually comes through with reasonable clarity; and in an exceedingly large set, it *almost always* comes through clearly, i.e., the relative frequency of odd and of even will *almost always* be in the neighborhood of ½. (For the "almost always" clause, see page 17, above.)

Consider now also the following: The reader may convince himself of the fact that our statements about the collective which Mises has constructed from his experiment remain valid if we consider only every second drawing of those registered in Mises' matrix—say the drawings in the first, third, etc., row, or those in the first, third, etc., column. They remain valid also if we omit the first half or the second half of a large number of drawings. Indeed, they continue to be valid regardless of what arbitrary rule we adopt for omitting and retaining entries placed one way or another (so long as the rule is not deliberately constructed in such a way as to be *selective* for odd and even). The set of events of which the collective consists satisfies the conditions of randomness. This is another way of saying that no useful statement can be made about the *individual* characteristics of the successive drawings that yielded even or of those that yielded odd. When faced with such a collective, the decision maker has no possibility of inventing a gambling system.[2]

It has become usual to call an observation such as "r even numbers in a total of n drawings" a sufficient statistic if the collective of drawings satisfies the condition of randomness just described, i.e., the condition that no additional useful knowledge is conveyed by information about the characteristics of the individual drawings (or groups of drawings) which produced this or that result. The elementary events of which such collectives of events consist—here the events even and odd—are called random events, and numerical variables which stand for random events (Mises' 0 and 1) are random variables. Collectives which have the property of almost always producing convergent frequency ratios, and of being made up of random events, disclosing no relevant individual characteristics such as could explain the differences between the outcomes in individual instances, are said thereby to satisfy the Law of Large Num-

[2] The following is a corollary of the two properties described in the text, i.e., of the convergence on a limit value and of the impossibility of a gambling system (randomness). If a long sequence of drawings becomes established where each member of the sequence consists of a *great many* individual drawings, then the tendency will be toward the identical relative frequency in the overwhelming majority of these many separate large sets of drawings. Almost all individual collectives of which such a supercollective is made up show a tendency toward identical frequency ratios, provided the number of items included in each collective is made large enough. This must be true of the collectives to which Mises' theory—the strict frequency theory—is applicable at all. The value on which the observed frequency ratios of (say) even converge, when the number of items included in the collective is increased further and further, is here defined as the probability (p) of drawing even.

bers. At least, this is what we shall mean here by this term (which is mostly used in this sense).

Given a Mises-type collective, which is defined by the properties of convergence and randomness, it is possible also to make essential statements about the probability of obtaining any specified number of successes, and of obtaining the corresponding "success *ratio*" or "frequency *ratio* of success,"[3] in trials of any given length (e.g., in Mises' case the probability of 49 even in 100 drawings, or the probability of no less than 49 and no more than 51 even in 100 drawings, etc.). These probabilities will tend to establish themselves if an experiment involving n drawings is repeated many times. In his Lectures, Mises used a particularly simple illustration of a collective possessing the traits of convergence and randomness—i.e., of a *Mises-type* collective—and the statement we have just made will now be explained with reference to the kind of collective he used for illustration. But even at this point the reader should remember that analogous propositions about the probabilities of various outcomes in trials of various lengths can be deduced for Mises-type collectives in cases where we wish to distinguish more than just *two* elementary events (say clubs, diamonds, hearts, and spades), so that the distribution becomes multinomial rather than binomial; and also for collectives in which the probabilities depend on events in other collectives, etc.

If the experiment consists of trying for one of two events, and if the event in question—say the drawing of odd—has a well-defined and stable (equal) probability in the various drawings, then the probability of r successes in n drawings is called a binomial probability (P_b). A binomial probability can be assigned to the prospect that in any specific number of drawings the actually observed number of successes will assume any specified value.[4] Thus, we can also deduce the cumulated binomial probability of the prospect that in n drawings the observed

---

[3] The term "relative frequency" of successes is also used for expressing this ratio.

[4] The derivation of these probabilities (P_b) is based on reasoning which is closely related to that underlying the binomial expansion in algebra. If in a process generating independent events with stable probability ("Bernoulli process," named for Jacques Bernoulli) the probability of success is p and the probability of failure is q (where $q = 1 - p$), then the binomial probability of obtaining precisely r successes in n trials is

$$P_b(r|n, p) = \frac{n!}{r!\,(n-r)!}\, p^r q^{n-r}$$

The relationship between this formula and the binomial theorem is described by the following: If the value of the foregoing expression is summed for all values of r from zero to n, then the resulting expression equals $(p + q)^n$. That is,

$$\sum_{r=0}^{n} \frac{n!}{r!\,(n-r)!}\, p^r q^{n-r} = (p + q)^n$$

Note that the binomial probabilities for which numerical values will be given in the text are

number of successes, or (alternatively) the observed frequency *ratio* of successes, will fall between any two chosen limits around any specified

---

cumulated for a *range* of successes, that is, for a range of possible values of *r*, given the value of *n* (say, for no less than four and no more than six successes in ten trials, etc.).

With an *unlimited increase of the number of trials* (*n*) the number of possible outcomes also increases without limit, and any precisely specified outcome (*r*) becomes infinitely improbable. Yet, if the continuous distribution, which is thus being approached as the number of trials (drawings) grows, is a *normal* (Gaussian) distribution, as is here the case, then the following becomes true: Multiplication of *that proportion* of all trials in which the *mean outcome* (*np* successes) is observed—i.e., multiplication of the relative frequency of the outcome "*np* successes in *n* trials"—by the standard deviation of the outcomes about the mean yields an algebraic product which tends to a numerical *constant*; the value of this constant is $\dfrac{1}{\sqrt{2\pi}}$ (approximately 0.4).

Hence, when $n \to \infty$, then in the resulting continuous frequency distribution in which we express all our magnitudes in terms of units of standard deviation, the *mean outcome* (*np* successes) is assigned the relative frequency $\dfrac{1}{\sqrt{2\pi}}$ (as measured in standard deviation units). Furthermore, the relative frequency of an outcome that *deviates from the mean outcome* (*np* successes) by *t* standard deviations (in either direction) can be shown to tend, with $n \to \infty$, to $e^{-\frac{1}{2}t^2}$ times the relative frequency of the mean outcome. That is to say, when $n \to \infty$, then, for given values of *t*, or for given ranges of *t*, the ratio of the relative frequencies tends to a constant.

In general, the Gaussian (normal) distribution may be written, in standardized form, as $P_N^*(t) = \dfrac{1}{\sqrt{2\pi}} e^{-\frac{1}{2}t^2}$. Accordingly, as was seen a moment ago, we obtain for $t = 0$ the value $\dfrac{1}{\sqrt{2\pi}}$. The symbol *t* expresses, in units of standard deviation, the deviation of the outcome (*r*) from the mean outcome (*np*).

For any sufficiently large *n*, the foregoing implies a method of very closely approximating the probability of the outcome described as "the number of successes will deviate from *np*, in a specified direction (up or down), by *t* times the standard deviation." The method is to divide $\dfrac{1}{\sqrt{2\pi}} e^{-\frac{1}{2}t^2}$ by the *standard deviation*. The latter is $\sqrt{npq}$ for the distribution in question. Integration of the P_N^* function over finite ranges enables us to approximate in this fashion the probability of the outcome's (*r* successes) falling in the range over which we integrate.

If *p* is not very different from *q* (i.e., from $1 - p$), then it takes a smaller value of *n* to make the normal approximation to the binomial distribution a good approximation than if *p* and *q* are very different from one another.

The conclusion that, when $n \to \infty$, the binomial distribution becomes the normal distribution with the foregoing properties, follows from the Central Limit Theorem.

Note that while, according to the theorem, the standard deviation of the *number of successes* about the mean number is $\sqrt{npq}$ and hence grows with *n*, the standard deviation of the *success ratios* about the mean *ratio* is $\sqrt{\dfrac{pq}{n}}$, and hence declines with rising *n*. The frequency distribution of the success ratios (i.e., of the frequency ratios of successes) is of course derived from the distribution of numbers of successes by substituting $\dfrac{r}{n}$ for *r* in describing an observed outcome, and by substituting *p* for *np* in defining the mean outcome. In Mises' case, $n = 100$; $r = 51$ if odd is defined as success; and $r = 49$ if even is defined as success ($\dfrac{r}{n}$ equals 0.51 and 0.49, respectively, and $p = 0.5$).

value. It can be shown that *regardless of how narrow we decide to make the range between the two limits around the true probability* (*p*) *of an event*, the probability P_b of the actual *frequency ratio's* falling in that narrow range around *p* will tend to *one* as the number of drawings (*n*) is made ever greater. For example, in the experiment we have described, the value of *p* for drawing odd is ½, because even and odd happen to be equiprobable events, although all that matters for the present problem is that each of the two events should have the same probability in any one drawing as in any other; given *p* = ½, the value of P_b for obtaining in *10* drawings (*n* = 10) a frequency ratio[5] of no smaller than 0.4 and no greater than 0.6 is nearly ⅔; by the time we get up to *100* drawings (*n* = 100), the value of P_b for obtaining a frequency ratio which is no smaller than 0.4 and no greater than 0.6 has risen to 0.96; and for 100 drawings the value of P_b for obtaining a frequency ratio of no smaller than 0.47 and no greater than 0.53 is already in excess of ½. For *n* = 1,000 and *p* = ½, the probability P_b of the range from 0.47 to 0.53[6] is about 0.95. Tangentially, it may be mentioned that Mises needed a little bit of luck to hit the range "no more than 51 and no less than 49 odd" in merely 100 drawings. The probability (P_b) of this range is somewhat less than ¼.

As we have seen, in some of the best-known pieces of reasoning of the early writers, these theorems have been deduced from the postulate that odd and even are equally possible (equiprobable), and that the results of the successive drawings are independent of each other. Already in the seventeenth century, Jacques Bernoulli justified this initial judgment of equiprobability by the Principle of Insufficient Reason, that is, by the principle that the decision maker has no more reason to expect even than to expect odd. On the other hand, Mises' way of looking at the matter led him to say (in effect): By experiments, we can convince any reasonable person of the proposition that in certain collectives the frequency ratios tend to a specific value, and that these tendencies remain the same if by some *ad hoc* rule we omit variously placed items from such collectives; hence, we conclude that in these collectives the frequency ratios have a theoretical (or true) value, which we call the *probability* of the event whose frequency is being measured. Having thus demonstrated all this, it becomes appropriate to apply to such physical collectives the theorems of probability theory which were deduced for idealized collectives possessing the foregoing properties by definition.

---

[5] This means here the ratio of odd to odd plus even.
[6] In symbols, the binomial probability of this particular range would be expressed as P_b (470 ≤ *r* ≤ 530 | *n* = 1,000, *p* = ½).

Mises would no doubt have wanted us to add that for such collectives the cumulated binomial probability P_b of the frequency ratios' falling between specific limits around the true values p of these ratios is also empirically observable, in that a series of experiments will convince any reasonable person of that tendency, too. Of this, the early writers were surely aware, even if, when stating the equiprobability of odd and even, or of red and black from a half-and-half urn, they relied on the Principle of Insufficient Reason rather than on a set of initial observations. Mises criticized them sharply for their reliance on the Principle of Insufficient Reason, because the latter is capable of being extended to situations of subjective ignorance, while Mises wished to limit the concept of probability to collectives with "observably" converging frequency ratios.

The real benefit which we may derive from Mises' presentation does not, I feel, coincide precisely with what he intended this benefit to be. To the present writer, as to subjectivists in general, probabilities mean degrees of belief concerning prospects of all sorts, rather than observable values on which frequency ratios converge in particular collectives. Indeed, I consider it objectionable even to state without qualification that the convergence of some frequency ratios is observable. Yet, I do believe that the collectives with which Mises was concerned, to the exclusion of others, possess certain distinctive characteristics, and that these deserve to be emphasized in any theory of probability and of decision making.

(3) Appraisal of the Frequentist Position: What to Think of Its Objectivist Claims

A person may watch drawings of odd and even, or of red and black, to the end of his days, and yet he will not observe the theoretical value of any frequency in the sense in which he observes that a number is odd or a color is red. Nor will he ever observe the theoretical value in the sense in which he observes the actual values of frequencies in finite samples. Insofar as a person makes a probability judgment about a physical process *of any kind*, he is making the subjective judgment that it is appealing to apply a mathematically defined measure to that process. This is *always* a subjective judgment. It is a subjective judgment not only if the decision maker is applying it to an event with distinctive individual characteristics, but also if by that judgment he merely approves of the proposition that in Mises' matrix the frequencies appear to converge.

Consequently, the frequentist-objectivist position would be acceptable only if it were possible to establish empirically a very sharp distinction between (on the one hand) sets of physical events which to practically all intelligent persons appear to be closely analogous to the hypothetical events generated by ideal coins and (on the other hand) events which do not compel the decision maker to use this analogy. Further, it would have to be an observable trait of practically all intelligent persons that while their degrees of belief are capable of being interpreted probabilistically when they relate to close physical analogues of the idealized processes, these beliefs are not capable of being so interpreted when the events are of a different kind.

Neither of these two conditions is satisfied. First, there exists a wide range of physical processes which are *more or less* analogous to the idealized processes of mathematical probability theory. Even the frequentists must admit that the phenomena which they accept as having a probabilistic character make up a spectrum ranging from *strong* cases, such as Mises' drawings from a bag, to *much weaker* cases, such as those illustrated by some of the less conventional insurance problems. Where one draws the line is clearly a matter of subjective judgment. This in itself greatly weakens the methodological foundations of the frequentist-objectivist position. Secondly, it has become obvious by now that a considerable number of highly intelligent people—including the prominant representatives of purely probabilistic decision theory—consider it compelling to apply the rules of probability to sets of events *in general*, that is, also to events which no one would consider more or less analogous to the idealized processes generating convergent frequency ratios. The frequentist-objectivist position is inadequate.

Yet the class of phenomena to which the strict frequentists limit their concern includes a hard core which does have a distinctive property. The category which a moment ago I called that of strong cases is more inclusive in the appraisal of some individuals than that of others, depending on the subjective characteristics of each person, but it is possible to find a number of physical processes about which there exists practical consensus among reasonable people. These processes have the property that, when faced with them, reasonable people can be convinced of its being advisable to rely exclusively on "straightforward" rather than on "elusive" hypotheses (page 13); and that it is useful to conclude that the observed frequency ratios tend to converge on a *numerically uncontroversial value or at least on some value which falls with practical certainty within an exceedingly narrow range.* In this particular sense, expectations relating to such specific collectives do have an "objective" character. Furthermore, many reasonable individuals feel differently about the numerically uncontroversial probability judgments relating to such collectives—numerical judgments which are almost certain to be confirmed by subsequent long-run experience—than they feel about numerically controversial degrees of belief and probability distributions relating to events in general. The highly controversial beliefs may be illustrated most vividly with events in relation to which the concept of converging frequency ratios would seem quite irrelevant. Many events bearing on the success of typical investment decisions in the economy belong in this category. Judgments concerning these events are controversial even among individuals who do their best to share their information.

Those who go along with my semiprobabilistic position should say: The collectives which belong in the hard core of frequentist illustrations have the property of being convenient points of reference in relation to which a reasonable person's system of discounts and premiums can be described. This is because in a world in which all events would fit into one of these hard-core collectives, no discounts or premiums would exist. Even the purely probabilistic group of the subjectivists—even those thoroughly convinced by the de Finetti–Savage views—should admit the validity of a proposition which to me seems crucial in this context. Going along with the purely probabilistic appraisal of some of Mises' "mass phenomena" *comes more naturally* than going along with the rule that if according to a person's momentary best guess a common stock is five times as likely to rise as not to rise, then he should act precisely as if he were trying to roll a nonace with a regular die. The advocates of purely probabilistic decision theory do, in fact, admit the existence of this difference. But they maintain that it is possible to convince intelligent decision makers of its being a requirement of consistency to overcome their initial inclinations and to behave identically in the two types of situations. This, of course, involves conditioning decision makers by means of some sort of extra effort. As the reader knows, I doubt that all (or practically all) intelligent decision makers would yield to this kind of conditioning, or that it would be in their interest to try to make them yield to it.

Having thus completed our brief discussion of the frequentist position, we shall now first consider the purely probabilistic approach in Section 4 and then turn to semiprobabilistic modifications in Section 5.

(4) The Purely Probabilistic Subjectivist Position: All Degrees of Belief Strictly Comparable, with No Discounts or Premiums

Those maintaining the position described by the title of this section consider the strict comparability of an individual's degrees of belief about events of various sorts a maxim of reasonable behavior. To be precise, in

L. J. Savage's presentation (**45**), this maxim is a corollary of seven explicit postulates—the maxim *follows* from seven explicit postulates—which relate to the preference ordering of acts and are of a very general character (see Chapter 6, Section 9). The purely probabilistic-subjectivist attitude can be well described with the aid of Bayesian analysis, which explains how the initial (prior) degrees of belief of a consistent decision maker become combined with conclusions based on subsequent factual observations when he forms his "posterior" probability judgments concerning future events. The validity of Bayesian analysis does not depend on whether, *given* the subjective prior probabilities, the numerical effect of the factual observations on the probabilities of future events is or is not interpersonally uncontroversial. But this effect *is* interpersonally uncontroversial *if* the factual observations are made on a sample drawn from a collective which is well behaved by frequentist criteria. In their illustrations, Bayes and Laplace did assume the availability of samples from such well-behaved collectives, and this procedure has the advantage of making it clear that the analysis links "subjective" with "objective" probabilities on an equal footing whenever well-behaved samples in the foregoing sense are available. In the present and in the next section of this chapter, we shall be concerned with such Bayesian blends of subjective probabilities with probabilities that would be acceptable even to thoroughgoing frequentists; but later, it will be explained that Bayes's theorem possesses general logical validity and hence is applicable also in frameworks which·are of subjectivist *or* of frequentist character *across the board.*[7]

A. *The Nature of the Bayesian Approach.* As we have already said, one of the simplest and best-known illustrations of this approach is found in Laplace's *Essai philosophique* (**32**) which in this regard was strongly influenced by Thomas Bayes's contribution (**4**).[8]

There are two balls in an urn, and we are guaranteed that *either* both balls are red, *or* both black, *or* one red and the other black.[9] The guarantee leaves the question open which of these possibilities holds for the specific urn we are actually facing. We draw a ball from the urn and observe that it is red. We replace the ball and draw once more at random from the same urn. We again draw red. We again replace the ball and ask ourselves the question *what the probability is of drawing red from*

[7] See Section 6 of the present chapter, and particularly Chapter 3, Section 3.

[8] See notes 4 and 5, p. 26; and p. 27.

[9] In Laplace's classic presentation the colors are white and black. In various illustrations of similar problems, I shall be using red and black (e.g., for cards), and I do not want to complicate the color scheme of the presentation at this point.

the same urn on the third drawing, too. The question is obviously analogous to questions one would like to be able to answer accurately for oneself in many situations of real life. It clearly relates to the testing and weighting of hypotheses. The decision maker's conjectures about his being possibly faced with one urn and about his being possibly faced with the other urn are hypotheses each of which is described by the value it assigns to the parameter "the true proportion of red." The task here is to weight these two hypotheses (on the basis of what may be regarded as a higher-order hypothesis relating to the proper weights). The problem is analogous to various problems involving economic materials (see Section 5, below, and Chapter 8).

The Bayes-Laplace[10] answer implies that it is obviously convincing to rely here on the rules of probability theory, even though the number of frequency observations is small. Being thus unable to observe the values on which frequency ratios converge, we must accord the status of probabilities also to our highly subjective guesses.

At the time when Laplace wants us to start the analysis—i.e., after two drawings—we know that the urn we are facing cannot contain two black balls but is either an *all-red* urn or a half-and-half *mixed* urn. Along Bayesian lines, Laplace assumed that our complete ignorance leads us to assign equal *prior* probabilities to these two hypotheses. That is to say, it is assumed that prior to any drawing, we considered these two hypotheses equiprobable. In forming our *posterior* probability judgment (after the drawing of red and red), we shall take account of the fact that on the all-red hypothesis the event which we have actually observed—the drawing of red and red—has unitary probability, while on the mixed-urn hypothesis, this result has the probability $\frac{1}{4}$. Hence, we assign to the all-red hypothesis a *posterior* probability which has four times the value of the *posterior* probability we assign to the mixed-urn hypothesis. On the all-red hypothesis concerning the urn, the probability of drawing red in the third drawing is *one*; while on the mixed-urn hypothesis, this probability is $\frac{1}{2}$. The probability one for drawing red on the next occasion must be weighted four times as heavily as the probability $\frac{1}{2}$, and this gives us the probability $\frac{9}{10}$ for obtaining red in the third drawing.

We shall now present these results with the aid of concepts and symbols the use of which has become conventional in the meantime, and which may be employed in a generalization of the analysis.

B. *Presentation with Reliance on the Now Usual Concepts and*

10 As was explained in n. 4, p. 26, Bayes used a different illustration.

Symbols. Let $P_i(A)$ stand for the prior probability (initial subjective probability) of the decision maker's becoming faced with an A-type urn, i.e., in our case with an all-red urn; $P_i(M)$ for the prior probability of his becoming faced with an M-type urn, i.e., in our case with a mixed urn (half red, half black); $P(A, RR)$ for the joint probability of his becoming faced with Urn A and of his drawing red and red from it; $P(RR|A)$ for the conditional probability of his drawing red and red, *given A*, i.e., assuming the condition that he actually is faced with A; $P(M, RR)$ for the joint probability of his becoming faced with Urn M *and* of his drawing red and red from it; $P(RR|M)$ for the conditional probability of his drawing red and red, *given M*. Then, according to what now usually is referred to as *Bayes's theorem:*

$$P(A, RR) = P_i(A) \cdot P(RR|A) \ \ldots \ldots \ldots \ldots \ldots \ldots \ldots \qquad (1)$$
$$P(M, RR) = P_i(M) \cdot P(RR|M) \ \ldots \ldots \ldots \ldots \ldots \ldots \qquad (2)$$

In words, the joint probability of becoming faced with A *and* of drawing red and red [the joint probability denoted by $P(A, RR)$] is the alegbraic product of the prior probability of becoming faced with A *and* of the conditional probability of drawing red and red, *given A*; and the analogous proposition holds for $P(M, RR)$. The conditional probabilities of making the observations which were actually made—i.e., terms such as $P(RR|A)$ and $P(RR|M)$—are said to represent *likelihoods*. It will be seen in a moment that Bayesian estimates are derived from likelihood *ratios* and from the *ratios* of prior probabilities. As a result of the fact that merely likelihood ratios are employed in any essential analysis, it is usual to define the likelihoods as functions of parameters describing the hypotheses (in this case, of parameters describing alternative potential urn compositions), *up to an arbitrary constant* for any given sample composition (e.g., for RR). Thus, we obtain a likelihood function for any given sample and for alternative hypotheses.[11]

We know that Laplace's urns carry the following guarantee: $P(RR|A) = 1; P(RR|M) = 0.25$. Equation 3, which follows now, is derived by dividing the left-hand side of equation 1 by the left-hand side of equation 2, and by recognizing that the resulting ratio is equal to the ratio of the right-hand side of equation 1 to the right-hand side of equation 2; however, in writing the right-hand-side ratio, we shall take

11 We say that the conditional probabilities *represent* likelihoods because the likelihoods are defined up to an arbitrary constant (and thus *could be* multiples or fractions of the conditional probabilities, as long as we multiply the conditional probabilities of the sample, given all hypotheses, by the same factor).

cognizance of the fact that $P(RR|A) = 1$ and $P(RR|M) = 0.25$. We obtain:

$$\frac{P(A, RR)}{P(M, RR)} = \frac{P_i(A)}{0.25 \, P_i(M)} \quad \cdots \cdots \cdots \cdots \cdots \quad (3)$$

The Bayes method, which Laplace uses here, postulates that *after the drawing of two balls* and after making the observation "red and red," the correct way of estimating the *posterior* probability, $P_2(A)$, of the individual's being faced with an A-type urn, and the correct way of estimating the *posterior* probability, $P_2(M)$, of his being faced with an M-type urn, is based on the judgment that $P_2(A)$ bears the same proportion to $P_2(M)$ as $P(A, RR)$ does to $P(M, RR)$. The correctness of this method of arriving at the ratio of $P_2(A)$ to $P_2(M)$ follows from the fact that by analogy to equation 1, we may write:

$$P(A, RR) = P_i(RR) \cdot P(A|RR) \quad \cdots \cdots \cdots \cdots \cdots \cdots \quad (1a)$$

and by analogy to equation 2, we may also write:

$$P(M, RR) = P_i(RR) \cdot P(M|RR) \quad \cdots \cdots \cdots \cdots \cdots \quad (2a)$$

so that the ratio of the left-hand-side joint probabilities in equations $1a$ and $2a$ must give us *the ratio of the posterior probability of being faced with A to the posterior probability of being faced with M after having observed "red and red."* Hence the posterior probability ratios are indeed correctly expressed by joint probability ratios such as those appearing on the left-hand side of equation 3. This insight enables us to derive from equation 3:

$$\frac{P_2(A)}{P_2(M)} = \frac{P_i(A)}{0.25 \, P_i(M)} \quad \cdots \cdots \cdots \cdots \cdots \quad (4)$$

Laplace took it for granted that on these grounds the observation "red and red" makes the probability of our being faced with an A-type urn four times as great as that of our being faced with an M-type urn— i.e., that $P_2(A) = 4P_2(M)$—and we see from equation 4 that this particular inference results from the assumption that the decision maker's initial ignorance concerning the urn with which he is faced led him to assign the same *prior* probability to the two possibilities [that is, $P_i(A) = P_i(M) = 0.5$]. Therefore, Laplace concluded that $\frac{P_2(A)}{P_2(M)} = 4$, this being the crucial numerical assumption in his reasoning (see page 49). If the ratio of the prior probabilities is *one*, then the ratio of the joint probabilities, and hence also the posterior probability ratio, simply equal the ratio of the conditional probabilities of making the observations which were actually made [such as the ratio of the conditional probability terms $P(RR|A)$ and $P(RR|M)$ in equations 1 and 2]. Ratios of such conditional probabilities are called likelihood ratios. Given the guarantees concerning the two urns—that is, given the hypotheses to which we limit ourselves here—the likelihood ratios can be computed objectively, by the use of frequency-probabilistic procedures. But this is, of course, not true of the prior probabilities which are subjective guesses.

In modern versions of Bayesian analysis, it is not taken for granted that the initial hunches always neutralize one another in this form—i.e., that $P_i(A) = P_i(M)$—but at present, we are giving an interpretation of Laplace's numerical results, and these do imply symmetrically distributed (uniform) prior probabilities. If Laplace had not assumed $P_i(A) = P_i(M)$, then it would have been necessary to multiply the likelihood ratio by the ratio of these prior probabilities to arrive at the ratio of the posterior probabilities $P_2(A)$ and $P_2(M)$. At any rate, once the ratio $\dfrac{P_2(A)}{P_2(M)}$ is known, $P_2(A)$ and $P_2(M)$ are known individually, too, since $P_2(A) + P_2(M) = 1$. Hence, if $\dfrac{P_2(A)}{P_2(M)} = r$, then $P_2(A) = \dfrac{r}{r+1}$ and $P_2(M) = \dfrac{1}{r+1}$.

A more general version of Laplace's problem can be expressed in the following way without taking uniformly distributed prior probabilities for granted. Each urn—Urn V and Urn W—contains a good many balls, red and black, but the red-black composition of the two urns is different. The composition of both urns has been guaranteed to us (i.e., we know the precise characteristics of all hypotheses that will be considered in the present context), but we do not know with which of the two urns nature has confronted us. From the urn with which we are confronted, we draw $m + n$ balls, replacing each individual ball before drawing the next, and we examine this sample of size $m + n$. We find m red and n black, that is, $mR + nB$. Our prior probabilities before the drawing—our initial guesses—concerning the question whether we are faced with Urn V or Urn W were $P_i(V)$ and $P_i(W)$. After examining $m + n$ balls, we wish to form the posterior probabilities of being faced with V and W, respectively, i.e., we wish to estimate $P_{m+n}(V)$ and $P_{m+n}(W)$. The Bayesian estimate of these posterior probabilities is based on the conception that the ratio of $P_{m+n}(V)$ to $P_{m+n}(W)$ should be judged identical with the ratio of joint probabilities analogous to the magnitudes in equations 1 and 2. Therefore, we obtain:

$$\frac{P_{m+n}(V)}{P_{m+n}(W)} = \frac{P_i(V) \cdot P[(mR + nB)|V]}{P_i(W) \cdot P[(mR + nB)|W]} \quad \cdots \cdots \cdots \cdots \quad (5)$$

where $P_{m+n}(V)$ and $P_{m+n}(W)$ stand for the posterior probability (after $m + n$ drawings) of being faced with V and with W; $P[mR + nB)|V]$ stands for the conditional probability of drawing m red and n black balls, *given Urn V*; and $P[(mR + nB)|W]$ stands for the conditional probability of drawing the same sample, *given Urn W*. These are the conditional probabilities which represent likelihoods.

Once the right-hand ratio in equation 5 is found, the problem is solved. The basic idea of the reasoning as a whole always remains the same: If the joint probability of making the actual observation—say, the observation "red and red"—*and* of being faced with one urn is some given multiple of the joint probability of making the same observation and of being faced with the other urn, then the posterior probability of being faced with the first urn is *this same multiple* of the posterior probability of being faced with the other urn. The joint probabilities, which are thus needed for arriving at the posterior probabilities, are derived from the "priors" (initial guesses) and from the likelihoods of making the observation actually made, given the various possible urns (hypotheses).

It should be added that having derived, after two drawings, the posterior probabilities P_2 of being faced with one or the other urn, we may in the Bayesian framework regard these posterior probabilities as the *prior probabilities for a third drawing*; after the third drawing, we may derive the posterior probabilities $P_3(A)$ and $P_3(M)$ in the way in which $P_2(A)$ and $P_2(M)$ were derived from the original P_i terms and from the observed result of two drawings. Unless it is very costly to engage in further drawings—i.e., to acquire further experience—it will in most cases pay to continue this procedure for a while, because $P_3(A)$ and $P_3(M)$ may be appreciably different from $P_2(A)$ and $P_2(M)$, and it is, of course, preferable to rely on a large number of observations. However, as the size of the sample grows, it becomes increasingly less profitable to bear the cost of further observations because the posterior probabilities of sizable samples are less likely to change when further observations are added.

There is nothing in the Bayesian approach that would limit its applicability to a comparison of two hypotheses (two urns). While it is convenient to present the problem for two alternatives, the method can easily be extended to analysis concerned with the relative probabilities of being faced with one of many urns (each defined by a specific composition). Laplace's more general proposition, called his Law of Succession, illustrates this extension clearly, since the proposition assumes that *prior to any drawing* all conceivable red-black proportions are judged equiprobable in a deck of cards.[12]

Indeed, the Bayesian approach is applicable to many significant cases in which it is useful to reason as if the number of possible "true proportions of red" were infinite, and as if only ranges of the value of this parameter—only sets of hypotheses relating to such ranges—had positive (nonzero) probabilities. Such a conception reflects merely a technique because the hypotheses which in the mind of the decision maker are worth distinguishing from one another are always at finite distances from each other, regardless of the kind of parameter to which the hy-

---

[12] Say that we have drawn n cards from a deck containing only red and black cards, with replacement of each card before the next drawing. We have absolutely no prior information about the red-black ratio, but having observed m red cards and $n - m$ black cards in a drawing of n, we want to estimate the probability of drawing red on the next occasion. Then we tell ourselves that if the next card should be red, we shall be faced with a situation where the ratio of red to the total number of cards will be $\frac{m + 1}{n + 1}$ (Hypothesis I), while if the next card should be black, then the ratio of red to the total number will be $\frac{m}{n + 1}$ (Hypothesis II). Given Hypothesis I, the conditional probability of our having found m red among the first-drawn n cards is $\frac{m + 1}{n + 1}$, this being the conditional probability of drawing red on any one occasion. Given Hypothesis II, the conditional probability of our having found m red among the first-drawn n cards is $1 - \frac{m}{n + 1} = \frac{n - m + 1}{n + 1}$, this being the conditional probability of drawing black on the $(n + 1)$th occasion in circumstances where, for $n + 1$ drawings, the ratio of red to the total number is $\frac{m}{n + 1}$. The relevant likelihood ratio therefore results from dividing $\frac{m + 1}{n + 1}$ by $\frac{n - m + 1}{n + 1}$. The division yields $\frac{m + 1}{n - m + 1}$. This expression gives us the ratio of the likelihood of Hypothesis I to the likelihood of Hypothesis II in view of the result of the first n drawings. Laplace assumed that the subjective *prior* probabilities assigned to the two hypotheses were equal and that the prior probability ratio thus being *one*, the likelihood ratio $\frac{m + 1}{n - m + 1}$ gives us directly the joint probability ratio (and hence also the posterior probability ratio of drawing red or black on the *next* drawing). From the fact that on these assumptions the ratio of the probability of drawing red on the next occasion to the probability of drawing black on the next occasion is $\frac{m + 1}{n - m + 1}$ it follows that the probability of drawing red on the next occasion is $\frac{m + 1}{n + 2}$. The probability of drawing black on the next occasion is $\frac{n - m + 1}{n + 2}$. (For example, prior to our making any observation—i.e., for $n = 0$, $m = 0$—the probability of drawing red on the next occasion is ½; if we have observed one red in a drawing of two, the probability is ½; if we have observed nine red in a drawing of ten, the probability is ⅚, etc.)

pothesis is made to relate. But if the number of relevant hypotheses (say concerning the specific numerical value of the "true proportion of red") is sufficiently large, and if these hypotheses are sufficiently close to each other, then it is convenient to proceed analytically as if the number of such hypotheses were infinite, and each precise value of the parameter had zero probability, because in such cases a technique involving *continuous probability distributions may be employed for prior probabilities and for likelihoods*. In our illustration the probability *ratios* for *individual values* of the "true proportion of red," as well as for ranges of this parameter, may be treated as definite magnitudes even in the framework of a technique involving continuous distributions.[13] But if this technique is used, then only sets of such hypotheses (i.e., ranges of the "true proportion of red") can be assigned nonzero probabilities. At the same time, in this case a finite number of hypotheses relating to *precise values* of the parameters of continuous probability *distributions* acquire positive (nonzero) probabilities. In the mind of the decision maker finite intervals always do exist between the relevant values of the "true proportion of red," either because any of the specific values in a sufficiently small range is acceptable to him for representing the range, or because only one value in the range is capable of being interpreted as emerging from an understandable theoretical structure. But if the intervals between the relevant "true proportions of red" are small, it is convenient to analyze the judgments of the decision maker with the aid of technical methods that bridge the intervals and that assign positive probabilities not to "true proportions of red," but to hypotheses (specific parameters) describing a continuous probability distribution of "true proportions of red." The same methods lead to the assignment of positive probabilities to sets of hypotheses relating to *ranges* of the "true proportion of red," and the decision maker is of course free to regard some specific value within each range as representative of the range. At any rate the Bayesian approach remains applicable in such cases too.

Furthermore, equation 6 below and the subsequent discussion in this chapter will demonstrate also that there is no need to limit the ap-

---

[13] Reference to the normal distribution suffices to illustrate the proposition that the relevant likelihood ratios and ratios of "priors" may assume definite values even if the number of possible cases is viewed as tending to infinity (see n. 4, p. 42). Note, however, that the likelihood ratios are ratios of the likelihoods of a *specific, observed sample composition, given alternative hypotheses*. The hypotheses imply likelihoods for all potential sample compositions and therefore imply likelihoods *also* for the specific, observed composition for which (after making the observation) we define the likelihood function, thus obtaining the likelihood of the observed sample for alternative hypotheses.

proach to problems involving composition merely by *two* characteristics of an "urn" (red and black); the approach fits also problems in which the "urn" is described by a considerable number of such characteristics (drawing red or black or green, etc.).

The Bayesian approach of our times—sometimes referred to as the neo-Bayesian approach—differs from the original Bayes-Laplace version in that two additional elements have been added. In the first place, it is now emphasized that the decision maker is entitled to formalize his hunches into prior probabilities which need not be symmetrically distributed among the various possibilities (need not be uniform). Indeed, listing a given number of possibilities frequently involves arbitrariness in the grouping of more elementary possibilities, not all of which can in practice be considered separately. Secondly, it is now usual to combine the Bayesian reasoning with utility analysis, that is to say, to assume that a reasonable decision maker maximizes the probabilistic expectation (mathematical expectation) of the *utility* of wealth to him, and thus his probabilistic expectation of the utility of the potential consequences of the acts he is considering. In a general way, we have already commented on the fact that there exist situations in which it becomes operationally testable whether an individual does or does not satisfy the assumption of probabilistic utility maximization (pages 19 ff.). Problems of utility theory will occupy more space in the later course of our analysis.

Returning to the first point, the real purpose of Bayesian analysis is to establish internal consistency within an individual's system of degrees of belief, and the individual is no less entitled to initial guesses that on balance favor one of the possible alternatives than to initial hunches that happen to neutralize each other precisely and thereby to result in initial equiprobability. If, for example, Laplace's decision maker had started out not with the prior probabilities $P_i(A) = P_i(M) = 0.5$, but (say) with $P_i(A) = 0.20$, $P_i(M) = 0.80$, then these would have been the values which it would have been necessary to substitute into equation 4, so that we should have had to infer $\dfrac{P_2(A)}{P_2(M)} = 1$. This is equivalent to $P_2(A) = P_2(M) = 0.5$. In other words, given initial subjective probabilities such as favor the mixed-urn hypothesis in the ratio $4:1$, the observation "red and red" would just offset the lopsidedness of the initial guess, and the probability of drawing red on the next occasion would be 0.75.

(5) The Case for the Bayesian Approach, and a Suggested Modification

We may now make a further step toward generalizing Bayes's theorem, and we may reformulate equation 5 of the preceding section in the following way:

$$\frac{P_D(H_1)}{P_D(H_2)} = \frac{P_i(H_1) \cdot P(D|H_1)}{P_i(H_2) \cdot P(D|H_2)} \quad \cdots \cdots \cdots \cdots \quad (6)$$

Here, H_1 and H_2 stand for two hypotheses; $P_D(H_1)$ and $P_D(H_2)$ express the posterior probabilities of the validity of these hypotheses for the events which we are facing, where *posterior* means "after observation of the data D;" $P_i(H_1)$ and $P_i(H_2)$ stand for the initial probabilities, *prior* to observing the data D, of the validity of the hypotheses; and the two conditional probability terms represent likelihoods of observing D, given the two hypotheses, respectively. The equation does not limit the content of H_1 and H_2 to conjectures about merely *two* elementary events, such as red and black (see page 55). Also, there could be a great many hypotheses such as H_1 and H_2. Once the posterior probability *ratios* of n hypotheses are known, the individual posterior probabilities of the hypotheses are also known, provided the n hypotheses concerning the probabilities of events are assumed to exhaust the possibilities (for $n = 2$, see page 52). The last sentence implies that the hypotheses have positive—nonzero—prior probabilities (or that if only sets of hypotheses relating to ranges of parameter values have positive priors, then H_1, H_2, etc., stand for sets relating to such ranges). However, as was explained on page 55, usefulness of the *ratio*-equation (6) does not necessarily require positive priors for H_1, H_2, etc.

In the present section, we shall assume that, given the controversial prior probabilities attached to each hypothesis, the numerical effect of factual observations on the probabilities of future events is uncontroversial. This, of course, is implied also in the original Bayes-Laplace illustrations. We, too, shall have our decision maker draw balls from an urn. It may be needless to stress that problems such as sampling a delivery of some raw material for its composition, or sampling the output of a plant, etc., give rise to questions similar to that posed by sampling an urn. So the problem unmistakably does have economic meaning.

Before turning to an appraisal of the Bayesian approach, it will be useful to make clear the meaning of the assumption of an uncontroversial

effect of observed events on the probabilities of future events. Any decision maker who relies on observed facts for forming or improving his
probability judgments concerning future events considers himself faced
either with events that are exchangeable or with events that, with allowances for the effects of changes in other variables on the probabilities of
the events, he is willing to treat as exchangeable. A set of "exchangeable" events consists of events—such as red on successive occasions
—which the decision maker regards at any time as possessing the
same probability under the conditions under which he will observe
them.[14] It is part of the definition of a set of exchangeable events *also*
that while observation of an event belonging in the set may well lead the
decision maker to change his probability judgments about all other events
in the set, this should happen *exclusively* because, in the light of experience, he will be improving his probability judgment about the events
and *not* because he believes that a reasonable person who has had
much experience with these events would consider the probability
of any one event dependent on the occurrence or nonoccurrence of another event of the set.[15] Now, if a reasonably observant decision maker
regards the events he faces as outright exchangeable (as exchangeable
under the conditions under which he observes them, without having to
make allowances for the effects of ever-changing other variables), and
if he persists in this judgment after making a good many observations,
then in most such situations there is a presumption that other reasonable
decision makers will also regard the events as exchangeable. The drawings from Laplace's urn yield exchangeable events. The conditional
probabilities of events being necessarily uncontroversial for any properly
specified hypothesis, exchangeability of the events now to be observed
with future events assures the uncontroversial character of the effect of
observed events on the probabilities of future events. If, on the other
hand, the events could be made exchangeable only by correcting for
changes in other variables, such as do in fact change from event to event,
then it may well prove impossible to formulate all the relationship
between all these variables in such a way as to render the numerical
effect of factual observations on the probabilities of future events interpersonally uncontroversial. Such cases we shall consider in the next sec-

[14] At any time, he considers it equally probable that one drawing will yield red as that
another drawing will (provided he faces one of Laplace's urns).

[15] More operationally expressed: Given enough experience with them, our decision
maker would (or will) consider these events *independent*. See Chatper 3, Section 3.

tion. In the present section, we shall be concerned with exchangeable events (exchangeable under the conditions under which they are observed), although, as will be seen later, the Bayesian approach incorporates a valuable rule of consistency even in cases in which the decision maker needs to rely on controversial correction factors in order to be willing to treat the events as exchangeable.

Assuming now a decision problem which relates to a set of exchangeable events, we first submit the following proposition: The Bayes-type approach is superior to an approach which limits itself to frequentist-objectivist considerations except in situations where it may be taken for granted that the two approaches lead to results which, for the purpose at hand, are not worth distinguishing. In the latter case the frequentist-objectivist procedure has the advantage of being less complex and thus of providing a useful short cut, which, however, as a matter of principle, should even in this case be interpreted as a short cut *within the Bayesian framework.*

The frequentist-objectivist short cut makes good common sense if, for example, we try to form an opinion of whether the result of a one-hundred-ball drawing (with replacement of the ball after each single drawing) comes from a half-red and half-black urn or from an urn containing 20 per cent red and 80 per cent black balls. This is true because we may describe the range in which the sample observation from the half-and-half urn is practically certain to fall in such a way that the range so described should not overlap with the range in which the sample observation is practically certain to fall if we draw from the predominantly black urn. In the event that we are comparing hypotheses the essential contents of which differ from one another much less widely than does the 50–50 composition from the 20–80 composition of these two urns, then it takes a much larger sample to give us this practical certainty of ranges that do not overlap.

Generally speaking, if—in view of how near the values of the parameters describing the hypotheses are located to each other—the sample size is *large enough*, then it is possible to describe the range in which the result is practically certain to fall, given the validity of one hypothesis (say, given one urn), in such a way that it should not overlap with the range in which the result is practically certain to fall, given the validity of the other hypothesis. In this case, we are practically certain to obtain a result which has the double quality of testifying strongly in favor of one hypothesis *and* of testifying strongly against the other. In such cases the frequentist-objectivist approach often performs well, provided that the decision maker wishes to know merely whether one of the hypotheses is or is not to be *very* greatly favored relative to others (i.e., provided he is prepared to neglect, rather than to weight probabilistically, the other hypotheses). In cases of sufficiently large sample size the approach is almost certain to lead to very strong indications as to the validity of one hypothesis and the invalidity of others. When the sample size is sufficiently large, essentially the same statement can be made about the strong performance of the frequentist-objectivist methods even if the a priori possible compositions of our urns lie rather near each other (note that it may be worth while to distinguish many potential compositions). With an exceedingly large number of drawings the true frequency ratio in an urn is practically certain to lie within a very narrow range of the ratio observed in the sample.

But in these cases where—in view of how near the parameter values describing the hypotheses lie to each other—the sample size generated by independent drawings is sufficiently large, the Bayesian procedure will almost always point to the same hypothesis (to the same urn composition) as the frequentist-objectivist. For example, if the composition of one a priori possible urn is 50–50 and that of the only other a priori possible urn is 20–80, and if, therefore, with a sample size of one hundred balls, we may be practically certain that the conditional probability of drawing the actually observed sample, given one of the two urns, will be a *very* high multiple of the conditional probability of drawing the actually observed sample, given the other urn, it would take an extreme *contrary* asymmetry of the prior subjective probabilities (initial guesses) to offset the effect of such a conditional probability ratio on the Bayesian ratio of joint probabilities. If it may be taken for granted that the asymmetry of the *prior probabilities* is not so extreme—and that there exists also no extreme asymmetry between the *utility* of the potential pay-offs on staking one's fortunes one way versus staking them the other way—then an extreme asymmetry in the sample evidence (likelihood ratios) makes it reasonably safe to replace the Bayesian technique with the frequentist-objectivist technique. *Even in these cases, it is important to remember that the numerical value of a reasonable decision maker's odds in favor of one or the other hypothesis should depend on the subjective elements which the exclusively frequency-oriented reasoning disregards.* But there exist important classes of decision problems for which the individual wishes merely to know whether the probabilities do or do not speak *very strongly* for one hypothesis and against its rivals. In otherwise favorable circumstances, large samples may in themselves decide *this* question "objectively."

The difference between the frequentist-objectivist and the Bayesian results gets to be important not so much in these cases as in the situations where—considering how near or far the hypotheses lie relative to each other—the sample size is insufficient to enable us to describe nonoverlapping ranges in which the sample observations are practically certain to fall. For example, a *one-hundred-ball* sample is not large enough in this sense if one of two possible urns is half red and half black and the other contains *45 per cent red and 55 per cent black*; and a sample can easily be small enough to be insufficient in the sense here considered, even if the urns differ quite widely in composition. These are the situations in which it is impossible to describe one range of sample observations into which we shall get with near certainty if one hypothesis is valid, and to describe another *nonoverlapping* range of sample observations into which we shall get with near certainty if the other is valid. Once there is an appreciable overlap, either the frequentist-objectivist approach becomes admittedly unhelpful, or the decision maker is forced to rely on a makeshift. Those relying on this makeshift introduce into the frequentist-objectivist approach an element of subjectivism, but they do this in a much less articulate fashion than those relying on the Bayesian blend.

Where ranges overlap significantly, the frequentist—if he feels compelled to make a statement about the problem—says, in effect, to the decision maker: You must make up your mind whether one hypothesis (say the hypothesis of being faced with a 45-to-55 urn) *is acceptable to you only if, given the other hypothesis, a proportion of red as low as or lower than that observed in the sample would occur very rarely,*[16] or whether the other hypothesis (the hypothesis of being faced with the half-and-half urn) *is acceptable to you only if, given the 45-to-55 hypothesis, a proportion of red as high as or higher than that observed in the sample would occur very rarely.* The hypothesis which thus gets the benefit of the doubt by the use of a rule of thumb is usually called the *Null Hypothesis*, while the hypothesis which is accepted only if the observed sample composition is exceedingly unlikely in the event of the validity of the Null Hypothesis is called the *Alternative Hypothesis*. The Alternative Hypothesis is accepted only if the data testify *significantly* against the Null Hypothesis. The method can sometimes be handled in such a

---

[16] In practice, the phrase "would occur very rarely" is frequently interpreted as meaning "would occur with a probability of less than five per cent (or of less than one per cent)."

way that the decision maker gets an opportunity to decide just how safely he wants to play against rejecting a valid Null Hypothesis in view of the corresponding degrees of risk of his rejecting a valid Alternative Hypothesis; but such a procedure, nevertheless, is less desirable than the Bayesian line of approach. This is because the makeshift we have just sketched is *at its best vaguely reminiscent* of putting it up to the decision maker to weight his hypotheses in accordance with his initial guesses, and in accordance with conclusions derived from the sample, and also to take account in his decisions of the utilities he assigns to the potential consequences of his acts. When such a makeshift is employed, it is not made clear that the procedure should involve consistent and systematic handling of prior-probability assignments and of utilities.

The reader will notice that, in contrast to Bayesian theory, the makeshift we have described builds on one hypothesis and *dispenses* with another. The makeshift does not *weight* the potentially valid hypotheses when deriving a probability judgment concerning events, as does Bayesian analysis. Hence the makeshift suggests playing safe in favor of one hypothesis not by playing safe on likelihood *ratios*—any variant of rule-of-thumb subjectivism which *does* suggest this thereby becomes a halfway house toward Bayesianism[17]—but the method suggests playing safe in favor of one hypothesis by recommending that the hypothesis receiving the benefit of the doubt be accepted unless likelihood considerations testify too strongly against that hypothesis viewed by itself. This attitude of acceptance or rejection, rather than of weighting, makes it necessary to practice such methods of rule-of-thumb subjectivism by exploring not just the conditional probability of the observed sample, given the Null Hypothesis, but by exploring the *cumulated* conditional probability of the actually observed sample and of any sample even more unfavorable to the Null Hypothesis. The conditional probability of merely the observed sample itself is admittedly uninformative, because the conditional probability of any precisely described sample becomes arbitrarily small,

---

[17] Such variants of rule-of-thumb subjectivism do exist. They suggest deciding for or against a hypothesis depending on whether the decision maker considers the likelihood *ratio* favorable enough for a hypothesis. But this is an unsatisfactory half-way house toward the Bayesian approach because "favorable enough" cannot have any meaning other than "favorable enough in view of the decision maker's prior probabilities and his utility assignments to the potential consequences of his acts"; and if we do add this, then we are in the midst of Bayesian analysis. Furthermore, the idea of exploring likelihood *ratios* is much more compatible with a Bayesian *weighting* of the various potentially valid hypotheses than with the conventional practice of *selecting* one from among them, except if the special circumstances of the case justify the objectivist short cut (in which event all roads lead to Rome, anyhow). For example, the finding that the likelihood of one hypothesis is five times as great as that of another would, I think, normally carry the suggestion that the second hypothesis should be weighted less heavily, not that it should be disregarded.

given *any* hypothesis, if the potential shadings of sample composition are made arbitrarily fine.[18] The likelihood *ratios* of the observed sample itself for various hypotheses do tend to definite magnitudes, irrespective of the fineness of shadings (this is essential for the *Bayesian* approach); but if, instead of exploring likelihood ratios, we wish to look at the conditional probability given the Null Hypothesis alone—a desire which is motivated by planning to accept one hypothesis and to reject another without considering the possibility that both should be weighted—then it is necessary to make the cumulated conditional probability of the observed sample *and of something even less favorable to the hypothesis* the criterion for the choice.[19]

Generally expressed, as soon as it becomes impossible to take non-overlapping ranges more or less *for granted*, the allegedly "frequentist-objectivist" approach to decision problems introduces a substantial subjective element into its procedure through a back door. If one thinks along frequentist-objectivist lines, this becomes inevitable because it would be so patently unsatisfactory to suggest to the decision maker that, without further regard to subjective factors, he should reject one hypothesis and accept another *in circumstances where the observed result, or worse,[20] would occur quite frequently, even on the hypothesis which he contemplates rejecting.* This is the reason why, in such circumstances, even an approach that *attempts* to be frequentist-objectivist needs to bring in a subjective element. But from a logical point of view, little can be said for introducing this element in a highly casual manner, by reliance on various rules of thumb. We have just seen that at this point the allegedly "frequentist-objectivist" methods become highly arbitrary—tend to rely on rule-of-thumb subjectivism—even where only two hypotheses are considered; and the logical clarity of the procedure is further reduced in cases where a choice needs to be made from among more hypotheses. The Bayesian principles are surely superior to this kind of rule-of-thumb subjectivism.

However, the fact remains that any literal or unmodified interpretation of the Bayesian method implies a decision process which is based

---

[18] The conditional probability of precisely 500,000 "red" in 1,000,000 drawings is of course exceedingly small, even if we draw from a half-and-half urn, and such conditional probabilities become arbitrarily small if we increase the number of drawings further. But the *ratio* of the conditional probability of r successes in n trials, given an urn in which $r = np$, to the conditional probability of r successes in n trials, given an urn in which r is (say) at a distance of one standard deviation from np, tends to a definite limit with rising n.

[19] For what to me seems an unconvincing justification of this cumulation (integration) over the sample space, see n. 22, p. 65, and Chapter 8, Section 2.

[20] We mean the observed result or a result even more unfavorable for the hypothesis the rejection of which is contemplated.

exclusively on straightforward hypotheses, that is, on hypotheses to the numerical effect of which on probability judgments the decision maker is willing to commit himself in his acts. For example in Laplace's problem the decision maker's conjectures—including his initial guesses which result in his prior probability assignments to the urns—are interpreted as straightforward hypotheses. If the decision maker regards the conjectures from which his prior probabilities are derived as elusive hypotheses (in the sense of our Introduction, page 13), then some of the simplicity of the Bayesian procedure is lost, since the observable decision weights are then derived from the true Bayesian probabilities by a process of slanting or distortion.

In our *semiprobabilistic* approach, we can take account of the effect of elusive hypotheses by recognizing that decision makers "slant" their probabilities, provided they feel that allowances must be made for the role of such hypotheses. In practice, this means that a good many reasonable individuals are apt to place those Bayesian probability judgments which are strongly influenced by shaky subjective appraisals at a discount relative to probability judgments which are less strongly influenced by such factors or are not influenced by them. This modification—allowance for slanting—is in accordance with our semiprobabilistic approach. The modification makes room for Bayesian methods even in cases where elusive hypotheses do play a part. Bayesian analysis does, of course, require that the hypotheses exhaust the possibilities assumed to exist at any time (see page 57), but this can be postulated also in a semiprobabilistic framework, provided elusive hypotheses are included. The feeling that "something else might also turn out to be at work" is not a hypothesis but is accorded merely the role of rendering some hypotheses "elusive," in view of the suspicion that the weights (positive or zero weights) assigned to, and suggested by, these hypotheses might turn out to be unconvincing. We have defined hypotheses by specific parameter values which they suggest, and as determining the undistorted probabilities of events. These probabilities are additive to unity; hence the hypotheses exhaust the possibilities assumed to exist at any time.

Here again, we have been using the terminology of Version 1 rather than that of Version 2 (see Section 3 of the Introduction to the volume). Even Version 1 suggests that notwithstanding elusive hypotheses, a consistent decision maker must have in his mind a degree of belief—a genuine, undistorted subjective probability—relating to the events he faces when making a decision. But in Version 1 the semiprobabilistic decision maker is represented as using not these genuine probabilities themselves but slanted probabilities as his decision weights. This is how he takes account of the nonmonetary (or nondirectly monetary) consequences of relying on shaky and interpersonally controversial judgments. Version 2 would formulate a utility function for these nonmonetary consequences, or would incorporate the corresponding utilities into the individual's utility-of-wealth function, and would apply the undistorted probabilities to utilities so defined.

Does our argument leave any room whatever for the rule-of-thumb subjectivism involved in accepting or rejecting a Null Hypothesis (rejecting or accepting an Alternative Hypothesis) according as the cumulated conditional probability of the observed data and of data which are even less favorable for the Null Hypothesis is or is not sufficiently small (say less than 5 per cent), given the Null Hypothesis? Performance of such *tests of significance* cannot be justified by systematic decision-theoretical considerations. The question should be asked in this form: Recognizing that rules of thumb of the kind we are now considering may sometimes be convenient, what are the conditions under which they are reasonably harmless, in the sense of not obscuring the true problem with which the decision maker is faced?

As concerns this particular rule of thumb, its three main implications would seem to be the following: (*a*) Very high prior probability is assigned to the Null Hypothesis, and/or the Null Hypothesis is such that grave disadvantage develops from not acting on it, if it should be valid; (*b*) alternatives other than that with which we compare the Null Hypothesis may, for the time being, be disregarded;[21] (*c*) adopting in a mechanical fashion various devices which make this particular rule of thumb manageable does not inadvertently lead the decision maker to an unintended decision (e.g., the significance level of, say, 5 per cent or of 1 per cent takes account of (*a*), above, moderately well; and the lumping-together of the observed outcome with outcomes even more unfavorable for the Null Hypothesis makes sense in the given context, etc.).[22]

---

[21] However, such hypotheses may be conjectures merely about ranges in which the true values of parameters fall, or they can be mere *denials* of parameter values (see p. 66).

[22] In the illustration which follows in the next paragraph, the lumping-together of the observed sample with samples even more unfavorable to the Null Hypothesis does, it seems to me, make some sense (because it is intuitively not meaningless to ask oneself the question whether the observed data fall in a very unexpected range of observations). However, sometimes it is argued that this lumping-together—i.e., integration over the sample space—is justified because if the rule so defined is followed, say, on the 5 per cent significance level, then this tends to lead to rejecting a valid Null Hypothesis in 5 per cent of the cases over a very long period of time. The conception that, in deciding a specific problem, one should think of an exceedingly large number of separate decision situations, in which the parameter to be estimated has the true value corresponding to the Null Hypothesis, is in most cases quite unconvincing. One should concern oneself with the sample one has observed, and not also with samples one *might have* observed. See also Chapter 8, Section 2.

Modern decision theorists maintain (I think rightly) that the rule of thumb in question—the rule on which significance tests are based—is being widely used in circumstances in which these conditions are *not* satisfied. But I shall first point out that in the present chapter, we have discussed a case which satisfies the conditions reasonably well. What I called the objectivist short cut to the large sample Bayesian problem illustrates a situation in which the method now under consideration is convenient and harmless. After all, if the decision maker has observed a large number of drawings from an urn and the outcome was nearly 50–50 for red and black, he may from there on place a high prior on this being a half-and-half urn; and as for future drawings from what he believes confidently to be the same urn, he may formulate the 50–50 composition as his Null Hypothesis. He may decide to proceed henceforth on the definite assumption of 0.5 probability for red, except if he should encounter a sample in which the proportion of red falls in a range which is sufficiently far removed from 50–50 to be a range of very low conditional probability (given a true ratio of 50–50); and if he should encounter such a sample, he may for the time being be satisfied with concluding that a so-called "Alternative Hypothesis" may well be correct—e.g., that his previous expectation of the identical urn's being used again may well be wrong. Subsequently, he may turn to exploring other hypotheses which are hypotheses in the true sense of the word. (Note that the "Alternative Hypothesis" in the foregoing formulation is merely the denial of a hypothesis rather than a hypothesis in the true sense. An "Alternative Hypothesis" of this kind may be interpreted as a doubt which, if not overcome, renders a true hypothesis elusive, in the terminology of our Introduction.)[23]

Analogous statements can be made both with respect to Bayesian analysis and with respect to objectivist short cuts and to rule-of-thumb subjectivism for problems involving the probabilities of more elementary events than two, i.e., for problems concerning which the relevant hypotheses relate to processes generating many events (analogously to the four suits drawn from a deck of French cards, or to the six sides of a die). In these problems, we are faced not with a binomial but with a multinomial distribution, unless we are interested merely in the probability of a six versus that of a nonsix. The Bayesian formulation of equation 6 on

[23] Such an "Alternative Hypothesis" is not truly a *hypothesis*, because it suggests no parameter values by which it could be described. However, the Null Hypothesis of the present illustration is a hypothesis in the true sense; and in some cases, both hypotheses formulated for a significance test are hypotheses in the sense in which we are using the term in this volume.

page 57 holds for these problems, too. Furthermore, here too a long sequence of trials may in some cases suggest the acceptability of the objectivist short cut, because the long sequence may convince a person that each of the six sides of a die comes with a specific probability (say ⅙). Also, on special occasions a check on this objectivist short cut by rule-of-thumb subjectivism may be appropriate, i.e., the decision maker may, for example, ask himself the question whether the relative frequencies which he has just observed would or would not be exceedingly unlikely, given the Null Hypothesis that each side of the die has probability ⅙. (This latter type of significance testing—the variety involving multinomial distributions and their continuous counterpart—makes use of what statisticians call the chi-square test).

So far, so good. But having said this, I shall repeat that the critical attitude of Bayesians to many current uses of the rules of thumb implied in significance tests seems convincing to me. In particular, modern decision theory says that the decision maker, when considering potential true values (or ranges of true values) of a relevant parameter, should *usually* weight many of these potential true values probabilistically, and that he should do so in view of his prior probabilities and in view of the likelihood of the subsequently observed data, given alternative true values. The theory also tells us that the utilities of the potential consequences of alternative acts need to be taken into account, because what matters is the probabilistic expectation of these utilities. The conventional significance test procedure, on the other hand, leads to *accepting* or to *rejecting* a hypothesis concerning the true value of a parameter. The procedure *chooses* from among alternatives true values, or sometimes from among ranges of these, with allowance for sampling errors, instead of *weighting* a good many possible true values; and it does this by the use of an inevitably arbitrary formula. Only in special cases is this harmless. But as has been argued, in some cases it *is* reasonably harmless and also convenient. These are mostly cases in which the decision maker regards it as safe to cut the Bayesian procedure short by objectivist methods, and in which nothing unintended will happen to him if he crudely checks on the validity (to him) of this assumption by rule-of-thumb subjectivism. We shall return to this problem in Chapter 8.

(6) Correction for Changes in Other Variables

Our illustrations have mostly suggested that important decision problems involve a question *analogous* to that of the true proportion of red in urns, or in decks of cards, etc.; and, of course, they involve also the question of dispersion around true values in samples of various sizes. It is not misleading to present the matter in this fashion, but it should be added that decision problems often require judging what the true proportion of red is for different values of some other variable (or of several other variables), i.e., of variables on the values of which the true proportion of red depends. What this means is that in such cases, judgments concerning the probability of parameter values expressing the proportion of red at each level of some other variable need to be made consistent with judgments concerning the probabilities of parameter values expressing the dependence of one variable on the other, including allowance for error terms. These are essentially judgments about conditional probabilities, such as the probability of red, given the values of other variables on which the urn composition is assumed to depend; or the probability of finding that the volume of a specific quantity of a gas falls in a specific range, given the temperature; or the probability of finding that consumer outlay is in a specic range, given the values of other variables.

Unless the other variables can be held constant by laboratory techniques, it is usually impossible in these cases to base probability judgments on the assumption that the relevant events form a set of *exchangeable* events[24] (exchangeable under the conditions under which they were actually observed). For example, the variables determining consumer outlay change from period to period, and even if we should estimate our relationship from cross sections, we are at the end interested in the probability of events[25] such as that consumer outlay will fall in one or the other numerical range *in future periods*. Such events are not equiprobable, since each event occurs at different values of other variables. Even a very long sequence of observations will not establish a Mises-type collective for these events; observed consumer outlay will not converge on a specific value. On the other hand, the investigator hopes to be able to infer in such cases that the conditional probability of the event, given the values of other variables, will stay reasonably stable (see above). What this amounts to is that one hopes to find a relationship—say a regression equation—which provides *correction factors* for the effect of changes in other variables, and that *with allowances for the effect of changes in these other variables*, it will appear more or less convincing to the decision maker to treat the events in which he is interested (the occurrence

---

[24] For the concept of exchangeable events, see p. 58, above; and Chapter 3, Section 3, below.

[25] These are "compound" events (not "elementary" events such as even or odd in Mises' illustration).

of now observable and of prospective consumer outlays of various sizes and the like) as if they were exchangeable events. However, the technical operations in question rarely lead to generally acceptable—i.e., to objective or uncontroversial—judgments about the effect of factual observations on the probabilities of prospective events. Two of the difficulties may be mentioned here.

In the first place, some of the effects of changes in other variables are apt to be of a kind for which it seems hopeless to correct by uncontroversial methods. Consequently, exchangeability of events after such corrections will be a controversial assumption. Say, for example, that the decision maker has the hypothesis H_p, according to which if the political event E'_p happens next year then the probability of a particular kind of consumer outlay's falling in a specified numerical range will be 10 per cent less, and the probability of its falling in other ranges correspondingly more, than the probability which a regression equation would otherwise lead one to infer; and say that E'_p is *at best vaguely analogous* to past events and also to events expected in other future periods. If, next year, E'_p does occur, and our individual engages in an appraisal of the conditional probability of the observed data, then he *may* discover by the use of uncontroversial methods that for the year in question his hypotheses are well supported; yet any inference he may want to base on this concerning the prospective effect of *vaguely similar* political events the year after will be a highly subjective inference. Political events illustrate the point especially well, but they are not the only ones which could be used for illustration.

Secondly, intelligent individuals are well aware of the fact that they are never capable of formulating all relevant hypotheses about the effect of other variables on the probabilities of prospective events. Consequently, where the problem of changing other variables acquires importance, the decision maker will usually have not only hypotheses, as this concept was defined in the Introduction, but—to a greater or to a lesser extent—also the vague feeling that "something else, too may turn out to be at work here." Such a feeling we do not call a hypothesis. But this is the kind of feeling which is apt to render some of the well-formulated hypotheses "elusive" and to lead to interpersonal differences of judgment (particularly to the use of slanted decision weights).

The Bayesian suggestion is to *weight* alternative potential values of the parameters on which the relationship between the probabilities of events and other variables depends, and to engage in this weighting in view of the prior probabilities concerning the values of all these parameters, as well as in view of the likelihood of alternative parameter values, given the observed data (and then to base one's decision on the probabilistic expectation of the utilities attached to the potential consequences of various acts). The procedure is particularly fruitful in cases where, given the controversial priors, the effect of observed data on the probabilities of future events is uncontroversial, but the method incorporates a valuable rule of consistency even where this is not the case. The semi-probabilistic version of the theory recognizes that in their acts, decision makers may place their highly controversial and shaky probability judgments at a discount, or conceivably at a premium, relative to their firm judgments. In the decision processes of some individuals, this semi-probabilistic slanting is likely to acquire particular prominence in cases where the correction for changing values of other variables cannot be based convincingly on technical-statistical analysis of a sample but must be undertaken with reliance on general and somewhat casual observations. It should never be overlooked that a great many decision problems have this character.

When faced with the same problems of correcting for changing values of other variables, the technical-statistical approach involving rule-of-thumb subjectivism suggests relying on those parameter values of (say) a regression equation which on the basis of the observed data (and on this basis alone) appear to have the greatest likelihood, *provided* the observed data fall in a range in which they would be exceedingly unlikely to fall if the true values of the parameters were *very* different from their maximum-likelihood values. If the data do *not* point to an exceedingly small probability of such very different values, then rule-of-thumb subjectivism usually favors abstention from acting on the basis of the parameter values which get the relatively strongest support from the data. In practice, this abstention involves either failure to act at all or an effort to frame other hypotheses concerning the relevant parameter values (or in many cases, this abstention no doubt leads to action based on probability judgments derived from a less systematic organization of the factual materials, without the use of technical-statistical procedures).

In Section 5, we commented on the question of the pros and cons of a rule of thumb of this kind, by which decision-theoretical complexities can be avoided. We commented also on the critical attitude of recent contributors toward these devices. We shall return to this problem in Chapter 8.

Chapter 3	POSTULATES UNDERLYING MODERN THEORIES OF UTILITY AND PROBABILITY

(1) Introduction

The position at which we have arrived so far may be described briefly by the following statements:

a) We are interested in the scope of applicability of probability theory to physical events, particularly those which bear on economic decisions. From our point of view, it would be question begging to define probability in terms of converging frequency ratios in repetitive processes (such as underlie the Mises-type collectives). This definition would *decide* the scope of applicability from the outset, and it would do so with a substantial bias toward narrowness.

b) Probability is a measure which should be defined by the rules in accordance with which it must be employed to qualify as a probability. It is possible to describe these rules in a very general way, as will presently be done, but it is particularly easy and convenient to *illustrate* them with reference to idealized processes such as random coin tosses. These idealized processes lend themselves well to the purpose because the theoretical values on which the frequency ratios tend to converge in them (almost always tend to converge in them)[1] satisfy the postulates which the measure "probability" must obey.

c) It is up to the decision maker to arrive at a judgment whether in a real-world situation he does or does not regard it as appealing to weight the alternative prospects with which he is faced by the measure called the probability of the prospective events. The narrowest (still significant) view about the scope of applicability is the frequentist-objectivist view, prominently represented by Richard von Mises. According to this view, it is appealing to employ this measure only in relation to collectives for which the behavior of frequency ratios suggests that kind

[1] For the meaning of the "almost always" clause, and for its unimportance from our point of view, see p. 17, above.

of convergence which is a definitional property of idealized coin processes and the like. Here, we have the narrowest (still significant) scope of application. The *broadest* position concerning the scope is that of the purely probabilistic version of the subjectivists, at present prominently represented by L. J. Savage (**45**), a position according to which a reasonable person should regard it as compelling to apply the measure to all risky prospects viewed as sets of (prospective) events. Most risky prospects do not fit into a collective in which the behavior of frequency ratios suggests an analogy to idealized repetitive processes.

d) The semiprobabilistic view expressed in the present volume accepts the basic conception of the subjectivist school but makes allowances for the fact that reasonable decision makers, when contemplating a move under the guidance of probabilities, may develop a system by which they place some of their highly unstable and controversial subjective probabilities at a discount (or at a premium) in relation to Mises-type probabilities. Not all the directly observable decision weights of such individuals need satisfy the specific rules by which probabilities are defined. This amounts to recognizing that a reasonable person may attach specific disutility to exposing himself to a loss by reliance on controversial and unstable hunches, and that this need not be neutralized by the specific disutility which attaches to a gain forgone through failure to make a move under the guidance of such hunches. Individuals whose behavior is semiprobabilistic arrive at the decision weights which they attach to some types of prospects by *slanting* the degrees of belief (probabilities) associated with these prospects.

e) Whether in a decision situation a person behaves probabilistically or semiprobabilistically (with consistent allowances for vagueness), or whether his behavior is incapable of being understood in the light of probabilistic considerations, is operationally testable if the person tends to maximize the weighted expectations of the utility of wealth to him. In our general analysis, we *shall* make these assumptions concerning utility maximization and the testability of probabilistic and semiprobabilistic behavior, although we shall recognize that in some cases nonoperational methods—discussions with the subject, etc.—need to be employed to throw light on his conception of a decision problem.

Let us now turn to a detailed discussion of the foregoing propositions.

(2) The Basic Rules of Probability

What are the rules by which the measure "probability" can be defined?

a) It must be possible to place an event,[2] the probability of which we are measuring, into a set of events to which we assign the probability *one*. That is to say, if *E* stands for the event we are considering, then we must define a set of events *S* of which *E* is an element and subset, and decide that $P(S) = 1$ (the probability of *S* is one).

That part of *S* which is not *E* is called the *complement* of *E* (in *S*), and we shall denote it by $\sim E$. That part of *S* which is defined as made up of *E* and of some other specified element of *S* is called the *union* of *E* and of that other specified element of the set *S*. The union includes all parts of *S* which are identified as belonging in *E* and also all parts of *S* which are identified as belonging in the other element of *S*, regardless of whether these parts of *S* belong in only one of the two elements forming the union or in *both* elements. Hence the union is a "this *or* that *or* both" concept. The symbol $\cup$ is used for denoting a union; and we must therefore postulate that $P(E \cup \sim E) = 1$. This relationship must hold for *any E* in *S*; i.e., it must hold for any *E* which has the property $S \supset E$ (*S* includes *E*). In the limiting case, $E = S$, which implies that $P(\sim E) = 0$, and $P(E) = 1$.

In whatever way one has decided to determine the limits of *S*, it is possible, for the sake of some other piece of probabilistic analysis, to place the entire set *S* into a set *S'*, and to make $P(S') = 1$, where *S* then is regarded as a subset of *S'*. The latter must be made larger than *S* or, in the limiting case, equal to *S*. Generally, an element of a set of "subsets" is itself a set which in some cases we may wish to view as being divisible into *further* elements.

b) $P(E) = 1$ is the upper limit of any probability assignment and $P(E) = 0$ its lower limit. $P(E)$ is always a real number satisfying the condition $1 \geqq P(E) \geqq 0$.

c) The *union* of any two events E_i, E_j is assigned a probability which equals the sum of the probabilities of the events in question minus the probability of their intersection. The concept of a union has been defined under (*a*). The intersection of two elements is defined as that part of the universe under consideration (in our case, that part of *S*) which belongs to *both* elements whose intersection we are forming. Conversationally, an intersection may be called an "overlap." It is expressed by the symbol $\cap$, and the rule which we are describing here may therefore be written:

$$P(E_i \cup E_j) = P(E_i) + P(E_j) - P(E_i \cap E_j)$$

[2] The term "event" stands here for a prospective event, as explained in the Introduction.

It will be seen presently that failure to deduct the intersection—i.e., the overlap—on the right-hand side of this equation would involve us in double counting to the extent of this overlap. If, however, E_i and E_j are mutually exclusive events, then, by definition, $E_i \cap E_j = 0$. For example, if the possibility of a coin's coming to rest on its edge is disregarded, "either heads or tails in a single toss" has the same probability—unitary probability—which can be obtained by adding the probability of heads to that of tails. The two events are mutually exclusive; and hence, there exists no intersection that would have to be deducted. (While mutual exclusiveness logically implies that no positive probability can be assigned to the intersection, absence of mutual exclusiveness—i.e., logical possibility of joint occurrence—is compatible with assigning zero probability to the intersection.)

Rules (a), (b), and (c) can be illustrated with the aid of "Venn diagrams." These were named for the English mathematical logician

FIGURE 1

Events of Various Sorts in a Venn Diagram

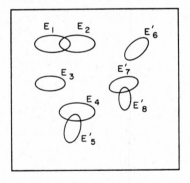

Legend: Preliminary Bayesian Exercise with Laplace's Urns in Mind (see p. 49)

Divide the entire square, which we shall call S, into two equal parts, to be labeled E_1 and E_3. Disregard in this exercise the other symbols which appear in Figure 1. Let E_s consist of the whole area of E_1 and of half of the area of E_3. This expresses the fact that to Laplace's subject the prospect of becoming faced with either of the two urns (E_1 and E_3) has probability 0.5; and the fact that drawing red (E_s) has unitary probability given E_1, and probability 0.5 given E_3. Subsequently, Laplace's subject observes red (E_s) in each of two drawings, and he concludes that this observation is four times as likely given E_1 as given E_3. Therefore, after this observation we make the ratio of the size of E_1 to the size of E_3 four times what it initially was (i.e., we make E_1 occupy four fifths of S and E_3 one fifth, and we continue to let E_s occupy all of E_1 and half of E_3).

In this exercise we limited ourselves to events that have nonzero probability, although zero *conditional* probabilities were not excluded (e.g., the conditional probability of E_1 given E_3 is zero). In the following analysis we shall observe this same limitation, except for the hints given in n. 8, p. 76.

John Venn. The diagrams are helpful; they have various limitations, which, however, do not interfere with their usefulness for our purposes in this volume.

The area of the entire square in Figure 1 represents the set S, to which unitary probability is assigned. We have drawn into the square eight elements (events), from among which we shall later want to distinguish two types, namely, E elements and E' elements. At present, we do not distinguish between these two types. If we draw E_1, E_2, etc. (also their intersections), with areas that correspond to their probabilities,[3] and assume that E_1 and E_3 are mutually exclusive, then $P(E_1 \cup E_3) = P(E_1) + P(E_3)$. But E_1 and E_2 are not mutually exclusive, and their intersection (joint occurrence) is represented as having positive probability. *If* both actually occur—which has positive probability but need not happen—then they overlap in the sense in which the event "at least one heads" overlaps with the event "at least one tails" in two successive random tosses of a perfect coin.[4] Therefore, $P(E_1 \cup E_2)$ is not equal to $P(E_1) + P(E_2)$. For example, for two tosses of a perfect coin, "at least one heads" has probability $3/4$; "at least one tails" has the same probability;[5] but the probability of "either at least one heads or at least one tails or both"—that is, the probability of the union of these two events—is obviously not $3/2$. From $3/2$, we must deduct the intersection of the two events to obtain the probability of the union. In general, this gives us the formula on page 73. In the heads-or-tails case for two tosses, which we have just been using as an illustration, the probability assigned to the intersection is $1/2$, since of four equiprobable events, two are overlapping ones.[6] From $3/2$, we deduct $1/2$, and we obtain unitary probability—as, indeed, in two tosses "either at least one heads, or at least one tails, or both" has unitary probability.

This completes our discussion of rules (a), (b) and (c). A measure on a set of events must be used in accordance with these rules to qualify as a probability. These rules have the force of axioms. A person deciding to apply the Calculus of Probabilities to a problem thereby expresses willingness to attribute axiomatic validity to these rules in the given context. This is true regardless of whether he applies probabilities to well-

---

[3] This device is unsuitable for representing any event which has zero probability.

[4] Denote heads by H, tails by T, and place subscripts under these face symbols expressing whether the face in question shows on the *first* or on the *second* toss. Then the following four equally probable outcomes exhaust the possibilities: $H_1 H_2$, $H_1 T_2$, $T_1 T_2$, $T_1 H_2$.

[5] Only one of the four combinations listed in the foregoing footnote contains no H, and only one no T.

[6] These are the second and fourth items listed in n. 4.

behaved collectives of the frequentists or to any other set of events (or of hypotheses).

(3) Conditional Probability and Joint Probability

The rules we have just been considering possess implications concerning the significant question of conditional probability. For example, we may now conclude that if two events are mutually exclusive—such as (say) E_1 and E_3 in Figure 1, or heads and tails in a single toss[7]—then the probability of one event, given the other event, is zero. The probability of an event, given another event, is called a conditional probability. The symbol $P(E_1|E_3)$ stands for the conditional probability of E_1, given E_3; and analogous symbols are used for conditional probabilities in general. In our case, $P(E_1|E_3) = 0$, $P(E_3|E_1) = 0$. In such a case[8] the joint probability of the two events must also be zero, that is, $P(E_1, E_3) = 0$. But of course, the probability of the occurrence of E_1 or that of E_3 is *not* zero; $P(E_1) \neq 0$, $P(E_3) \neq 0$.

The relationship of mutual exclusiveness provides merely one illustration of a relationship between two events which can make the conditional probability of an event different from the probability of its occurrence. In situations where $P(E_i|E_j) \neq P(E_i)$, we say that E_i is not independent of E_j. If E_i and E_j are mutually exclusive, so that, by definition, $E_i \cap E_j = 0$, then surely these events cannot be independent of each other. Indeed, in this case, $P(E_i|E_j) = P(E_j|E_i) = 0$. But even if they have a positive intersection—as do E_1 and E_2 in Figure 1—the events *need not* be independent of one another. The probability of an event's happening *may* still be different according as the occurrence of another event is or is not taken for granted. To refer to an example: The event "the first of two random tosses of a perfect coin yields heads" and the event "both tosses yield heads" are not mutually exclusive, but they are not independent because the probability of the second of the two events is ¼, while the (conditional) probability of that same event, *given the first event*, is ½.

Subjectivists have rightly stressed that the concept of independence

---

[7] For two tosses the first and the third item listed in n. 4, p. 75, are mutually exclusive with the event "heads and also tails will be observed."

[8] Only if we wanted to include here a discussion of logically possible zero-probability events, such as may occur in sets viewed as consisting of an infinite number of elementary events, would it have to be considered *possible* at all that $P(E_i|E_j) = 0$, while $P(E_j|E_i) \neq 0$. In the discussion that follows, some other statements would also have to be modified in the presence of such zero-probability events: Independence would not always have to be a *mutual* relationship between events; while exclusiveness *would* have to stay mutual, it would not necessarily imply lack of independence.

can prove confusing in cases in which a decision maker is firmly convinced that a person knowing the composition of a set of events would have to regard the events belonging in the set as independent, and as satisfying Mises' criteria; but the decision maker himself assigns probabilities to each event (say, to successive random drawings from a nonguaranteed deck) which *do* depend on the preceding events (on the outcome of the previous drawings) because, in view of the already observed results, he will be improving his probability judgment. In such cases the events should be called *exchangeable* rather than independent, as was done in Chapter 2, Section 5. All elements of a set of events viewed as exchangeable have the same probability, which depends on observed events of the same set in the identical fashion.

From the three rules described in Section 2, we may now draw certain conclusions concerning conditional probabilities. Say that according to these rules, we have assigned a probability to the event E_1, and that we are now viewing E_1 as a subset containing further elements. The intersection of E_1 and E_2 may, for example, be viewed as such an element of E_1, since $E_1 \supset (E_1 \cap E_2)$. But we might be concerned with *any* element of E_1—say, in general, with E_s (not marked as such in the diagram in Figure 1). Let us first try to determine the probability of this element where $E_1 \supset E_s$. For this purpose, we *could* take E_1 (instead of S) as our universe; we could assign unitary probability to E_1, thereby narrowing our focus to those situations in which E_1 may be taken for granted; then we would have to assign a probability to E_s in a universe consisting merely of E_1. This is the *conditional probability* of E_s, given E_1. If now, returning to the larger set S, we wish to arrive at the *joint* probability of E_1 itself *and* of E_s, then we must multiply the probability of E_1 (in S as a whole) by the conditional probability of E_s, given E_1.

For illustration, we may use an example involving the traditional frequency probabilities. Someone might guarantee to us that only if a fair coin falls heads twice in a row (of which the probability is $\frac{1}{4}$) shall we draw a ball from an urn, and that in this case we shall draw the ball from an urn containing eight red and two black balls; then we may want to denote the event of becoming faced with the eight-to-two urn as E_1, and we may denote the event of our drawing a red ball as E_s. The conditional probability of E_s, given E_1, is $\frac{4}{5}$ or, in symbols, $P(E_s \mid E_1) = \frac{4}{5}$; the joint probability of E_1 and E_s—i.e., $P(E_1, E_s)$—has the value $\frac{1}{4} \times \frac{4}{5} = \frac{1}{5}$. This is the joint probability of our becoming faced with the eight-to-two urn *and* of drawing red from it. In general,

$$P(E_1, E_s) = P(E_1) \cdot P(E_s \mid E_1) \quad \ldots \ldots \ldots \ldots \ldots \quad (1)$$

It follows from this immediately that the joint probability of two mutually independent events is simply the algebraic product of the probabilities of the two events. This is because independent events are defined by the criterion that the conditional probability of such an event (say a differently chosen E_s), given the other event (say, given E_1), is precisely the same as the probability of the first event (i.e., of E_s). In this case the condition has no significance for the probability of E_s, and the right-hand side of equation 1 becomes $P(E_1) \cdot P(E_s)$. For example, in our illustration the outcome of a first random toss is independent of that of a second random toss, and thus the joint probability of (say) two heads in a row is simply $\frac{1}{2} \cdot \frac{1}{2}$. But the rule for handling the problem of the joint probability of independent events is merely a special application of the rule for computing joint probabilities (see equation 1).

Many significant problems have the property that an element E_s belongs potentially in E_1 and potentially in E_3. Those who in our previous illustrations guaranteed to us that if a fair coin falls heads twice in a row, then we shall draw a ball from an urn containing eight red and two black balls could also have guaranteed to us that if the coin to be tossed will *not* fall heads twice in a row (of which the probability is $\frac{3}{4}$), we shall be drawing from an urn containing four red and six black balls. The event "drawing red" (E_s) may then be interpreted as a potential element of the event "becoming faced with the eight-to-two urn" (E_1), and also as a potential element of the event "becoming faced with the four-to-six urn" (E_3). The events E_1 and E_3 are mutually exclusive.

The earlier version of the guarantee, discussed on page 77, gave us the joint probability $\frac{1}{5}$ of being faced with the eight-to-two urn and of drawing red from it; this second version of the guarantee gives us at the same time the joint probability $\frac{3}{10}$ of being faced with the four-to-six urn and of drawing red from this latter urn. All told, our probability of drawing red then is $\frac{1}{5} + \frac{3}{10} = \frac{1}{2}$. When a probability, such as $\frac{1}{2}$ in this example, is computed by adding up all the weighted conditional probabilities, then the probability in question is sometimes referred to as a *marginal probability*.

In general, we have, in addition to equation 1 above:

$$P(E_3, E_s) = P(E_3) \cdot P(E_s|E_3) \quad \ldots \ldots \ldots \ldots \ldots \ldots \quad (2)$$

Various algebraic operations involving equations 1 and 2 for E_1, E_3, etc., and for various elements such as E_s, lead to alternative forms of "Bayes's theorem." One form of this theorem was used and discussed in

Chapter 2. There the theorem was applied to a blend of numerically controversial prior judgments with *de facto* uncontroversial judgments based on a collective which was well behaved by frequentists criteria. The narrative of the present passage has referred to frequency probabilities alone (across the board). But what matters in the present section as a whole is obviously not the narrative, that is, the method of *illustrating* various formal propositions. What matters here is that all these propositions—including Bayes's theorem—follow from the general formal properties of the measure called "probability," regardless of what leads the decision maker to assign this measure to events (or to hypotheses).

This concludes our brief survey of the properties of the measure "probability." The basic axioms to which this measure is subject are those described in Section 2. The corollaries relating to conditional probabilities and to joint probabilities are of substantial significance for a good many problems. These are the foundations from which the complex theorems of the theory of probability can be derived.

Coins, cards, dice, and the like lend themselves particularly well to the illustration of these rules and their corollaries, but this is no excuse for prejudging the scope of applicability of the rules.

(4) *The Standard Process Postulate and the Utility Axioms*

In their *Theory of Games and Economic Behavior* (**38**), John von Neumann and Oskar Morgenstern have proved the existence of cardinally measurable utility for an individual satisfying certain axioms. Before turning to a survey of modern utility theory, which is a theory based on the von Neumann–Morgenstern utility axioms, I shall introduce a postulate which I shall call the *Standard Process Postulate*.

Mathematicians sometimes try to construct their utility analysis and their analysis of numerical subjective probability without reliance on this postulate because the postulate has a distinctly empirical character. Savage once called postulates of this sort "flagrantly ad hoc"; and in his analysis, he avoids them consistently. But our Standard Process Postulate is clearly reasonable. The task of interpreting the essential content of modern theories of subjective probability and of utility is made *very* much easier by recognizing the reasonableness of this postulate. Later, in Chapter 6, Section 9, we shall express our conclusions also by using Savage's postulational system as our point of departure.

Call a physical process a standard process of an individual if he is willing to regard the sets events generated by this process as strictly analogous to idealized coin tosses and card drawings (and to similar idealized processes) which have the definitional property of randomness and of creating frequency ratios such as converge on some *known* value. Ideally, we should assume that a standard process is capable of generating events with probabilities of *any* value in the range of real numbers bounded by zero and one; but what matters from our point of view is that it should be able to generate events with any probabilities needed for the analysis of problems we shall encounter. The known values of the probabilities of the events generated by a standard process may depend on various conditions, since such questions as whether a deck of cards will have one or the other guaranteed composition may depend on whether one or the other condition is satisfied; but unless the probability of one or the other of these conditions' being satisfied is itself a standard process probability of a value known to the individual, the problem posed by this conditionality must be a trivial one. I mean trivial in the sense that a process qualifies as a standard process only if the decision maker acts either as if he knew with certainty which of the relevant conditions will be satisfied for any bet he may want to place on an event generated by the process, or as if he knew with certainty that the question of which condition will be satisfied depends exclusively on the outcome of another standard process governed by probabilities the values of which he knows with certainty. That is to say, any *nonstandard process event* on which the probabilities of standard process events are conditioned must belong in the special class of nonstandard process events to which firm unitary probability is assigned (such as that a specific guarantee will be fulfilled). In particular, the probabilities of standard process events must not depend on the occurrence or nonoccurrence of any nonstandard process events the probabilities of which we shall want to measure by comparing them with the probabilties of standard process events. Such nonstandard sets of events, on the one hand, and standard process events, on the other, must be independent.

Many real decks of cards, real coins, real dice, and many physical entities of other sorts produce repetitive processes which to most reasonable individuals are standard processes in our sense. Our Standard Process Postulate maintains that *each reasonable individual has at least one standard process*, and that the great majority of reasonable individuals have at least one standard process in common. To the prospects offered by such a process, they assign decision weights which equal the "textbook probabilities" (i.e., probabilities of known numerical value, although if the computation of the theoretical probabilities in question is complicated enough, the individual may, of course, require expert advice). In the terminology which was explained on page 13, above, the probability judgments of an individual concerning events generated by his standard processes may be regarded as wholly uninfluenced by elusive hypotheses.

In cases where the willingness of an individual to accept a physical process as a standard process rests on his own personal observations relating to the behavior of frequency ratios, it takes considerable experience with a physical process to make it one of his standard processes. But this is not the only way in which a person may decide that a concrete physical process is acceptable to him as a standard process.

To become testable—operationally meaningful—the Standard Process Postulate must be supplemented with further postulates (axioms) relating to the acts in which the individual will engage after having weighted each prospect by its probability. If, for example, in addition to the Standard Process Postulate, we introduce also a set of axioms implying the maximization of the probabilistic expectations of utility in these processes, then the existence of a standard process for an individual can be tested by the criterion that his betting behavior in his standard process must disclose a consistent utility function on the basis of numerically known probabilities. One obvious implication of this is that he must be indifferent between accepting a prize contingent upon some set of events in the standard process and accepting the identical prize contingent upon any other set of events which is generated by the same process and which has the same theoretical probability. Generally expressed, if a person's behavior is such as to show consistency and to be predictable, on the joint assumption that (a) he satisfies the Standard Process Postulate for a specific physical process involving known probabilities *and* (b) in this process he is guided by the von Neumann–Morgenstern axioms which imply the maximization of probability-weighted utility expectations, then it is reasonable to infer that he does in fact satisfy this postulate and these axioms. The following section contains a brief survey of the von Neumann–Morgenstern axioms. We shall postulate that reasonable individuals do satisfy them *in their standard processes*.

(5) Summary of the Utility Axioms

First: Utilities are subject to complete transitive ordering by means of the relation $\leqq$ or $\geqq$. That is to say, if $u, v, w \ldots$ are utilities, then for any u and v, either $u < v$, or $v < u$, or $u = v$. Also, the transitivity requirement is satisfied—i.e., $u < v$ and $v < w$ implies $u < w$, etc.

Second: It is possible to derive a third utility w from any two utilities u and v by the operation $\alpha u + (1 - \alpha) v = w$, where α is a real number with the property $0 < \alpha < 1$. Note that before we are through, the number α—i.e., the weight in question—will be endowed with the properties of a probability, though probabilities of zero and one can be avoided in the reasoning.

Third: The so-called "Independence Axiom" must be satisfied. That is to say, $u < v$ implies $u < \alpha u + (1 - \alpha) v$, and $u > v$ implies $u > \alpha u + (1 - \alpha) v$. This is the von Neumann–Morgenstern statement of the Independence Axiom (38). The statement requires that if v, taken in isolation, is preferred to u, then the joint appearance of u and v in the option $\alpha u + (1 - \alpha) v$ should not change this ranking. The essential meaning of the Independence Axiom is this: *Mutually exclusive prospects of utilities must exert no complementarity effect on each other.*

Essentially the same postulate is sometimes expressed as the constant-column axiom because the absence of complementarity *for mutually exclusive* prospects may also be formulated in the following way: If one option promises the prospect of something (call it good A) with probability α, *and* promises B with probability $1 - \alpha$, and a second option promises the prospect of another thing (call it C) with probability α, *and* promises B with probability $1 - \alpha$, then substituting something other than B for B in both options must not change the preference ranking of the two options, as long as the identical thing (say D) is substituted for B in both options, i.e., as long as the same entry appears in that column of the payoff matrix which indicates what will happen in the first option if A is not gained and in the second option if C *is* not gained. In other words, neither the prospect of B nor that of D must be complementary with the prospect of A or with that of C, since these prospects are mutually exclusive. However, the von Neumann–Morgenstern formulation of the no-complementarity requirement is that expressed in the preceding paragraph.

Fourth: A continuity condition must be satisfied which may be expressed as follows: "If $u > v > w$, then there exists an α_1 such that $\alpha_1 u + (1 - \alpha_1) w < v$, and also an α_2 such that $\alpha_2 u + (1 - \alpha_2) w = v$, and also an α_3 such that $\alpha_3 u + (1 - \alpha_3) w > v$." In other words, by using the proper α, we can mix probabilistically *any* two utilities in such a way that the probabilistic mix should be any utility located between the two.

Fifth: In forming new utilities, it must make no difference whether we apply to any utility (say, to u) the weight α, or whether we apply to the same utility the weight $\alpha_{11} \cdot \alpha_1 + \alpha_{22} \cdot \alpha_2$, provided that $\alpha_{11} \cdot \alpha_1 +$

$\alpha_{22} \cdot \alpha_2 = \alpha$. That is, if $\alpha_{11} \cdot \alpha_1 + \alpha_{22} \cdot \alpha_2 = \alpha$, then it must be true that in the preference ranking of the individual, $\alpha_{11} \cdot \alpha_1 u + \alpha_{22} \cdot \alpha_2 u = \alpha u$. This expresses the conditional probability rule for the preference system of the individual—i.e., it assures that the α terms obey the rules by which probabilities can be compounded. (The axiom is slightly differently formulated in von Neumann and Morgenstern's *Theory of Games*, but this is its meaning.)

The authors of the book have shown that for an individual satisfying these conditions, there exist operationally testable utilities the mathematical expectations of which he maximizes and which are measurable up to a positive linear transformation. Measurability up to a positive linear transformation means that a numerical measure can be assigned to any quantity of the entity in question (here, to utility) and that *only* in the following two respects is the number so assigned arbitrary: The zero point of the scale and the unit of measurement are arbitrary. If, for example, to two quantities the numerical measures m and n are assigned, then (with a different zero point and a different unit of measurement) these numbers could alternatively become $a + rm$ and $a + rn$ where $r > 0$. Such transformations do not alter the order of ranking of the quantities in question, since if $m > n$, then and only then is $(a + rm) > (a + rn)$; furthermore, positive linear transformations do not alter the order of *ranking of the differences between the quantities in question*, since each difference of the form $(a + rm) - (a + rn)$ is equal to r times the difference $(m - n)$.

It is an essential property of measurability up to a positive linear transformation that not only the first condition expressed in the preceding sentence is satisfied (the condition of the determinate ranking of the quantities themselves) but also the second condition (the condition of the determinate ranking of the *differences*). This is the same kind of measurability as that of temperature on the Fahrenheit or on the centigrade scale, where, too, the zero point and the unit of measurement—the origin and the slope—are arbitrary, but where, nevertheless, *both* the following statements are valid: "Warmer" means warmer on *either* scale, *and* "a bigger rise in New York than in New Haven" is a bigger rise on *either* scale. If measurement were possible only up to all positive transformations which leave the ranking of the quantities themselves unaltered (but may change the ranking of the differences), then we would not speak of numerical or cardinal measurability. Instead, we would say that our quantities can be fitted only into an *ordinal* system. In these cases of mere ordinality, one may alternatively speak of measurability up to a positive monotone transformation; but in ordinary language, it is not usual to call this measurability. The Hicks-Allen indifference curve apparatus provides a well-known illustration of such ordinal systems. For the validity of that system, *only* the *first* utility postulate of Section 5— i.e., the postulate of complete, transitive ordering—is necessary. The other elements of the von Neumann–Morgenstern axiomatic construction narrow the permissible range of transformations from all positive monotone transformations to positive linear ones, that is, they lead to the assignment of utility measures which are measures in the same sense as is the degree Fahrenheit. It must, however, be emphasized that each person who satisfies these axioms has his own individual utility function: The system creates no room for interpersonal comparisons. Acceptance of the axioms results in numerical or cardinal measurability for each individual separately.

Given the foregoing axiomatic system, the required ranking of utility differences (or utility distances) and the assignment of numerical values to utilities may be achieved in the following way: Say the individual ranks the utilities themselves (not differences) in this order: $u > v > w$; and his behavior discloses that he judges $\alpha u + (1 - \alpha)w = v$. We then assign numbers to the utilities in u, v, and w in such a way that the utility distance from u to v should bear the proportion $\dfrac{1 - \alpha}{\alpha}$ to the utility distance from v to w.

In Chapter 1, this principle was implied in an illustration in which an individual was observed to assign one third of a utile to the first dollar which he acquires over and above his present wealth. The zero point of his utility scale was set at his initial no-bet position, and one utile was defined as the amount of utility carried by the *last* dollar already in his possession. The conclusion that the *next* dollar was worth only one third as much was derived from the observation that the individual proved indifferent as between putting up and not putting up $1.00, for a potential gain of $1.00, provided his probability of winning was ¾ ($\alpha = 0.75$). The same principle permits measurement of the utility of successive quantities of *specific goods*, assuming that exchange of these goods for other goods can be effectively barred.

(6) A Historical Note concerning Cardinal and Ordinal Utility

As concerns the history of the subject, we shall limit ourselves to a few brief comments. The Swiss mathematicians Daniel Bernoulli and Gabriel Cramer were the first to develop (independently of each other) the hypothesis that the unwillingness of individuals to accept bets even at actuarially better than fair odds reflected decreasing marginal utility of wealth. Neither Bernoulli nor Cramer suggested a method for actually *measuring* utility functions, although, in retrospect, one cannot help but feel that they did have the insight on which modern utility theory depends. It seems to me that not all the conclusions which the work of these two masters suggest have as yet been fully developed, and I shall return to this problem in the Appendix to the present chapter.

Alfred Marshall (**35**) was aware of Daniel Bernoulli's contribution; but he, too, refrained from basing on it a general theory of measurable cardinal utility. However, along different lines, he suggested that the utility of a specific commodity is (for all practical purposes) cardinally measurable if the commodity has a very small weight in the budget of the individual. This is because the rational individual buys those quantities of all goods which equate the ratio of the marginal utilities of any two goods to the ratio of their prices; thus, we may take a commodity which has a small weight in the budget of the individual, and we may select the aggregate of all other goods (called "money") as the other commodity, postulating that *the small weight of the first commodity will assure that the marginal utility of money remains constant irrespective of how much of this particular commodity is acquired;* and then we arrive at the conclusion that whatever the price of the "small" commodity may be, this known price will be made to bear that proportion to the number one (namely, to the price of money) as the marginal utility of the "small" commodity bears to the *constant* marginal utility of money. Hence the marginal utility of the "small" commodity is cardinally measurable in terms of a unit which is defined as the marginal utility of money to the individual. This is the analysis on which Marshall based his cardinal measurement of the marginal utility—and, through integration, also of the aggregate utility —of goods which are very small in the budget of the consumer. The consumer surplus (aggregate utility minus outlay on the good) also becomes cardinally measurable for such goods. The method is admittedly inapplicable to goods *in general*, because the marginal utility of money is not independent of how much is spent on any single major item in the consumer's budget. Hence, in general, the marginal utility of money cannot be used as a constant unit of measurement.

Marshall and many of his contemporaries did postulate a concept of cardinal (numerical) utility, but this was essentially an intuitive-introspective, nonoperational concept. For goods *in general* their "cardinal utility" was not measurable in any operational sense, i.e., was not even in principle measurable by observing the behavior of individuals. The concept of indifference curves, on the other hand, has been defined operationally all along but, prior to J. R. Hicks and R. G. D. Allen, even those authors who made occasional use of the merely ordinal (noncardinal) indifference curve approach placed reliance *also* on a purely intuitive concept of cardinal utility which lacked operational content. This is true particularly of the first three of the authors to whom we now turn, but it is not true of Hicks and Allen, who in order to move onto the operational level *limited themselves* to the use of indifference functions (and thus "gave up" cardinal utility just about the time when this concept too' was about to acquire operational meaning).

The indifference curve approach was used for specific and limited analytical purposes by F. Y. Edgeworth (**13**), Vilfredo Pareto (**39**), and Irving Fisher (**20**). The indifference function was made the central tool of purely ordinal utility theory by J. R. Hicks (**24**) and R. G. D. Allen (1934). This approach implies merely the axiom of complete, transitive ranking of utilities (i.e., of "desirables") by means of the relations $\leqq$ and $\geqq$. Only measurability up to a positive *monotone* transformation (rather than a positive linear transformation) is postulated, and this is not measurability in the usual sense. For example, while Hicks's "compensating variation" does express the *money* equivalent of the gain in well-being which the consumer acquires through access to various markets, the ordinal approach does not enable us to express the utility equivalent of this gain in numerical terms. In such a framework, in which the consumer is conceived of as being faced with absolutely certain (not with probabilistic) prospects of various commodities, it is not possible to base measurement on the ranking of utility mixes which would be analogous to our probabilistic mix $\alpha u + (1 - \alpha)v$ in Section 5. The reason is that if commodities are mixed *physically* (i.e., actually), then complementarities become inevitable. In other words, the Independence Axiom for *mutually exclusive* probabilistic prospects is thoroughly unconvincing for simultaneously available goods.

In the meantime, in a posthumously published essay, Frank Ramsey of Kings College, Cambridge, had suggested that utility and probability were cardinally measurable and that measurement could be based on the observation of the individual's choices from among risky prospects (**43**). Ramsey died very young—at not quite 27—and he did not go very far in axiomatizing his approach. The modern, probabilistic theory of cardinal utility was developed by von Neumann and Morgenstern in Princeton (1944). They based their theory on the axiomatic system discussed in the preceding pages. Frederick Mosteller and Philip Nogee (**37**) of Harvard were the pioneers in the game experimental measurement of utility.

(7) Derivation of the Utility Function from the Bet-Acceptance Boundary in a Standard Process

An individual can be made to disclose the least favorable probabilities of winning at which he is still barely willing to risk a definite amount of money in his standard process.[9] This risk-acceptance boundary stands in a unique relationship to his operationally detectable utility function for monetary pay-offs. The utility function so derived is a *utility-of-gains* function or, alternatively expressed, the individual's *local utility-of-wealth* function, in which x dollars of wealth means x dollars more than the initial wealth of the present period (rather than x dollars more than no wealth at all), and $-x$ dollars of wealth means x dollars less than the initial wealth of the present period. Given an unchanging global utility-of-wealth function (in which x dollars of wealth means x dollars more than no wealth at all), the local function—i.e., the utility-of-gains function—must be expected to change as the initial wealth of the decision maker changes. This is because in each period the local function shows the same shape in the neighborhood of $x = 0$ as does the global function in the neighborhood of a point on the abscissa expressing the amount of wealth already accumulated.

In Figure 2 the curve labeled $s = 1$ represents the risk-acceptance boundary when the individual gets an opportunity to put up a stake of one (small) unit of his money. The curve shows that if the potential net gain is zero, then the minimum probability of winning on which the person insists is one. This is clearly a limiting case of no interest. The significant points of the curve are such points as B or F. Point B, for example, indicates that if the potential gain is one monetary unit—one being the abscissa of B, that is, its distance from the ordinate—then BC

---

[9] I shall not here go into a question which has attracted the attention of several recent investigators, namely, the question of the operational meaning of the minimum acceptable odds.

On the continuity assumptions implied in the discussion, one should visualize a bet-acceptance region, a bet-rejection region, and a boundary line which separates the two. This boundary marks indifference. But in what precisely does indifference express itself in a universe in which a bet, after all, is always either accepted or rejected? Does indifference express itself in a 50 per cent acceptance ratio? Does preference for accepting the odds then express itself in a somewhat higher acceptance ratio and preference for staying in the no-bet position in a somewhat lower ratio? Do these acceptance and rejection ratios change in a predictable way with the odds, and is the presumptive strength of the preference thus made to change? Or does indifference show in erratic behavior, while acceptance and rejection might then show in (almost) consistent acceptance or rejection whenever the subject is well informed and has time to reflect? We shall not take up a discussion of this question, but the reader will find an illuminating analysis of this problem and an interesting suggestion in Frank T. Dolbear's doctoral dissertation, "Individual Choice under Uncertainty" (11), published in *Yale Economic Essays*, Fall, 1963.

FIGURE 2

BET-ACCEPTANCE BOUNDARIES

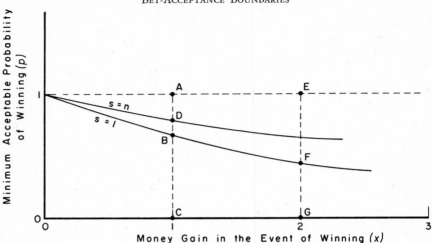

expresses the minimum probability of winning at which the individual will put up one unit of his monetary wealth. To be precise, the curve is a boundary line defined as follows: All combinations of *probabilities* of winning and of *sizes* of winnings within the area *between* the curve and the axes are rejected, and all combinations on the other side of the curve are accepted.

Let us for the present exposition again select the individual's no-bet position as the zero point of his utility scale, and the utility carried by a stake of one money unit ($s = 1$) as his unit of utility (one utile). This means that the last monetary unit in his possession is worth one utile. We then conclude that to him the utility of a gain of one money unit is $\frac{AB}{BC}$, and that the aggregate utility of all other gains is expressed by the analogous ratio of two vertical stretches. For example, the aggregate utility of a gain of two money units is $\frac{EF}{FG}$. The common-sense explanation of this proposition is that to our individual, BC times the utility of one money unit's worth of gain is the same as one minus BC times one utile; and FG times the utility of two money units' worth of gain is the same as one minus FG times one utile. Hence the utility of the gain of one money unit is one minus BC divided by BC, and this is the ratio $\frac{AB}{BC}$; the utility of two units of gain is one minus FG divided by FG, and this is $\frac{EF}{FG}$.

An individual who, throughout the range of gains, has constant marginal utility shows an $s = 1$ curve which goes through the point $p = \frac{1}{2}$ for $x = 1$; through the point $p = \frac{1}{3}$ for $x = 2$; and generally through $p = \dfrac{1}{r+1}$ for $x = r$. However, even a curve that lies everywhere above the curve so described does not *necessarily* imply *monotonically* decreasing marginal utility, but may merely imply that in no range does marginal utility increase enough to offset decreases in other ranges, when a direct jump is considered from the zero point to any point on the abscissa. In general, the marginal utility at each level of gain—i.e., at each level of wealth consisting of the no-bet wealth plus alternative gains measured on the abscissa—is the *difference* between the aggregate utilities corresponding to nearby points on the abscissa divided by the distance between these to points on the abscissa (or rather the limit to which this ratio tends when the two points on the abscissa are brought ever closer to each other).

So far, we have stayed on the $s = 1$ curve; that is to say, we have faced our individual with various choices, all of which involved putting up or not putting up *one* monetary unit of his money. If we face the individual with the option of putting up or not putting up *n* monetary units rather than one monetary unit, at alternative probabilities and for alternative potential gain, then we obtain the curve which is labeled $s = n$. The relationship between the $s = 1$ curve and the $s = n$ curve must satisfy a consistency requirement which will be explained in the next section and will be summarized in the last paragraph of that section.

(8) Algebraic Derivation of the Utility Function in a Standard Process

Let us denote the values measured along the abscissa of Figure 2 by x and those measured along the ordinate of the figure by p; let us denote the function graphed as $s = 1$ by $p = p(x)$ and the utility of a gain of x by $U(x)$. The initial no-bet position of the individual is marked by $x = 0$ (so that we say that if he loses $100, he has "minus $100"); we make $U(0) = 0$; and we define one utile as $-U(-1)$, which is the utility of the last money unit possessed in the no-bet position.

Then, from the maximization postulate:

$$pU(x) = 1 - p \quad \ldots \ldots \ldots \ldots \ldots \ldots \quad (1)$$

we obtain the aggregate utility function:

$$U(x) = \frac{1-p}{p} \quad \ldots \ldots \ldots \ldots \ldots \ldots \quad (2)$$

It is obvious from equation 2 that if one money unit of gain brings the individual less utility than is represented by the stake $s = 1$, then he will insist on better than actuarially fair odds to put up one money unit for a potential gain of one money unit. In this case, $U(1) < 1$, and this implies that $p > (1 - p)$; hence, it implies that $p > 0.5$.

For marginal utility, we obtain:

$$\frac{dU(x)}{dx} = \frac{dU(x)}{dp} \cdot \frac{dp(x)}{dx} = -\frac{1}{p^2} \frac{dp}{dx} \quad \ldots \ldots \ldots \ldots \ldots \quad (3)$$

There exists a whole family of boundary lines such as the curve $s = 1$. Each member of the family relates to different *money* amounts which the individual must put up out of his own monetary wealth. Let us consider $s = n$. On this curve, we may observe, for example, point D. What is the meaning of the ratio of vertical distances $\frac{AD}{DC}$? This is the ratio of the utility of $x = 1$—i.e., of the wealth consisting of the initial no-bet wealth plus one money unit's worth of gain—*to the utility of the last n money units' worth of wealth already in the individual's possession*, i.e., to $-U(-n)$. The foregoing statement, too, is derived from a maximization postulate:

$$p_n U(x) = -(1 - p_n) U(-n) \quad \ldots \ldots \ldots \ldots \ldots \quad (4)$$

where $p_n = p_n(x)$ stands for the function graphed as $s = n$. Hence, for any x, we obtain:

$$\frac{U(x)}{-U(-n)} = \frac{1 - p_n}{p_n} \quad \ldots \ldots \ldots \ldots \ldots \quad (5)$$

Note that by dividing equation 2 by equation 5, we obtain $-U(-n)$. Thus the following is the method by which we obtain the utility of the last n money units which the individual posesses in the no-bet position. We divide the $\frac{AB}{BC}$ ratio by the $\frac{AD}{DC}$ ratio. The ratio of such ratios must be the same all along the $s = 1$ and $s = n$ curves, regardless of the value of the abscissa for which we observe these horizontal stretches, except that the ratios themselves are zero (and *their* ratio meaningless) in the point of origin.

Unless the ratio of ratios such as $\frac{AB}{BC}$ divided by $\frac{AD}{DC}$ is the same for all nonzero points of the abscissa, the individual does not maximize the correctly computed probabilistic expectations of the utility of wealth to him. (I did not try for high geometric precision in this regard.)

(9) The Utility of Gambling and the Higher Moments of Frequency Distributions

A comment needs to be added on the utility of gambling. An element which one might be inclined to designate by this term may well enter into the utility function just discussed—the von Neumann–Morgenstern utility function[10]—but only if by the term "utility of gambling" we refer to a factor that escapes operational identification. This needs to be expressed more specifically.

It is, of course, quite conceivable that the operationally defined von Neumann–Morgenstern utility function differs from the Jevons-Menger-Walras-Marshall introspective utility function (the neoclassical utility function) because of the fact that the operational function is influenced by specific attitudes to moving out of one's initial position *by an act of betting*, i.e, by reliance on probabilistic motivations. If this is meant by the utility or disutility of gambling in a standard process, one may merely *assert* or *deny* the presence of that element on intuitive grounds. Operationally, one cannot *test* for this element in the standard process because the neoclassical utility function cannot be identified operationally. However, intuitive assertions and denials of this sort may, of course, convey very valuable insights, and it would be a mistake to overlook the fact that for the foregoing reason the operational utility function *may* be an impure equivalent of the neoclassical function.

On the other hand, the von Neumann-Morgenstern postulates exclude that sort of utility or disutility of gambling which would make a person react differently to a prize depending on whether the prize is promised with a probability of 0.5 if an event with probability 0.4 does occur and with a probability of 0.25 if the event with probability 0.4 does not occur, or is promised on condition that a simple event with probability 0.35 occurs. This sort of utility of gambling would lead an individual to behavior which is inconsistent with the assumption of his having a von Neumann–Morgenstern utility function. An individual to whom gambling has utility or disutility in this latter sense would make choices which contradict the predictions based on his operational utility function.

In the present volume, *we shall assume that in his standard process (or standard processes) a reasonable individual observably tends to behave according to the von Neumann–Morgenstern axioms, that is, that he satisfies these axioms with α terms that are standard process probabilities.* A more detailed analysis of behavior outside these standard processes—i.e., of behavior in regard to nonstandard sets of events—will follow later; however, it has already been pointed out that Version 1 attributes to the decision maker the same utility-of-wealth (monetary wealth) function in standard and nonstandard processes alike—this being the function observable in standard process bets—and attributes to

---

[10] As was explained in Section 7, we have been deriving a local function of this type, but these remarks on the utility of gambling apply to operational utility functions in general.

semiprobabilistic decision makers an inclination to use slanted probabilities as decision weights in nonstandard processes. (Version 2, which other investigators might prefer, would no doubt insist on behavior according to the von Neumann–Morgenstern axioms for behavior in relation to all types of events; but the resulting concept of the utility function would, in some respects, be appreciably less manageable than our utility-of-monetary-wealth function).

For standard processes the maximization of the mathematical expectation of utility—as axiomatized by von Neumann and Morgenstern —is intuitively very appealing. I believe that on reflection, most readers will agree with this statement. Modified axiomatic systems, incorporating the same basic principles, might do equally well; but I should like to point out here that there exists a specific kind of modification, the idea of which has tempted some contributors but which in reality has no justification. I mean the idea of postulating that a rational decision maker may wish to weight his *utility prospects* not exclusively by their probabilities but also by some measure of the possible deviations from the probabilistically expected utilities. This is a confusing suggestion because the utility function itself takes account of the deviations from the actuarially expected outcome of the monetary pay-offs. It takes account of the fact that the decision maker will either gain or lose as compared to the mathematical expectations of *money gains*, and these money gains are linked by the utility function to utility gains. If an individual wishes to pay attention *once more* to the deviations from the probabilistically expected outcome—i.e., if he is not prepared to weight the *utilities* by their probabilities—then this is another way of saying that he is introducing considerations the foundations of which are not probabilistic and which therefore cannot be expressed by the variance, or by the higher moments, or by any other properties of frequency distributions. As the reader knows, in our analysis we shall make room for deviations from purely probabilistic behavior; but this will have to be done by a different method, and it will be done only for sets of events falling outside the category of standard processes.

(10) The Problem of Imperfections Contrasted with the Problem of Semiprobabilistic Modifications

While, in this volume, we shall build on axiomatic foundations described by the Standard Process Postulate and by the von Neumann–Morgenstern utility axioms (as applied to standard processes), it should be remembered that neat postulational systems of this sort must always be interpreted as idealizations. Even on reflection, no one acts *in all respects* as if he were motivated by the principles incorporated in an orderly axiomatic system. When it comes to testing behavior based on such systems, certain types of situations must be avoided, because in these situations the observed results would be strongly influenced by various kinds of imperfections. A discussion of this problem will be found in the Appendix to the present chapter.

The adherents of purely probabilistic decision theory would relegate even the semiprobabilistic elements of the theory which is presented in this volume into the realm of imperfections. According to such a view, the fact that many reasonable individuals are less willing (or in some cases more willing) to bet on an unstable and controversial hunch than on a standard process probability may be the result of confusion, or it may be the result of imperfections similar to that which makes many reasonable people disregard the difference between a prize of $100 and a prize of $100 plus a nickel. Such a conception of the matter seems unconvincing to me, and this is why I am making an attempt to take account of the unstable and controversial character of specific probability judgments by making systematic allowances for different degrees of willingness to rely on appraisals of different kinds.

As will be argued in the Appendix, some phenomena must indeed be dealt with as imperfections. But it is detrimental for a theory if it shifts into the realm of imperfections phenomena of major significance which cannot be circumvented in empirical investigations. The phenomena which in my opinion call for the semiprobabilistic interpretation of the decision process are of major significance; they cannot be circumvented in empirical work without serious loss of substance, and they are capable of being incorporated into an orderly system. Hence, they will not be lumped together with the imperfections which will be examined in the Appendix to the present chapter.

(11) *Observations on Ramsey's Earlier Method, and on Davidson's and Suppes' Recent Argument in Its Favor*

Frank Ramsey, an important pioneer in operational utility and subjective probability theory, developed his concept of cardinal utility by a piece of reasoning which is different in some details from that present in Sections 7 and 8. The distinctive feature of Ramsey's method (**43**) was that he visualized the individual as faced with two options, of which one gave him the prospect of money gain *a* with probability 0.5 and at the same time the prospect of money gain *b* with probability 0.5, while the other gave him the prospect of money gain c with probability 0.5 and at the same time the prospect of money gain d with probability 0.5. Thus the procedure suggested by Ramsey requires making money gains contingent on events which the individual considers equiprobable. Given such events, we make the gain a in Option I *greater* than c in Option II; and we make b in Option I *smaller* than d in Option II, so that a configuration of this sort should result:

$$
\begin{array}{c|c}
\text{I} & \text{II} \\
a & \\
 & c \\
 & d \\
b &
\end{array}
$$

The money difference $(a - c)$ and also the money difference $(d - b)$ must then be so adjusted that the individual should be indifferent as between the two options. From this indifference, we conclude $U(a) - U(c) = U(d) - U(b)$, and we may now rely on the theorem that ability to rank *utility differences* establishes the cardinal measurability of utility, i.e., its measurability up to a positive linear transformation (see page 83). Once we have measured the individual's utilities in terms of utiles for a sufficiently wide range of money incomes—which implies discovering what amount of money represents to him the same amount of utility at various levels of wealth as does $1.00 at some given level of wealth—we can also measure his subjective probabilities, since these will be disclosed by the odds he is barely willing to accept on various bets, provided these odds are expressed *in units of utility*. For example, if he is indifferent as between receiving five utiles if a stock exchange event occurs and ten utiles if it does not occur, then he assigns probability $\frac{2}{3}$ to the event's happening and $\frac{1}{3}$ to its not happening. It is implied that the individual maximizes strictly probabilistic expectations for all sets of "ethically neutral" events. Ramsey limited his approach to such events; but for such events, his approach was purely probabilistic (not semiprobabilistic).

Donald Davidson and Patrick Suppes, in co-operation with Sidney Siegel (10) have recently used experimental methods of utility measurement which are rooted more in Ramsey's ideas than in those considered in Sections 7 and 8. These authors have applied the method to standard processes. Contrary to my own beliefs, Davidson and Suppes feel that, when applied to these processes, Ramsey's two-option method has a specific advantage, in that it does not involve putting up a stake and thus avoids the potentiality of actual loss, thereby minimizing the impurities entering through the utility or disutility of gambling.

The following is my reason for being unconvinced of the existence —or, at any rate, of the importance—of any such difference. We have seen that the disutility or the positive utility of gambling may mean one of two things. It may mean some degree of reluctance (or occasionally of particular eagerness) to move out of one's initial position under the guidance of probabilistic considerations, and thus an inclination to display an operational utility function which is different from one's introspective neoclassical utility function of wealth. For this impurity the operational utility function *cannot* be corrected because the neoclassical utility function has no operational equivalent. For example, while it is true that in Sections 7 and 8 the individual was confronted with a choice of putting up or not putting up some of his own money in a bet, it is equally true that Ramsey's (or Davidson's and Suppes') Option I is more of a gamble than Option II, even though neither option calls for risking a stake. The range is wider in Option I than in Option II, and a person who is particularly reluctant or eager to make his destinies dependent on a gambling decision will notice this difference. Say that our individual illustrates the case of reluctance in the foregoing sense. Then his operational utility function will show a tendency toward diminishing marginal utility more strongly than does his operationally nontestable, intuitive neoclassical utility function. This will be true regardless of whether we employ the procedure described in Sections 7 and 8 or the two option method just discussed. It must simply be taken for granted that the charatceristics of the operational utility function may be influenced by the utility or disutility of gambling in this sense.

On the other hand, we have seen that the utility or disutility of gambling may mean something else. It may mean that the individual has no standard process in which he would make his degrees of belief internally consistent by the criteria of probability theory. This possibility might, for example, be illustrated by the subject's making ratios such as $\frac{AB}{BC}$ to $\frac{AD}{DC}$ in Figure 2 different for different values of the abscissa. More generally expressed, the utility of given amounts of money to him may appear to depend upon how the identical probabilistic expectations of utility are arrived at (see page 91). If the individual displays utility or disutility of gambling in this sense, then he cannot be said to have a consistent operational utility function. We have postulated that the individual does not behave in this fashion; but if he does, then there is no point in hiding this prohibitive difficulty by confronting him exclusively with 50–50 probabilities.

I therefore consider the framework of Section 7 and 8 adequate. The Ramsey method is an alternative, but I see no reason for considering it a superior one.

(12) *The Shape of the Operational Utility Function*

We shall assume that our individual does have a consistent operational utility function which can be detected in his behavior in a standard process, and which possibly can be found also in various other processes or sets of events in which he behaves purely probabilistically. His utility function is described by equations 2, 3, and 5 on pages 89–90 (disregarding the imperfections to be discussed in the Appendix to the present chapter). The function relates to monetary wealth.

The utility function in question might, for example, have one of the two shapes shown in Figure 3. The labeling of the abscissa shows that we have here a local utility function in mind.

FIGURE 3

UTILITY FUNCTIONS

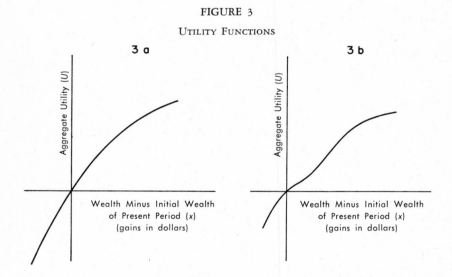

Figure 3*a* shows a utility function which is concave from below throughout its course. For this function the marginal utility $\left(\dfrac{dU}{dx}\right)$ is decreasing all along. In reality, the marginal utility may be increasing in some ranges and decreasing in others. For bets in specific ranges the individual may be willing to accept worse than actuarially fair odds; while

for bets in other ranges (particularly in ranges involving the possibility of a large loss), he is practically certain to insist on appreciably better than actuarially fair odds. Figure 3*b* has inflexion points which express these alternatives.

It is easy to verify the meaning of an observation of the following sort: "At its mid-point a chord connecting on the utility function the two end points of a range lies *below* the utility curve." What does this mean? Consider that mixing with equal probabilities the utilities marked on the utility curve by the two end points of such a chord yields the utility indicated by the mid-point of the chord; hence, if this utility, expressed by the mid-point height of the *chord*, is smaller than the utility indicated by the *utility curve itself* for the same mid-point value of x, then in that range the individual will prefer the utility which the U function expresses for the "sure" mid-point value of x to the 50–50 probabilistic mixture of the two end points of the x range. In the event of monotonically diminishing marginal utility, it is impossible to draw a chord that would not satisfy this condition. In Figure 3*a*, all chords that can be drawn lie below the curve at their mid-points. In Figure 3*b*, some do, and some do not; but if we include large enough potential losses, then all do.

Milton Friedman and L. J. Savage (**21**) concluded from common observation that many people do accept worse than actuarially fair odds in some ranges of betting and insist on better than fair odds in other ranges. They suggest that utility functions may frequently have several inflexion points. This is a reasonable suggestion.

(13) *The Postulate of Subjective-Probabilistic Behavior outside the Standard Processes*

Referring back to Figure 1 (page 74), I shall now use the following expository device: "Events" (i.e., prospects of events) such as E_1, E_2, E_3, E_4, . . . are generated by a standard process, while events such as E'_5, E'_6, E'_7, E'_8, . . . belong in various nonstandard sets of events.

An individual behaving according to the purely probabilistic-objectivist theory not only satisfies the von Neumann–Morgenstern utility axioms in his standard process—i.e., with α terms that are standard process probabilities—but satisfies *also* the following postulate which we shall call the *Postulate of Equivalent Degrees of Belief.* When faced with monetary pay-offs, he attaches to E'_5, E'_6, E'_7 (and, indeed, to all risky prospects on which pay-offs may be contingent) decision weights that are strictly equivalent to a probability attached to some standard process event such as E_1, E_2, E_3, ... His observable decision weights relating to risky prospects of any sort possess strict standard process probability equivalents.

The following are some of the most important corollaries of this postulate:

a) If such a person is equally willing to accept a prize when it is made contingent upon E'_5 as when it is made contingent upon E_1, so that we conclude that to him $P(E'_5) = P(E_1)$, then his betting behavior must disclose also that to him $P(\sim E'_5) = 1 - P(E_1)$. Illustration: If he is indifferent between a prize contingent upon the rise of a stock price and a prize contingent upon a standard process event of probability 0.75, then he must be indifferent also between a prize contingent upon the stock price's not rising and a prize contingent on the nonoccurrence of the standard process event that has probability 0.75. (The nonoccrrence of this event has, of course, probability 0.25.)

b) If, in betting tests of the foregoing kind, he discloses subjective equiprobability of E'_5 with E_1, and also of E'_6 with E_3, then he must disclose also $P(E'_5 \cup E'_6) = P(E_1) + P(E_3)$, provided E_1 and E_3 are mutually exclusive, and E'_5 and E'_6 also are. Illustration: If, in the betting tests, this individual proves indifferent between the chances of a specific political candidate from among three running for a single office and the probability that on both of the next two occasions a fair coin will fall heads, and if he proves indifferent also between the chances of a second candidate and the probability that on the next two occasions a fair coin will fall heads once and tails once (in either sequence), then he must prove indifferent between the prospect "either the first or the second candidate will win" and the probability that either one or the other of the two coin events will happen.

Corollaries analogous to those listed above can be formulated for all rules of the Calculus of Probabilities. These analogous corollaries state that once the purely probabilistic individual has disclosed that he is equally as willing to make a money gain dependent on the prospect of some nonstandard event as on a standard process prospect of given probability, then he consistently handles his degree of belief concerning the nonstandard event as a probability the numerical value of which is the same as that of the standard process probability in question. Some further illustrations of corollaries of the postulate, beyond (*a*) and (*b*), may be added here.

c, d, etc.) Once the individual has disclosed that he assigns positive probability to the joint occurrence of two nonstandard process events (such as E'_7 and E'_8), then he must deduct the standard process probability equivalent of this joint occurrence from the sum of the standard process probability equivalents of E'_7 and of E'_8 to arrive at the standard process probability equivalent of $E'_7 \cup E'_8$. *Further*, if his betting behavior shows that the probability he assigns to E'_5 does not depend in the least on whether E'_6 is or is not guaranteed to occur (and in this case also that the probability he assigns to E'_6 does not depend in the least on whether E'_5 is or is not guaranteed to occur), then the joint probability of E'_5 and E'_6 must be the algebraic product of the two individual probabilities; and in general, all degrees of belief of this person must obey the rules of conditional probability.

We see that it is relatively easy to define purely probabilistic behavior operationally for an individual to whom the *Standard Process Postulate* of page 80 applies and who in his standard process satisfies the von Neumann–Morgenstern utility axioms. The purely probabilistic version of the subjectivist theory then requires that this individual should also satisfy the *Postulate of Equivalent Degrees of Belief*.

If, on the other hand, one wishes to avoid using the Standard Process Postulate, then the postulational system which underlies purely probabilistic behavior becomes more involved. Yet, even in this case, it is possible to endow the theory of numerical subjective probability, and of all-around probabilistic utility maximization, with operational meaning. For example, we have seen that Savage avoids the Standard Process Postulate, because he considers it "flagrantly ad hoc." We shall give a brief characterization of Savage's system in Chapter 6, but it may be useful here to add a footnote on a specific postulate which suggests the lines along which subjective probability can be made measurable (i.e., numerical) without reliance on the Standard Process Postulate. I mean Savage's $P6'$.[11]

All this relates to purely probabilistic behavior. A semiprobabilistic individual will in this volume be interpreted as one who observably satis-

---

[11] This postulate requires that if the individual prefers to stake his fortunes on event (or set of events) E rather than on event (or set of events) $'E$, then it should always be possible to describe a set of sufficiently unlikely events $''E$ so that it should be true that the individual still barely prefers to stake his fortunes on E rather than on $'E \cup ''E$. This or some similar postulate is needed to enable us to *rank the differences* in numerical probability between sets such as E and $'E$ in terms of the probability of $''E$-type events (which can be used to fill in the difference). The events $''E$ should be independent of E and $'E$. For example, $''E$ could be a set of highly unlikely heads-or-tails outcomes—with a coin which the individual *need not* consider fair (but to which he attaches definite subjective probabilities).

As I have said before, in my opinion the assumption that a reasonable person satisfies the Standard Process Postulate is sufficiently mild to be acceptable. Its use simplifies matters very greatly.

fies the Standard Process Postulate—and also satisfies the von Neumann–
Morgenstern axioms when the α terms of the axiomatic system are standard process probabilities—but who deviates from the Postulate of Equivalent Degrees of Belief in a systematic fashion. This he does because the
loss caused by action based on various nonstandard degrees of belief is
more painful (or less painful) to him than the gain forgone by disregarding the availability of acts based on such beliefs. Some of his beliefs
are appreciably influenced by elusive hypotheses; and in practice, this
always implies that these beliefs are controversial and psychologically
unstable at the same time. In Version 1, which is in the foreground of
our presentation, the nonequivalence of a person's degrees of belief in
various processes is said to express itself in his using slanted probabilities
as decision weights in a good many processes. (In Version 2, this same
nonequivalence would be said to result in his utility function's including
allowances for the shaky and controversial character of some of his degrees of belief.)

Later, we shall consider systems of semiprobabilistic allowances
more closely. Rational semiprobabilistic behavior requires that these allowances should satisfy certain consistency requirements, which will be
discussed in detail in Chapter 6, Section 6.

(14) Group Decisions

How should we interpret the behavior of an individual making a
decision the direct benefits or harmful consequences of which fall upon
others? Does such an individual have a utility function of his own for
the wealth which, as a result of his decisions, accrues to others?

In most situations of this sort, it seems reasonable to postulate that
the decision maker does have a utility function of his own which is influenced by his idea of the shapes of the utility functions entertained by
the other beneficiaries. In the typical case the decision maker himself
is one of the interested parties, if for no other reason than because his
reputation and his ability to continue in his position depend on how successful his decisions are. This is particularly true of relatively decentral-
ized societies in which the individuals for whom the group decision
makers act have a wide range of choice of groups which they may join, or
to the formation of which they may contribute. However, semiprobabilistic slanting tendencies are likely to be particularly pronounced in situations involving group decisions, since the controversial nature of the
probability judgments is one of the prominent features of the problem
with which group decision makers are faced.

APPENDIX TO CHAPTER 3

The St. Petersburg Game and the Problem of Imperfections: A Warning Inspired by Gabriel Cramer

History

The Bernoullis are a Swiss family from Basle. In successive generations, during the seventeenth and eighteenth centuries, several members of this family played a prominent role in the intellectual life of the period, particularly a pioneering role in the development of various branches of mathematics and theoretical physics.

Nicolas Bernoulli (to be referred to as N. B.) formulated the problem known as that of the "St. Petersburg game." The first published analysis of this problem was developed by his younger cousin, Daniel Bernoulli (D. B.). The younger Bernoulli's paper was written during his stay in St. Petersburg as a visiting scholar (1725–33). The Latin original of the paper was read before the St. Petersburg Academy in 1730 or 1731, and the paper appeared in print in 1738. While still in St. Petersburg, D. B. sent a copy of the paper to N. B., who in his reply communicated to D. B. the results of a piece of analysis which the Swiss mathematician Garbriel Cramer, a pioneer on linear equations, had submitted to him in the meantime. Cramer's analysis related to the same problem, and his solution was remarkably similar to D. B.'s. This is known because in the published version of his essay, D. B. included a brief review of Cramer's analysis.

The Latin original of D. B.'s manuscript was published in the *Proceedings* of the St. Petersburg Academy under the title "Specimen theoriae novae de mensura sortis" (5); a German translation with commentaries by Alfred Pringsheim appeared in 1896 (Duncker Humblot); an English translation by Louise Sommer was published in *Econometrica*, January, 1954.

The Problem

You are made the following offer: Someone is going to flip a fair coin as many times as it takes to have it fall heads. When the coin falls heads for the first time, the game is over. You are paid one ducat if the first toss yields heads, two ducats if the first appearance of heads occurs on the second toss, and, in general, 2^{n-1} ducats if the first appearance of heads occurs on the nth toss. The question which N. B. asked was this: "What is the amount of money the outright receipt of which you would consider equivalent to the privilege of playing this game on the receiving side?"

Note that the game is defined in such a way that the mathematical expectation of your money gains from the game is *infinite*, since the rise in the potential money gains for increasingly late first appearances of heads precisely offsets the decrease in the probability of increasingly late first appearances. If the first appearance of heads occurs on the nth toss, then for all possible values of n the probability of this event is $\frac{1}{2^n}$, and the money gain is 2^{n-1}. The money gain multiplied by the corresponding probability is ½ for all tosses. This gives you for the game as a whole the following mathematical expectation of money gains:

$$\sum_{n=1}^{\infty} \frac{2^{n-1}}{2^n} = \tfrac{1}{2} + \tfrac{1}{2} + \tfrac{1}{2} \ldots \ldots = \infty \tag{1}$$

Your mathematical expectation of money gains is infinite; but as N. B. pointed out, it is intuitively obvious that no reasonable person would prefer the privilege of playing this game on the receiving side to the outright receipt of any appreciable amount of money. Search your mind, reader, and I am sure you will agree! This describes the so-called "St. Petersburg paradox," formulated by N. B. in Basle but discussed and resolved in D. B.'s St. Petersburg paper.

Daniel Bernoulli's Solution

The solution which D. B. suggested rests on the idea that the marginal utility of money gains diminishes to you with rising amounts of money gains. Therefore, while the declining probability of increasingly late first appearances of heads *is* fully offset by increasingly large *monetary pay-offs*, it is *not* fully offset by the *less steeply rising aggregate utility pay-offs*. What matters is the value of the utility pay-offs, not that of the money gains. The nonconvergent infinite progression (series) which was developed above for the money gains must be replaced by a progression expressing the utility equivalents of each potential pay-off. On the assumption of monotonically decreasing marginal utility, this operation yields a convergent progression. Indeed, D. B.'s specific assumptions led him to formulate for the utility gain a progression which tends to a sum the monetary equivalent of which is a *very small* amount.

The specific assumption in question was that the utility of a money gain is a logarithmic function of the size of the money gain. To D. B., this seemed a plausible function because it reflected the suggestion that the same *proportionate* addition to an amount of wealth carried the same *absolute* addition to utility, regardless of the absolute level of wealth at which this addition was accruing. Say that your initial wealth is negligibly small—less than a ducat—and the zero point of your utility scale is set in such a way that your initial wealth (a) has zero utility; and say that for any wealth (w) exceeding a the aggregate utility of wealth to you is $b \log \frac{w}{a}$, where b is a constant and w is measured in ducats. Then, while your mathematical expectation of money gain from the St. Petersburg game can be expressed by $\sum_{n=1}^{\infty} \frac{2^{n-1}}{2^n}$ (see page 102), your mathematical expectation of utility gains—i.e., your so-called "moral expectations"—will be shown by an expression in which, for each n, not the money gain 2^{n-1} but the utility gain $b \log \frac{2^{n-1}}{a}$ is weighted by the probability $\frac{1}{2^n}$. Hence, taking account of the fact that the weighting yields $\frac{b[(n-1)\log 2 - \log a]}{2^n}$, we obtain for the mathematical expectation of utility gains:

$$\sum_{n=1}^{\infty} \frac{n-1}{2^n} b \log 2 - b \log a = b \log \frac{2}{a} \quad \ldots \ldots \ldots \ldots \ldots \ldots \quad (2)$$

Equation 2 makes use of the relationship $\sum_{n=1}^{\infty} \frac{n-1}{2^n} = 1$. For this, see the footnote below.[12]

As we said a moment ago, the reasoning is based on the assumption of a utility function according to which the utility of w is $b \log \frac{w}{a}$. From

---

[12] The expression $\sum_{n=1}^{\infty} \frac{n-1}{2^n}$ obviously can be expanded in the following way (omitting the first term, which, for $n = 1$, has the value zero):

$$\tfrac{1}{4} + \tfrac{2}{8} + \tfrac{3}{16} + \tfrac{4}{32} + \tfrac{5}{64} + \ldots \ldots \ldots \ldots$$

This can be put together from the following geometric progressions:

$\quad\quad\quad \tfrac{1}{4} + \tfrac{1}{8} + \tfrac{1}{16} + \tfrac{1}{32} + \tfrac{1}{64} + \ldots$ (The sum of this line tends to $\tfrac{1}{2}$.)
plus $\quad\quad \tfrac{1}{8} + \tfrac{1}{16} + \tfrac{1}{32} + \tfrac{1}{64} + \ldots$ (The sum of this line tends to $\tfrac{1}{4}$.)
plus $\quad\quad\quad \tfrac{1}{16} + \tfrac{1}{32} + \tfrac{1}{64} + \ldots$ (The sum of this line tends to $\tfrac{1}{8}$).
plus $\quad\quad\quad\quad \tfrac{1}{32} + \tfrac{1}{64} + \ldots$ (The sum of this line tends to $\tfrac{1}{16}$.)
etc.

Add up vertically the numbers shown as the sum of the various lines. That grand total tends to the number one.

this, it follows also that the money equivalent of the right-hand side of equation 2 is two ducats. The outright receipt of a payment in this amount conveys to you the same utility as the privilege of playing the St. Petersburg game on the receiving side. The "infinite amount of money" has shrunk to two ducats!

Gabriel Cramer's Solution

We know from D. B.'s paper that Cramer communicated his analysis of the problem to N. B. in 1728, that is, four years before D. B. did, and that Cramer's letter to N. B. preceded also the time when D. B. presented his analysis to the Academy in St. Petersburg. Nevertheless, D. B. learned about Cramer's solution only after informing N. B. of his own (but, of course, before *publishing* his paper).

To be precise, we should say that Cramer had *two* solutions, which may be considered alternatives. According to N. B.'s letter to D. B., which is quoted in D. B.'s St. Petersburg paper, Cramer reasoned in the following way: In the first place, it is enough to assume that beyond some very large amount of money gain—say, beyond 2^{24} ducats—further gains carry zero marginal utility to you. This assumption would suffice to make your mathematical expectation of utility gains finite *and not very large*, even if your aggregate utility function were linear up to that point. Secondly, it is to be taken into account, however, that your aggregate utility function is practically certain to show diminishing marginal utility from the outset. This makes your mathematical expectation of utility gains from the game finite, even if you do not have zero marginal utility from any point on. In this second part of his brief analysis, Cramer did in fact not assume a ceiling to aggregate utility but developed his argument in terms similar to those of D. B.'s reasoning, except that Cramer illustrated the point with a function which represented the *utility gain as equal to the square root of the money gain*. This led him to express your mathematical expectations of utility gains from the game as

$$\sum_{n=1}^{\infty} \frac{\sqrt{2^n - 1}}{2^n} = \frac{1}{2 - \sqrt{2}} \tag{3}$$

It is immediately seen that the right-hand side of equation 3, for the derivation of which see the footnote below,[13] expresses the quantity of

---

[13] The left-hand term of equation 3 can be expanded in the following way for $n = 1$, 2, 3, . . . :

$$\tfrac{1}{2}\sqrt{1} + \tfrac{1}{4}\sqrt{2} + \tfrac{1}{8}\sqrt{4} + \cdot \cdot \cdot \cdot \cdot \cdot \cdot \cdot \cdot \cdot \cdot \cdot \cdot \cdot$$

This is an infinite geometric progression described by a first term, the value of which is $\tfrac{1}{2}$, and by a common ratio, the value of which is $\tfrac{1}{2}\sqrt{2}$.

utility conveyed to you by the outright payment of $\left(\dfrac{1}{2 - \sqrt{2}}\right)^2$ ducats. This is less than three ducats, very little more than the amount at which D. B. arrived.

The Recent Change in Emphasis

Neither D. B. nor Cramer suggested measuring the utility functions of individuals by examining what amount of sure money they would actually consider the equivalent of various risky prospects. Indeed, the St. Petersburg game is hardly suitable for experimental reproduction, since it is essential to the game that the person offering the payments should be able (or, at least, thought to be able) to pay out unlimited amounts of money.

The participants in this eighteenth-century discussion thought of the problem in the following way: It is obvious from introspection and from casual observation that no reasonable person would regard the privilege of playing the St. Petersburg game on the receiving side as the equivalent of more than a very small amount of sure money; this can be explained convincingly by assuming decreasing marginal utility and by postulating the maximization of the mathematical expectations of utility; the assumption of a logarithmic utility function (or of Cramer's square root function) leads to the intuitively plausible result that the money equivalent of the utility expectations is two ducats (or with Cramer's function, almost three ducats).

Our contemporary operational orientation led Ramsey, and particularly von Neumann and Morgenstern, to build from the elements of this kind of reasoning a somewhat different construction. We start by formulating axioms (postulates) of which the maximization of the mathematical expectation of utility is a corollary, and from which it follows that by observing the betting behavior of an individual, we can measure his utility-of-wealth function. If the behavior of the individual points to his acting consistently in accordance with a utility function so established, we conclude that the postulates in question have proved fruitful. Only after having observed a specific individual's behavior do we feel entitled to make statements about the shape of his utility function.

Still, it seems reasonable to conclude that the essential elements of modern utility theory were developed by Daniel Bernoulli and Gabriel Cramer in the second quarter of the eighteenth century. This is true in spite of the fact that the line of development from these authors to Ramsey and then to von Neumann and Morgenstern was by no means straight (see pages 84–86).

A Warning Inspired by Cramer

As has been seen, before introducing his square root function, Cramer stated that the St. Petersburg paradox could be resolved simply by making the assumption that gains exceeding (say) 2^{24} ducats carry no more aggregate utility than do 2^{24} ducats' worth of gains. Even if the utility function were linear up to that point, the mathematical expectations of the utility gains from the game would still become finite (and not very large) because the infinite number of further terms in the progression would not rise in units of utility and hence there would be nothing to offset the steep decrease in the probabilities which are associated with these terms. This assumption of a ceiling to the aggregate utility function Cramer considered clearly reasonable, and the assumption does make sense. But this does not decide the question whether an inclination to disregard the late terms of equation 1 on page 102, reflects this ceiling or whether it reflects something else.

I think it can indeed be maintained with overwhelming plausibility that the great majority of reasonable individuals would assign negligible, or perhaps zero, significance to the enormous monetary rewards set on exceedingly late first appearances of heads in the St. Petersburg game. One would not regard the expectation from the game as the equivalent of a larger outright money payment merely because the person offering the game might further raise the already enormous rewards set on *very late* first appearances of heads with a fair coin. Or to take a game with finite expectations of money gains, the outright payment for which a person would be willing to settle as an alternative to the prospect of $1 million promised with probability 0.8 may well stay *literally* unchanged if the risky prospect is made to include, in addition to the foregoing, also a reward of $10 billion with probability 10^{-5}. If we postulate the maximization of the mathematical expectations of utility, then such a finding would indeed point to a ceiling over this person's utility function at $1 million. But while many people might show this reaction to the problem we have just described, these same people may nevertheless show no ceiling in the same neighborhood when it comes to comparing the outright payment which they would be willing to consider the equivalent of $1 million with probability 0.8 with the outright payments they would be willing to consider the equivalents of increasingly larger amounts (beyond $1 million) with the same probability of 0.8. On these terms the additional amounts, beyond $1 million, might have quite a bit of utility to the same people.

This has to do with the fact that the inclinations of many people to disregard very small probabilities, very small probability differences, and also very small amounts of money cannot be fitted into an orderly axiomatic system. Observations which are influenced by this inclination cannot simply be interpreted as establishing a ceiling to the aggregate utility function of the individual, since this interpretation would frequently be contradicted by tests which circumvent very small probabilities. One might be tempted to try to reconcile this threshold-value proposition with the requirements of an otherwise probabilistic viewpoint by describing (say, for standard processes) an axiomatic system in which the individual's subjective probabilities are identical with the theoretical coin probabilities whenever the latter do not fall short of a threshold value but are smaller than the theoretical coin probabilities whenever the latter do fall short of the threshold value. But this attempt at reconciliation would be found wanting—and thus the inconsistency of the behavior would become exposed—as soon as it was pointed out that situations involving lower than critical probabilities can be derived from situations involving higher probabilities, provided the problem calls for multiplying the higher probabilities by one another. If the theoretical (textbook) probability as well as the subjective probability of the coin event E_1 is p_1, and the theoretical probability as well as the subjective probability of the coin event E_2 is p_2, and if E_1 and E_2 are independent, then there exists no reasonable system of subjective probabilities which would allow for a subjective probability of the joint occurrence of E_1 and E_2 such as would be less than $p_1 p_2$. If the subjective probability of the joint occurrence is less than $p_1 p_2$, then this is a violation of the rules of probabilistic behavior.

It seems safe to state that in the real world the problem of threshold values does exist, and that these difficulties need to be watched. Yet, what this calls for is not a reformulation of the axiomatic foundations of modern utility theory but recognition of the fact that axiomatic systems are idealizations; and that in an attempt to build a useful empirical approach on an axiomatic system, we must be aware of imperfections. We must not try fully to exploit an axiomatic system in all respects. The Standard Process Postulate is no exception. We must recognize that in their actions, some reasonable individuals deliberately disregard (knowingly wish to treat as zero) such probability terms as fall below a threshold value, a value which is different for different individuals and may vary also with the specific characteristics of decision situations. For the identical reason, individuals tend to disregard very small probability differences and, for similar reasons, very small differences in monetary pay-offs and in monetary costs. This limits the usefulness of our axiomatic systems for the understanding of observed economic behavior, but the region of higher than critical values is, of course, very broad; and hence, this limitation is on the whole not too severe.

As for Cramer's remarks concerning a ceiling to the aggregate utility function—remarks which he did not follow up in the main part of his analysis—I suggest that the argument he developed rests on an informal observation about human behavior which, as concerns the St. Petersburg series, can be explained more convincingly with reference to threshold values than with reference to a ceiling. It *is* intuitively appealing to argue that a good many reasonable people would pay no attention to the very late terms of the St. Petersburg game as formulated by Nicolas Bernoulli. But when it comes to explaining this phenomenon, then the proposition that for sufficiently high values of n the value of the probability $\frac{1}{2^n}$ is treated as zero would seem to be more revealing than the proposition that at sufficiently high levels of wealth the marginal utility of wealth is zero. At any rate, for establishing the second of these two propositions, it would not be enough to discuss the underweighting of the very late terms of progression 1, page 102. It is necessary also to argue for the hypothesis that at high probability levels an increase of the monetary reward is considered worthless beyond some point. To many people the level of wealth at which marginal utility becomes zero in the second type of experiment is likely to be much higher than the level at which negligible or unimaginably low probabilities deprive the further terms of the St. Petersburg series of any importance.

Chapter 4	# OUTLINE OF AN ECONOMIC THEORY OF PROFIT

(1) *Nature of the Theory*

The idea of profit maximization plays a crucial role in the economic theory of the firm, but the meaning of the concept of profit has stayed controversial among economists. This is because any consistent person's interpretation of the concept of profit must be in harmony with his position concerning the decision problems discussed in the present volume. These problems are controversial, although I believe that with the recent advances in probability theory the area of agreement has been growing and that it may now be easier to make a few concise statements on the remaining areas of disagreement.

Let us first take the purely probabilistic position in decision theory. This theory postulates that a reasonable person maximizes his "expected utility," that is, the mathematical expectations of the utility of wealth to him. In such a framework, profits ex ante may be conceived of as the *gain in expected utility which an investment project promises as compared to the initial position of the individual.* We may then postulate that the amounts of investment which the investor makes will be those amounts which maximize this ex ante profit. About profits ex post—by which I here mean profits, *given* the amounts invested—one can only say that they depend on luck as well as on the quality of the probability judgments by which the individual was guided. Outside the context of standard process bets the concept of luck—i.e., the concept of results which are better than deserved on the basis of the quality of the decision maker's probability judgments—becomes somewhat hazy. Yet, when it comes to the interpretation of an individual's record, it is intuitively appealing to increase the emphasis placed on the quality of judgment and to de-emphasize good or bad luck as the record is extended to an increasingly large number of decisions. Having made these general comments on ex post profits, we turn to ex ante profits, and thus to the determinants of amounts invested, about which probabilistic decision theory can develop a number of specific propositions.

It is to be hoped that future research will pay a good deal of attention to the question of what the guidelines are by which different types of individuals are mostly influenced in arriving at their subjective degrees of belief in various risky processes. About this, little is known at present, and one would imagine that careful research will be able to disclose some regularities in this regard. At any rate, we may start by tailoring the analytical structure to special situations in which the degrees of belief of reasonable individuals are formed in a way which is well understood. These are the situations created by various chance devices which generate standard processes. Heads-or-tails events with practically fair coins provide a good illustration. In a purely probabilistic decision theory, all degrees of belief of a reasonable individual are conceived of as strict equivalents of some heads-or-tails event, no matter what the event is to which the degree of belief relates.

Yet, if, in outlining a theory of profit, heads-or-tails probabilities are used for illustration—as will be done in this chapter and in Chapter 5, but not in Chapter 7—then it must be remembered that the illustration by-passes two problems. The first of these is concerned with how people employ guidelines of various sorts to arrive at beliefs about the outcome of a typical business investment project (and similar prospects). This problem has no analogy for heads-or-tails with a practically fair coin because the learning process by which reasonable people arrive at degrees of belief concerning fair coins has relatively well-known characteristics. The difference between the rather well-known *origins* of degrees of belief relating to head-or-tails events and the poorly understood *origins* of analogous degrees of belief relating to various other types of events is, of course, recognized even by those adhering to the purely probabilistic-subjective position. But if a theory of profit starts with the assumption of *given* heads-or-tails probabilities and *given* other subjective degrees of belief, then this whole question of origins is by-passed.

There exists also a second problem which is by-passed in a presentation based on heads-or-tails probabilities and on other degrees of belief interpreted as equivalents of these probabilities. This is the problem briefly discussed in our earlier chapters, a problem to be considered later in more detail. As we have seen, some people place their numerically controversial and shaky (vague) probabilities at a discount or at a premium as compared to probabilities of the heads-or-tails type.

Still, it will be useful to develop here the basic structure of the theory of profit for probabilistic appraisals which are interpreted as strict equivalents of heads-or-tails appraisals. But in our reasoning, we shall have to remain aware of the differences between the origins of various types of degrees of belief; and subsequently, we shall have to make room for the modifications required by systems of discounts and premiums. In other words, a useful theory of profit is a theory that can subsequently be fitted into a semiprobabilistic framework, as we shall attempt to do in Chapter 7, even if the skeleton of the theory is initially developed with reliance on the Postulate of Equivalent Degrees of Belief (page 97).

(2) Some Basic Propositions

The more technical analysis of the next chapter will center on a set of propositions which in the present section will be expressed merely in a very general way. These propositions—(*a*) through (*i*) of the present section—relate to the question whether the decision maker will or will not put up money on specific projects and, if so, how much he will put up on them.

a) The typical investment project confronts a person with the prospect of alternative monetary outcomes, to each of which he attaches a degree of belief or "subjective probability." Often, it seems convenient to assume that the decision maker conceives of a very limited number of classes of outcomes, where the highest possible outcome is unbounded from above. In the decision maker's mind, all these classes of outcomes, including the highest, may then be represented by some typical outcome falling in that class; and the decision maker assigns subjective probabilities to these representative values in each class of potential outcomes.

Only if the number of yield classes required for a fairly realistic representation of the decision process becomes very large, is it clearly preferable to approximate the resulting probability distribution by a continuous function and hence to approximate the sum of the weighted terms by integration. This procedure calls for introducing simplifying assumptions concerning the probability distribution itself—i.e., concerning the number and the values of the parameters needed for describing it. In some cases, these simplifying assumptions reduce the realism of the approach *more* than does the assumption of eight or ten representative yield classes.

b) It is possible to define for the decision maker two marginal functions which are essential to explaining his decision process and the role the concept of profit plays in that process. The first of these—the G function—we shall call the *weighted marginal utility of potential gains as a function of the amount to be invested in the project.* This function is obtained by limiting ourselves to those potential outcomes which are gains, as compared to the initial situation. Each potential money gain corresponding to alternative amounts that may be invested is expressed in terms of numerical utility; each such utility is weighted by the probability of the outcome; and the weighted utility of the outcome in question is differentiated with respect to the size of the stake, i.e., with respect to the amount invested;[1] finally, the resulting magnitudes for the various potential gains are added up. Unless economies of scale are involved in the individual decision maker's monetary investment, diminishing marginal utility must express itself in a downward slope of the G function for increasing amounts invested in the project (see Figure 4, page 119). On the other hand, unless diseconomies of scale are encountered for the individual investor's monetary investment, increasing marginal utility must express itself in an upward slope of the G function. (See Figure 6, page 127.)

c) The second of our two marginal functions—the L function—is defined as the *weighted marginal disutility of potential loss as a function of the amount to be invested.* Here, by the analogous procedure, the disutility equivalent of each potential loss is weighted by the probability of that loss. The resulting weighted disutility of each potential loss is differentiated with respect to the amount invested,[2] and the weighted marginal disutilities of all potential losses are added up. As for the shape of the L function, we are inclined to describe the normal case as one in which the function slopes *upward* with rising investments, and then to qualify this statement with regard to the possibility of economies of scale for the individual investor and (particularly) with regard to the possibility of rising marginal utility of wealth. These qualifications allow for cases in which the L function might slope downward. However, for sufficiently large amounts of investment—hence, sufficiently large dollar amounts of potential loss up to the point of bankruptcy—these qualifications are practically certain to become unimportant because, for a loss that is large enough (in view of the means available to the investor), the disutility of potential loss is practically certain to increase very sharply per money unit of further investment, i.e., of additional potential loss. By pushing himself into a region of sufficiently large potential loss, the investor

[1] Alternatively, we may interchange the two operations just described—i.e., we may first differentiate the aggregate utility of potential gain and subsequently weight the derivative probabilistically. The result is the same.

[2] Here, too, we may interchange the two operations just described by first differentiating the aggregate disutility of potential loss and by subsequently weighting the derivative probabilistically. The result is the same.

would practically always hit a range of very sharply diminishing marginal utility of wealth (very sharply increasing marginal disutility of loss, which means very sharply decreasing marginal utility of higher wealth positions corresponding to smaller losses). In other words, *while the L function may in some cases slope downward in its early ranges, for large amounts of investment it is practically certain to show a very steep upward slope.* For the sake of simplicity, we shall draw the L function with a monotonic upward slope in all three figures of the next chapter (Figures 4, 5 and 6).

d) Given these assumptions, the relationship between the G function and the L function may be of various sorts.

In Figure 4 (page 119) a single intersection marks stable equilibrium for a positive amount of investment in the project. The decision maker will invest the amount corresponding to the point of intersection. The area lying *between* the G function and the L function from the origin to the intersection expresses the maximum gain in expected utility which the investor can obtain from the project. For smaller or larger amounts of investment, this gain would be smaller; for sufficiently large amounts of investment the gain would "turn negative." The gain in expected utility is our profit (ex ante).

In Figure 6 (page 127) the number of points of intersection in the region of positive amounts of investment is greater than one. Unstable intersections, such as the first intersection in Figure 6, do not count. The decision maker will invest the amount corresponding to the second intersection—stable intersection—in Figure 6, provided the area lying between G and L from the origin to that intersection is positive on balance (as is the case in the figure). If that area is negative on balance, the investor will stay away from the project; if the number of stable intersections is greater than one, the equilibrium lies at the point of intersection for which the value of the area in question is a maximum.

In Figure 5 (page 126) G and L do not intersect in the region of positive amounts of investment. For no amount of investment is the probabilistically weighted utility of potential gain sufficient to compensate the decision maker for the probabilistically weighted disutility of potential loss. He will not invest in the project.

e) If the demand of a large number of decision makers for some specific type of investment increases—i.e., if the utility functions and/or the probabilistic appraisals get to be such that the amounts invested in some specific project tend to increase—then, other things equal, this will lead to a deterioration of the odds on the project, and vice versa. The market tends to shape the odds (available prospects) in such a way that the amounts which decision makers desire to invest in specific projects should be no greater and no smaller than the amounts for which various specific investment opportunities are made available at the given odds.

f) To the investors whom we have considered in the preceding pages, investment opportunities (or more generally, opportunities to accept risks of various sorts) are made available in part by other individuals, whose utility-of-gain functions, or whose disutility-of-loss functions, or whose probabilistic appraisals are different from his. Partly—indeed, much more importantly—these opportunities develop because of the fact that probabilities attach to gains and to losses which may be earned or suffered in processes of technical transformation. Neither the forces of nature, nor the workings of technology, nor the acts of consumers are securely predictable (to say the least). Through adjustments in the odds the market tends to conduct the investible funds into specific channels in such a way that the desire to engage in specific investments and the availability of specific investment opportunities at the given odds should become equated. Small changes usually will have small consequences.

However, the question of how aggregative demand-supply equilibrium is reached or restored for investment opportunities in the economy as a whole creates a problem the characteristics of which are different in an essential respect. If, for example, the desire to invest decreases *generally*—i.e., if this decrease is not limited to specific channels of investment—and if, therefore, effective demand as a whole tends to diminish, then output as a whole also tends to diminish. Unless an offsetting tendency is brought into life by an automatic process (e.g., the Pigou-Patinkin process [**40, 41**])[3] *or* an offsetting tendency is created by policy action, it cannot be taken for granted that the change in odds will equate demand and supply in the general neighborhood of the initial equilibrium.

g) Returning now to the question of the individual's decision to invest specific amounts in specific projects, the analysis here presented suggests that normally he will not put all his eggs in one basket. In this regard, the simplest proposition which is generally valid may be expressed in the following way: An individual whose utility-of-wealth function shows monotonically decreasing marginal utility will (aside from institutional costs) *always* find it advantageous to diversify among bets the *probabilistic properties of which are identical*. That is to say, such an individual will always prefer betting $1.00 on heads in each of

---

[3] This process operates through a reduction of the general money-wage and price level, and thus through an increase in the real value of the existing liquid assets, as a result of which the public decides to spend a larger amount of money on goods and services.

a hundred successive tosses to betting $100 on one toss of a fair coin. This follows from the fact that the probability of extreme outcomes decreases sharply with an increase in the number of tosses, and this *must* be considered an advantage by an individual to whom the marginal utility of wealth decreases throughout the relevant range. The case of monotonically increasing marginal utility may, I think, be disregarded because losses which are very large as compared to the initial wealth of the investor must be assumed to become exceedingly painful (and increasing marginal disutility of losses as compared to the initial position is equivalent to decreasing marginal utility of wealth in the region of losses). Nevertheless, the desire to diversify may be reduced by increasing marginal utility in *specific ranges* of the utility-of-wealth function.

Furthermore, our foregoing propositions relate to diversification among bets with identical probabilistic properties (such as bets on tosses of the same coin); and once we move onto a more realistic level of discourse, it must be realized that the desire to diversify is limited by the fact that investors are usually incapable of spreading their investments too thin without including in their holdings bets the probabilistic properties of which seem increasingly unfavorable to them. This, along with the institutional cost of spreading oneself thin, seems to set the effective limits on diversification in the real world. But it is difficult to think one's way through the propositions of the present paragraph without arriving at the conclusion that normally there exists a strong case for quite a bit of diversification.

h) So far, our statements about expected gains and losses in utility have disregarded the expected time of accrual of these gains and losses. Yet the element of timing would be important even if the utilities which the decision maker assigned to given quantities of total wealth were wholly uninfluenced by whether these quantities of wealth become available to him in this or in that period. Such intertemporal equivalence of the utilities attached to given quantities of wealth would express the absence of *pure* time preference.[4] Absence of *pure* time preference would indeed imply that *if* the decision maker knew for sure that he would have

---

[4] The assumption that the decision maker, when assigning utilities to given quantities of total wealth, is indifferent concerning time of accrual over an infinite period ahead of him—the assumption that he has no pure time preference in this particular sense—leads to absurd conclusions; and hence, models based on this assumption need not be explored. Indifference concerning the time of accrual during the lifetime of the decision maker—absence of pure time preference within each individual's life span—should perhaps not be brushed aside in quite this sweeping fashion, especially if institutional arrangements are visualized which would facilitate the appropriate clearings between successive generations. At any rate, as will be said in a moment, I believe that a reasonable theory of saving and investment *should* incorporate pure time preference.

at his disposal the identical initial quantity of goods in each subsequent period, then he would be indifferent as between two or more risky prospects which differ from one another exclusively in the timing (but not in the amount) of the potential gains and losses as compared to the initial quantity of goods. But even in this case—i.e., in the absence of *pure* time preference—an intelligent decision maker should not be assumed to take it for granted that the alternative projects about which he reaches decisions will bring additions to or deductions from the identical basic quantity of goods, regardless of when these additions or deductions accrue. On the contrary, most individuals expect their initial quantity of goods to be different at different future dates. They expect to be at different points of their global utility function; hence, they expect shifts in their local utility function (see Chapter 3, Section 7). This is what would introduce *time preference in the broader sense* into the individual's calculations even if he had *no pure time preference*, that is, even if one, two, three, etc., units of total wealth carried u_1, u_2, u_3, etc., units of utility to him irrespective of whether the wealth in question was present wealth, or wealth of the near future, or wealth of the distant future. For even in this event the individual would ordinarily care whether the addition (deduction) would accrue at a time of relative affluence or at a time of relative poverty. A person with diminishing marginal utility of wealth would, of course, prefer the accrual of additions in periods of relative poverty and the accrual of losses in periods of relative well-being.

Time preference in this broader sense must surely not be overlooked, but a reasonable decision model takes account of it more or less automatically. This is because in such a model the potential utility gains and losses involved in an investment project are viewed in relation to some initial position of wealth. One is hardly tempted to overlook the fact that the initial position may be different in different periods, and that therefore a given global utility function does not imply that the decision maker expects his local utility function to stay unchanged over time.

In some theories of investment, considerable emphasis is placed not only on time preference in this broader sense but also on *pure* time preference. Individuals may have utility functions which assign (say) smaller utilities to all potential quantities of total wealth if the wealth in question is distant-future wealth than if it is near-future or present wealth. Pure time preference may be expressed by the statement that an individual's global utility-of-wealth function includes the time of accrual as one of its variables, in the sense that the utility of any given amount of wealth depends on the time which will elapse from the time of valuation to the time of availability. I think Eugen von Böhm-Bawerk (6) was right in maintaining that pure time preference has an important place in the theory of rates of return on capital.

i) The essential trait of a theory of profit based on all these considerations is that, in such a theory, profit in the ex ante sense—the profit that is being maximized—is a utility surplus as compared to the initial position of the decision maker. To explain the phenomenon in language which is analogous to that employed in the explanation of other utility surpluses, we may say: *If, at given odds, the decision maker finds it worth his while to make an investment (a bet), then at these odds it must still be barely worth his while to invest the last dollar he puts up; and this normally implies that the intramarginal region, taken as a whole, carries a net utility gain.*

A purely probabilistic decision theory considers such utility gains equivalent regardless of how firm or shaky (numerically uncontroversial or controversial, psychologically stable or unstable) the probability judgments are from which the expectations were derived. A semiprobabilistic approach does not generally insist on this equivalence of probabilistic ex ante surpluses (or profits) in alternative situations in which the probability judgments of the individual are held with different degrees of firmness. In the semiprobabilistic approach, various kinds of probability judgments may be at a discount or at a premium relative to others. What rubs some protagonists of the purely probabilistic theory the wrong way in this approach is perhaps not so much the idea that the firm or shaky character (controversial or uncontroversial nature) of probability judgments may introduce nonmonetary consequences into the pay-offs, and that it would be desirable to take account of nonmonetary consequences, but the suggestion that it is analytically advantageous to "capture" this element by exploring distortions of the weighting systems of decision makers. But I think it *is* revealing to do so.

The propositions of the present chapter require some amount of technical elaboration, which will be undertaken in the following pages.

Chapter 5

ELABORATION
ON THE THEORY
OF PROFIT

(1) *The Risk Taker's ex ante Surplus*

Consider a person who may bet an amount of his choosing on the guess that the event E will happen. He assigns to E the probability p, and to $\sim E$ the probability $1 - p$. We assume that he is guaranteed n dollars of net gain in the event of winning for every dollar which he risks losing. Will he invest in this venture; and if so, how much?

In such a framework the known probabilities of various events may be of the heads-or-tails type. For expository reasons, it will frequently be useful to interpret them as applying to such "standard processes." This is true despite the fact that in most situations in which the economist is interested, these probabilities will be of a highly subjective kind. But as long as we stay within a purely probabilistic framework, the elementary formal characteristics of the decision problem will be the same for all sets of events, regardless of how the decision maker arrives at his degrees of belief. So we may use the heads-or-tails problem for illustration, and the semiprobabilistic element can then be introduced separately.

Figure 4 is drawn on the assumption that the probability of the investor's winning, as well as that of his losing, is 0.5, as when he bets on a fair coin's falling heads on the next occasion. Further, the graph will imply that the money odds are $2 \div 1$ in the investor's favor. For every dollar he risks losing, he wins two dollars net if the coin falls heads. But these numerical values do not matter, and the algebraic treatment will be somewhat more general. If this particular individual, along with many other individuals, wants to "buy" too much of this specific "risk," then these individuals will, of course, end up by spoiling the odds; while if there is too little willingness to take this risk, then the odds will tend to become improved. To these general economic aspects of the problem, we shall return later.

The broken line of Figure 4 is the present local von Neumann—

FIGURE 4

A SINGLE INTERSECTION OF $G(x)$ WITH $L(x)$
FOR POSITIVE STAKES

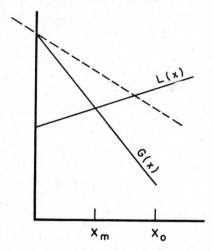

Morgenstern *marginal* utility function—i.e., the marginal utility-of-gains function—of an individual (for the difference between the local and the global function, see page 87). We may assume that the broken line is derived from a local *aggregate* utility function of the form

$$U(x) = ax - bx^2 \quad \ldots \ldots \ldots \ldots \ldots \quad (1)$$

with positive values for the constants a and b; however, this formulation is acceptable only for $x < \frac{a}{2b}$ $\left(\text{or perhaps up to } x = \frac{a}{2b}\right)$ because beyond $x = \frac{a}{2b}$ the value of U would diminish with rising x. The independent variable (x) stands here for *wealth possessed minus the initial wealth of the present period* (i.e., x stands for *gains*), as measured in money.[1]

The Function 1 gives us for marginal utility

---

[1] Quadratic functions of this sort, if bounded so as to exclude negative marginal utility, are convenient tools of exposition in several respects. even though some of their properties are unwelcome. I am told that the decision theorists of the Harvard Business School make good use of a measure of risk *aversion* which, for any level of wealth, is defined as $-\frac{U''}{U'}$. The fact that the numerical value of the ratio of the curvature of the utility function to its slope *is* indeed a convenient measure of the degree of risk aversion follows from what was said in Chapter 3, Section 12, about the position of points on the chord there defined relative to points on the utility curve itself. Now, for quadratic utility functions, $-\frac{U''}{U'}$ rises with rising wealth, which intuitively is not an appealing property.

$$U'(x) = a - 2bx \ldots \ldots \ldots \ldots \ldots \ldots \qquad (2)$$

Let us say that the *broken* line expresses $U'(x)$. For this local function the zero point of the abscissa is, of course, at the individual's no-bet position of wealth in the period for which the function is defined. The zero point of the utility scale is given by $U(0) = 0$. The unit of utility (utile) is defined here in such a way that the marginal utility of wealth is one utile for $x = \dfrac{a-1}{2b}$. This implies that $-U(-1) = a + b$ utiles, while in Chapter 3, we decided that $-U(-1) = 1$ utile. Choice of the zero point of the utility scale and of the unit of utility are merely matters of convenience, since utility is measurable only up to positive linear transformations. If we wanted to have $-U(-1) = 1$ utile, then we would have to replace equation 1 by $U(x) = \dfrac{ax - bx^2}{a+b}$.

From utility function 1, we now map the following two functions, $G(x)$ and $L(x)$, which are represented by the two *fully drawn* lines in Figure 4. When we consider either of these fully drawn functions, the *independent variable* (x) *stands for money staked* (i.e., now to be invested in a bet), not for "wealth minus the period's initial wealth," as was the case when we were considering the U function.

The declining fully drawn curve $G(x)$ *is the weighed marginal utility of potential gain as a function of the total amount to be invested in the bet*—i.e., as a function of the variable x, as this variable is to be interpreted when we look at the G or the L function. The $G(x)$ function is derived in the following way. First step: We obtain the aggregate utility of potential gains, as a function of the amount to be invested, by defining a function which gives us for all positive values of x those utility values which the aggregate utility function (in our case, $U = ax - bx^2$) gives for $2x$; this is because $2x$ is the potential gain associated with the invested amount; and thus, in our case, we obtain the transformed function $2ax - 4bx^2$. The transformation we have just described we shall call a "2x-to-x transformation." Second step: We obtain the marginal function corresponding to this transformed function by taking the derivative of the latter with respect to x; and thus, we arrive at $2a - 8bx$. Third and last step: We weight this function by the probability of the potential gain $2x$; in our case, the probabilistic weight being $\frac{1}{2}$, we obtain $G(x) = a - 4bx$. For odds of $n \div 1$, and for the same probabilities, this last function would be $\dfrac{na}{2} - n^2bx$. Our function $G(x) = a - 4bx$ represents the special form applicable to $n = 2$.

In some respects, it would be clearer to reverse the order of making the second and third step, that is, to weight the aggregate utility of potential gain probabilistically and then to differentiate the weighted function. But the result would be precisely the same; and for the present purpose, it is more convenient to proceed as we have done here (so that changing the probabilities will affect merely one step).

First Addendum, for later use in the analysis: G *functions with many components and the continuous case.* If, say, the $2x$ potential gain corresponding to the invested amount x had had merely probability $\frac{1}{4}$ (rather than $\frac{1}{2}$), and an alternative potential gain of $\frac{x}{2}$ had had probability $\frac{1}{2}$, then $G(x)$ would have been the sum of two constituents. In this event, too, we would have performed our "$2x$-to-x transformation" on $U = ax - bx^2$, but we would have used the weight $\frac{1}{4}$ instead of $\frac{1}{2}$ for weighting the derivative of the transformed function (the unweighted derivative is $2a - 8bx$); to the resulting $\frac{a}{2} - 2bx$, we would have added, with the weight $\frac{1}{2}$, the derivative of the function obtained through an $\frac{x}{2}$-to-x transformation of $U = ax - bx^2$; then, since the $\frac{x}{2}$-to-x transformation leads to $\frac{a}{2}x - \frac{b}{4}x^2$, and the derivative of this is $\frac{a}{2} - \frac{b}{2}x$, and since this would have had to be weighted by $\frac{1}{2}$, we would have obatined $\frac{a}{4} - \frac{b}{4}x$ as the second constituent of $G(x)$; and the sum of the two constituents would have been $G(x) = \frac{3a}{4} - \frac{9b}{4}x$.

This function will play a part in our later analysis. We should remember that *in the general case* G(x) *has many constituents and that this may lead into the problem of continuous distributions for which the analogous operations are carried out in the footnote below.*[2] For the time being, we are faced with the

---

[2] While the yield of a security may in principle be any amount lying within an infinite range, in the mind of the investor the range is made up of a finite number of yield classes, each of which is represented by some value in that range. As has already been said, if it takes a large number of yield classes and of representative values to give a realistic description of the decision process under consideration, then it becomes preferable to treat the distribution as if it were *continuous*, provided the needed simplifying assumptions concerning the number of parameters and their values do not reduce the realism of the approach more than would the use of fewer yield classes and of representative values.

In a model postulating a continuous distribution, we may write x for the stake interpreted as the maximum amount the investor may lose; n for the various odds interpreted as factors by which x must be multiplied to give the various possible monetary gains ($n \geqq 0$); and $f_g(n)$ for the probability (density) of the outcome's being such as to make any value of n the relevant multiplicative factor for obtaining the actual money *gain* nx; and we obtain for the probabilistically weighted aggregate utility of the potential gain the expression $\int_0^\infty U(nx)\, f_g(n)\, dn$, where $U(nx)$ is by definition the utility of any one of the potential gains. The corresponding probabilistically weighted marginal utility of the entire potential gain, as a function of the amount invested (x), is $\int_0^\infty nU'(nx)\, f_g(n)\, dn$. *This becomes the equivalent of our* G *function in such a model.* Note that integrating the $f_g(n)$ function from zero to infinity does not yield one, but merely the probability of outcomes which are associated with (nonnegative) gains.

function which was formulated prior to the First Addendum, that is with $G(x) = a - 4bx$. This completes the First Addendum.

The rising fully drawn curve $L(x)$ *is the weighted marginal disutility of the potential loss as a function of the amount to be invested in the bet*—i.e., as a function of x as this variable is to be interpreted when we look at the G or the L function. The L function is derived in the following way: We define a function showing the aggregate utility of the last x money units of wealth which the individual possesses in his present no-bet position—i.e., of those x units counted from his no-bet position as the zero point, which he puts up in a bet if he puts up precisely x units— and we find that in our case, this function is $ax + bx^2$; we take the derivative of this function with respect to x, and we obtain $a + 2bx$; and we weight this function by the probability of the loss of the invested amount, i.e., in our case, by ½. Thus, we obtain $L(x) = \frac{a}{2} + bx$.

Second Addendum, for later use in the analysis: L functions with many components and the continuous case. If we had been faced with the probabilistic conditions envisaged in the First Addendum, then the probabilistic weight of $a + 2bx$ would have been ¼, and we would have arrived at $L(x) = \frac{a}{4} + \frac{b}{2}x$. (Further, if there existed not only the possibility of losing the total amount invested with, say, a small probability p_1, but also the alternative possibility of losing one half of the amount invested with a somewhat greater probability p_2, then $L(x)$ would be the sum of the two constituents, where the second constituent would involve an $\frac{x}{2}$-to-x transformation[3] of $ax + bx^2$, and it would involve weighting the derivative of the transformed function by p_2.) *In the general case* $L(x)$, *too, has many constituents; and this again may lead into the problem of continuous distributions for which the analogous operations are carried out in the footnote below.*[4] For the

[3] By analogy to the transformation which was earlier described, I mean here a transformation such that for x the value of the transformed function should be the same as is the value of $ax + bx^2$ for $\frac{x}{2}$.

[4] If, by analogy to what was said in the second paragraph of n. 2, p. 121, we postulate a *continuous* distribution for the potential losses, we arrive at the following conclusion. We write x for the stake interpreted as the maximum amount the investor may lose; m for various fractions of x, so that any mx may constitute the actual loss $(0 \leqq m \leqq 1)$; and $f_1(m)$ for the probability (density) that the actual loss will be mx; and we obtain for the probabilistically weighted aggregate disutility of the potential loss the expression $\int_0^1 - U(-mx)\, f_1(m)\, dm$, where $-U(-mx)$ is by definition the disutility of any one of the potential losses. The corresponding probabilistically weighted marginal disutility of the entire potential loss, as a function of the amount invested (x), is $\int_0^1 m\, U'\,(-mx)\, f_1(m)\, dm$. *This becomes the equivalent of our* L *function in such a model.* Note that the integral of the $f_1(m)$ function from zero to one yields merely the probability of outcomes associated with nonpositive profits.

time being, we are faced with the function which was formulated prior to the Second Addendum, that is, with $L(x) = \frac{a}{2} + bx$. This completes the Second Addendum.

We shall return to the addenda later; but for the time being, we have the declining and the rising fully drawn curves of Figure 4. These are:

$$G(x) = a - 4bx \quad \ldots \ldots \ldots \ldots \ldots \quad (3)$$
$$L(x) = \frac{a}{2} + bx \quad \ldots \ldots \ldots \ldots \ldots \quad (4)$$

We may now deduce three propositions which are crucial to our argument.

a) The individual will put up money on this "bet" if, at least for some stakes (measured on the abscissa), the area lying under $G(x)$, from the origin to any of those stakes, exceeds[5] the area lying under $L(x)$. In Figure 4, this condition is satisfied for all positive values of x that are smaller than x_0.

b) If the foregoing condition is satisfied for a range of values of x and the individual is free to select the amount of his stake, the amount which he puts up will be determined by the intersection of $G(x)$ with $L(x)$. In Figure 4, this amount is x_m. This, of course, is a maximization condition: The last money unit up to x_m is still worth the commitment; the next would not be worth it. We are implying that the second-order condition of maximization is met, as is obviously the case in Figure 4. The magnitude to be maximized is the expected utility associated with the amount invested—i.e., it is generally $E[U(x)]$; and on the terms underlying Figure 4, this latter magnitude has the value of $\frac{1}{2}(2ax - 4bx^2) - \frac{1}{2}(ax + bx^2)$, a value which is maximized at the intersection of $G(x)$ with $L(x)$. Given this form of the functions, there exists no problem of multiple equilibria, although on more general assumptions, there may well exist such a problem (see page 127).

c) *The individual acquires a risk taker's surplus in relation to his no-bet position—a surplus which we regard as his ex ante profit—from being able to choose the amount he puts up under given market conditions.* The reason is that if at these probabilities and at these odds, we had faced him with an all-or-none choice, then he would have been barely willing to put up the amount x_0 rather than x_m. Indeed, it is his willing-

---

[5] If, for some amount of money, the area lying under $G(x)$ just equals the area lying under $L(x)$, and if the condition of a positive surplus is satisfied for no value of x, then the individual will be indifferent as between putting up this critical amount and not betting at all.

ness to put up x_0 which is felt out in the experiments establishing his von Neumann–Morgenstern utility function. This follows from the presentation in Chapter 3, Section 7. The amount x_0 which our individual would be barely willing to put up if he were faced with an all-or-none choice marks a position which from his point of view is inferior to that determined by x_m. The concept of this ex ante profit is analogous to the Marshallian consumer surplus, but we have here a magnitude which is cardinally measurable in utiles, even though constancy of the marginal utility of money is, of course, not assumed.

For the functions we have been using to illustrate our propositions, the reader may wish to verify the following algebraic relations.

The optimum stake:

$$x_m = \frac{a}{10b} \quad\ldots\ldots\ldots\ldots\ldots \quad (5)$$

The maximum stake which the individual would still barely be willing to put up if he had merely the choice of putting up this stake or staying away from the bet:

$$x_0 = \frac{a}{5b} \quad\ldots\ldots\ldots\ldots\ldots \quad (6)$$

The maximized risk taker's surplus at x_m, that is, the difference between the relevant areas under $G(x)$ and $L(x)$:

$$M = \frac{a^2}{40b} \quad\ldots\ldots\ldots\ldots\ldots \quad (7)$$

M is measured in utiles.[6] In a strictly probabilistic model, any given expected money gain carries the same amount of utility in one risky process as in any other. On semiprobabilistic assumptions, it is possible to take account of distortions caused by the fact that an ex ante surplus resulting from (say) very shaky probability judgments is not always interpreted as the precise equivalent of an ex ante surplus resulting from firm probability judgments. A prospect based on probabilities the numerical values of which are highly controversial and highly unstable in the mind of the decision maker need not yield the same amount of utility-of-money gain as a prospect based on *de facto* uncontroversial, firm numerical probability judgments.

[6] The derivation is the following:

$$\int_0^{\frac{a}{10b}} \left(a - 4bx\right) dx - \int_0^{\frac{a}{10b}} \left(\frac{a}{2} + bx\right) dx = \frac{a^2}{40b}\text{utiles}$$

It is necessary, however, to add a further word on the problem of time preference. Our formal analysis of the decision process has implied that the decision maker can realize all surpluses in the immediate future practically without a lag. Yet, if surpluses are realized at various time rates over alternative periods of time, then it is necessary, at any event, to take account of the fact that the decision maker's initial wealth—that is, the wealth corresponding to his no-bet situation—is likely to be different in these various periods, and that therefore the local utility functions shift with the passage of time. This is the problem of time preference in the broader sense. Allowance for *pure* time preference requires working into the global utility function a variable which expresses the period elapsing from the time of utility assignment to the time when the wealth, the utility of which is being measured, will become available (see Chapter 4).

(2) The Other Side of the Bet and the Question of Macroeconomic Adjustments

The person to whom Figure 4 relates will certainly not consider putting up money on the complement of the event on which he was betting in Section 1. Even if the odds had been 1 ÷ 1 instead of 2 ÷ 1 in favor of a person betting on E, he would not have considered betting on ~E, since his von Neumann–Morgenstern utility function shows decreasing marginal utility (see his broken line). Actually, the odds were 2 ÷ 1 *against* ~E. With these odds, the graph *applying to a bet on* ~E has the characteristics of Figure 5. This graph shows that there exists no stake for which a bet on ~E would offer a risk taker's surplus to our individual. Indeed, the surplus is negative for all stakes. A maximizer of expected utility will surely stay away from this bet.

The fact that our individual had a chance to bet at the odds implied in Figure 4 therefore requires explanation. What are the reasons to which such opportunities are attributable? The reader will notice that the three reasons—three possibilities—which will be discussed are not mutually exclusive. But it is convenient to separate them in the exposition.

First Possibility: Different Utility Functions. We should not overlook the existence of individuals whose tastes may be represented by a rising broken line—i.e., by a rising local von Neumann–Morgenstern marginal utility function—at least for some ranges of positive gains. For such an individual the $G(x)$ curve, which was first introduced in Figure 4, and was drawn again in Figure 5, is rising, at least in some ranges. Figure 5 relates to a bet on ~E. If we modify Figure 5 so as to show a

FIGURE 5

NO INTERSECTION FOR POSITIVE STAKES

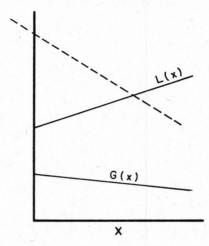

rising $G(x)$ function, this function may intersect with $L(x)$, and the two curves may intersect more than once. This is illustrated by Figure 6 for a person who has the same probability judgments as the previous bettor, but has a different utility function. Figure 6, too, applies to a bet on ~E. While Figure 6 implies that the individual in question has rising marginal utility in the region of gains, he is still represented as having decreasing marginal utility of wealth in the region of losses, and hence as having rising marginal disutility for increasing stakes. In the region of sufficiently large losses the L function is practically certain to slope upward (up to the point of bankruptcy), and we shall see that this is the fact that needs to be emphasized in the argument.

In these circumstances, the condition of a nonnegative total surplus in a bet on ~E may then be satisfied for the individual in question. Figure 6 shows that he may satisfy the condition expressed in the first proposition on page 123. If so, then *that* intersection of $G(x)$ and $L(x)$ will be optimal for which the total surplus is the greatest. Such an intersection in Figure 6 must satisfy the stability condition that to the right of the intersection, $G(x)$ falls below $L(x)$. If this were not the case, the total surplus would continue to rise with rising stakes. In other words, even if both $L(x)$ and $G(x)$ should be rising in the neighborhood of the equilibrium, the rise of the $L(x)$ curve must be steeper. On the other hand, the $G(x)$ curve might turn down to the left of the intersection, even if it should be rising in its early ranges. In that case the intersection

FIGURE 6

THE PROBLEM OF MULTIPLE INTERSECTIONS

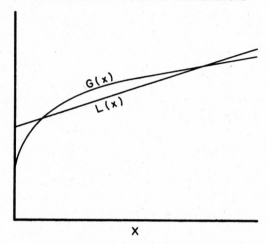

will, of course, always be stable. In Figure 6, only one intersection is stable; but generally, there could be several stable intersections, and in this case the *maximum maximorum* (global maximum) marks the true equilibrium, so that a set of inequalities must be solved to find that surplus maximum which is not merely a local maximum.

I am assuming that if the two curves of Figure 6 intersect at all— with $G(x)$ sloping upward either in its early range or throughout its course—then there will be at least one intersection which satisfies the stability condition, since for very large stakes the $L(x)$ function must be assumed to become very steeply upward-sloping. It follows that, given the heads-or-tails probabilities and the odds described on page 118, there may exist individuals who *are willing* to bet on the *complement* of the event E—i.e., on $\sim E$—even though the odds go against them. This willingness may simply be a consequence of the shape of the utility function of these individuals. Yet, if all bettors have the same probability judgments, then matching of bettors who stake their fortunes on the event favored by the odds with bettors who stake their fortunes on the complement of that event assumes that institutional reasons prevent many people from entering the bet on the more favorable side. Betting at more favorable odds is a preferable alternative to betting at less favorable ones, even to people who prefer betting at less favorable odds to not betting at all.

Second Possibility: Different Probability Judgments. Interpersonal differences between the G and the L functions are not the only differences that could explain why the bettor on the event E, who was discussed in Section 1, is matched by a bettor who stakes his fortunes on the complement of the same event ($\sim E$). To the second bettor (matching bettor) the same broken line of Figure 4—the same von Neumann–Morgenstern marginal utility function—may apply as to the first, but his probabilistic appraisal of E and $\sim E$ may be significantly different. It would be unreasonable to assume this for standard process events, such as heads or tails. However, as soon as we move out of the universe of standard processes, or of sets of events whose characteristics are very similar to those of such processes, the differences between the probabilistic appraisals of various individuals are apt to become significant.

It will be remembered that Figure 5, showing a situation in which no bet is forthcoming, related to the complement of E (i.e., to $\sim E$). The person to whom it applied had decreasing marginal utility; he assigned probability 0.5 to E and to $\sim E$ alike; the odds were 2 ÷ 1 in favor of E. As Figure 5 is drawn, no bet on $\sim E$ yielded a positive risk taker's surplus. However, the reader is requested to have a look at the operation by which the $G(x)$ and the $L(x)$ functions were derived on pages 120–22 (the First and the Second Addendums may be disregarded at this point). From these operations, it is quite obvious—as, indeed, it stands to reason by common-sense considerations—that the application of sufficiently higher probabilistic weights to $\sim E$, and the application of correspondingly lower probabilistic weights to E, will result in a positive risk taker's surplus for $\sim E$ in Figure 5. To a person using such weights, a bet on E will not yield a risk taker's surplus, but a bet on $\sim E$ will. He will belong among those who match bets on E.

Third Possibility: Observations on the Central Problem of Macroeconomics. The most significant betting opportunities in an economy—opportunities on terms such as those expressed in Figure 4 for some specific event E—are created *not* by the existence of matching bettors but by the fact that probabilities of gains and of losses attach to the transformation of resources into specific goods for which buyers are likely to have a demand. Those investing in risky production processes are indifferent as between investment and risk avoidance at the *margin* of their investments; and, as is generally the case in market situations in which choice exists (and all-or-none provisions are not imposed), a net utility gain tends to develop in the *intramarginal* region. The economic problem of risk and profit derives its significance largely from the possibility of engaging in technical transformations, not so much from our first two possibilities. Some combination of the first and the second possibilities does, ot course, possess considerable importance in speculative markets. Yet the typical business investment is a bet on which the powers of nature, technology, and the consuming public promise to pay odds if the coin falls the right way.

The prices to be paid for resources, the technological results of production, and the selling prices to be obtained for goods—all of these future variables are subject to uncertain expectations. Given the risky appraisals of these variables, and given the shapes of the utility functions of the investors, specific amounts of money will be made available for investment in various projects. Economic equilibrium requires that on the basis of the observable prices, and of the observable quantities bought and sold of all goods, risk takers should in each successive period form those appraisals of specific risky prospects which will lead them to utilize, or to hold, the supplied quantities of each existing type of resource; and this, in turn, requires the price behavior consistent with this condition. Stability of such equilibrium requires that in the event of a disturbance the various prices and quantities, and with them the investors' appraisals, should adjust in such a way as to clear each market at the adjusted values of these variables.

At this point, it is necessary, however, to remind ourselves once more of certain distinctive properties of the problem of *aggregative*—in contrast to specific—equilibria and disequilibria. As long as the level of aggregate economic activity is assumed as given, the demand-supply adjustments in any one of the many channels of investment may be conceived of as being guided by a worsening of the odds to investors on specific types of resources in the event of excess demand for these resources, and by an improvement of the odds on specific types of resources in the event of specific excess supply. Yet the possibility of aggregative disequilibrium, and the process by which aggregative equilibrium may be restored, pose problems which are in part of a different sort.

Take, for example, the case of insufficient aggregate planned investment relative to an increased amount of planned full-employment savings. If the *money wage and the price level were perfectly flexible*, aggregative equilibrium would automatically tend to become restored at capacity output. Yet, as was mentioned in Chapter 4, this process would have to operate through the Pigou-Patinkin real-balance effect **(40, 41)** that is—partly, at least—through increased consumption and thereby through a reduction of the amount of investment *needed* for full production rather than through an improvement of the odds to investors.

Even to the extent that the increased stock of real balances induces more private investment, this may happen not because of a change in the odds but because greater real liquidity may make individuals more risk-bearing, i.e., it may change their utility-of-gain and utility-of-loss functions. To be sure, to the extent that such a process of automatic market clearance became associated with a reduction of interest rates, one would indeed be inclined to speak of an improvement of the odds to investors, but here the qualification needs to be added that odds would deteriorate to lenders (buyers of bonds).

In the event of *money wage and price rigidities* the adjustment process may acquire some of the typical Keynesian features **(28)**, in which case it works through the permanent elimination of part of the investment opportunities (or options) which would be available at full utilization. Or if the central bank, or the government, intervenes to restore aggregative equilibrium, the policy measures used *may* be of the kind which tend to improve the odds to profit-maximizing private investors; but they may also be of a different sort; and at any rate, they operate partly through different mechanisms.

At the end, in macroequilibrium the odds to private investors must, of course, always be such that enough planned private investment is induced to take up that part of the aggregate output which is not taken up by consumption and by government expenditures. Also, even in the event of aggregative disequilibria, changes in the odds—in the inducement to invest—may in due time terminate the disturbance or reverse it. But even if the restoration of macroequilibrium were automatic—by way of the Pigou-Patinkin process—the adjustment would still not be carried primarily by changes in the odds; while at given levels of aggregate activity, specific disequilibria do call forth a response mechanism via changes in the odds with which investors are faced.

(3) The Surplus from Diversification among Independent Bets with Identical Probabilistic Properties

The ex ante surplus we were considering in Section 1 may be said to have resulted from diversification between the only riskless wealth which was included in our model—namely, money—and the only risky claim of which we have so far taken account. However, to call such a case one of diversification is somewhat formalistic, and we should now turn to situations where the investor can diversify between various risky events on which he can stake his fortunes. Earlier, we saw that ex ante profits are normally increased by diversification. There even exist types of profits—particularly insurance profits—that result entirely from far-reaching diversification.

Assuming purely probabilistic behavior, the nature of the problem can be made clear by introducing a simple modification into our previous analysis. The investor, who in the situation illustrated by Figure 4 was betting on a single event, will now be able to bet on two independent events. Previously, he was conceived of as putting up the whole stake he decided to risk (say, x_m) on one coin, thus acquiring an ex ante surplus of specific magnitude (say, M). Now we may think of him as being able to put up one half of whatever stake he decides to risk in the changed circumstances (say, one half of x_m*) on *one* fair coin's falling heads, and the other half of that stake on *another* fair coin's falling heads, in two simultaneous tosses. The odds remain the same as before, in the sense that heads in each toss bring him twice the amount of money which tails lose him. His probabilistic appraisal also remains the same for heads versus tails in any single toss. Even in a purely probabilistic model, we should not in general think of situations for which the probabilities can be looked up in a textbook but of sets of events for which the risk taker must form his subjective probability judgments. He must be guided by observations on the evaluation of which opinions differ. But the significance of the element of diversification—our theme in the present section—can be made clear by contrasting a bet on a single toss with a bet on two independent tosses.

This is the point at which the reader is requested to make use of the First and the Second Addendums on pages 121–22. There, we saw that the $G(x)$ function, which in the case of the single toss was $a - 4bx$, now changes to $\frac{3a}{4} - \frac{9b}{4}x$, and that the $L(x)$ function, which in the case of the single toss was $\frac{a}{2} + bx$, now changes to $\frac{a}{4} + \frac{b}{2}x$. This is because our individual now assigns the probability $\frac{1}{4}$ (the probability of two heads) to winning twice the amount invested in the two tosses; he assigns $\frac{1}{2}$ (the probability of heads once and tails once) to winning on one toss twice the amount invested in that toss and to losing on the other toss the amount invested in that toss—that is, he assigns the probability $\frac{1}{2}$ to winning one half of the amount invested in the two tosses—and he assigns $\frac{1}{4}$ to losing his investment in the two tosses (on two tails).

Hence, in view of the First and Second Addendums, the amount of investment which will now maximize his risk maker's surplus—call this amount x_m*—will be the x satisfying the condition that the $G(x)$ function just derived for the double-toss model should equal the $L(x)$ function derived for the same model, i.e.:

$$\frac{3a}{4} - \frac{9b}{4}x = \frac{a}{4} + \frac{b}{2}x$$

While, in the single-toss model, we had $x_m = \frac{a}{10b}$ (see page 124), we now have for the double-toss model:

$$x_m^* = \frac{2a}{11b} \quad . . . . \quad (5a)$$

Also, while, in the single-toss model, we had for the maximized risk taker's surplus $M = \frac{a^2}{40b}$ (see page 124), we now have for the double-toss model the expression:[7]

$$M^* = \frac{a^2}{22b} \quad . . . . \quad (7a)$$

We find $M^* > M$, both measured in utiles, because for a person with decreasing marginal utility, diversification *must* increase the risk taker's ex ante surplus, provided the probabilistic weights and all the potential gains and losses are the same in the two or more bets which go into his diversified commitment (or portfolio). The conclusion will hold for a person with monotonically decreasing marginal utility, *regardless* of what the other properties of his utility function are, and *regardless* of the nature of the frequency distribution of expected money gains, *as long as bets among which he diversifies have the identical characteristics* and the various events on which he places his diversified bets are not perfectly correlated. In our case, with an additional toss of a fair coin, the condition of identical probabilistic characteristics was satisfied, and the events were perfectly uncorrelated. These conditions would be satisfied also for the addition of any number of further tosses. Diversification of this sort leads to a reduction of the probabilistic weight of the extreme monetary outcomes in the diversified commitment, and to an increase of the probabilistic weight in the region around the mathematical expectation of money gains. This must please a person whose von Neumann–Morgenstern utility function shows decreasing marginal utility throughout the

---

[7] This expression results from

$$\int_0^{\frac{2a}{11b}} \left(\frac{3a}{4} - \frac{9b}{4}x \right) dx - \int_0^{\frac{2a}{11b}} \left(\frac{a}{4} + \frac{b}{2}x \right) dx = \frac{a^2}{22b}$$

range of possible outcomes of a bet. It would have to *displease* a person with rising marginal utility *throughout* the range in question, but the discussion on page 126 suggests that we may disregard this case. Whether reduced dispersion with unchanging mathematical expectation of the monetary outcome will please or displease a person who has decreasing marginal utility in part of the relevant range and has increasing marginal utility in another part depends on the details of the course of his utility function and on *how* (in what parts of the frequency distribution) the dispersion of outcomes is reduced.

We also obtained $x_m^* > x_m$, that is, the improvement in the investor's position led him to invest more (see equation 5a, page 132). This is indeed to be expected. The improvement of the investor's position *through improved odds*—rather than through diversification—*may* in some cases result in an unchanging or a reduced amount of investment. In Hicksian terminology, this is a matter of the weight of the income effect (or wealth effect) as compared to that of the substitution effect. But the piece of reasoning which leads to this conclusion has no analogy for the improvement of the investor's position by means of diversification.[8]

The question of the absolute amount of the surplus must, of course, not be confused with that of the surplus per unit of investment. One should remember that the surplus-raising effect of diversification makes it attractive to individual investors to accept risks even at worsened odds (if need be), and that therefore a worsening of the odds—and a lowering of profit rates—is a probable macroeconomic consequence of large-scale diversification. If a sufficient number of investors had similar utility functions and similar probability judgments, then—by setting up pooling agencies—they could raise the absolute amount of their risk takers' surplus even at expected profit rates which are very low relative to the amount of investment; and competition among such pooling agencies would, in effect, tend to establish very low profit rates. This problem is in some ways similar to that of insurance, although the conventional insurance problem has the specific property that the individual customer is getting rid of a risk which the circumstances of his life have *forced* upon him.

Insurance profits provide a good illustration of surpluses from diversification. These profits cannot be explained by the three factors—

---

[8] On much more complex assumptions, it could be argued that for different reasons the long-run effects of diversification on the amount of investment might come out either way, but I think it is unreasonable to expect anything but an investment-increasing effect.

three possibilities—discussed in Section 2. The companies issuing insurance policies enable people to *get out* of risky commitments which for these individuals carry disutility, i.e., from undesirable commitments which "come in a package" with desirable or with inevitable things in their lives. For this the companies charge a premium, and the fact that the owners of the companies can strike this bargain with the insured to the *mutual* benefit of the parties reflects the advantages of the diversification in which the companies can engage.

We have illustrated these benefits in a simple model in which each bet entering into the diversified commitment had the identical probabilistic properties. This condition was fully satisfied for our coin tosses. In reality, this condition is *not fully* satisfied for insurance companies, so that, in this regard, we have been drawing a somewhat oversimplified but not an essentially misleading picture of the insurance problem. The condition of identical probabilistic properties is definitely not satisfied for large groups of risky commitments, to which we now turn.

(4) Limits of Useful Diversification: Bets with Different Probabilistic Properties

In the previous illustration, additional diversification would always seem desirable. Not only does an amount of money staked on two independent coin tosses create a greater risk taker's surplus than would the identical amount of money staked on a single toss, but the same proposition stays valid for a general comparison of $n + 1$ independent tosses with n tosses. Is this a conclusion that can be extended to risky commitments in general? In the real world, is the institutional cost of minute diversification the only factor setting limits to the degree of diversification which seems desirable to an investor, provided he operates entirely in a range of decreasing marginal utility? This is not so, not even if we assume that he can diversify among assets between which the covariance[9] is not too great.

For various reasons the investor, who is faced with alternative securities rather than tosses of coins, must accept less favorable subjective probabilities if he carries diversification beyond a very moderate degree. The bets among which he can diversify have different characteristics. The simplest illustration of this proposition is provided by the investor who feels that the profitability of a specific enterprise is greater if in that single enterprise he can perform the function of a large-scale investor

[9] The covariance between two random variables is equal to the coefficient of correlation multiplied by the algebraic product of the standard deviations of the two variables.

and entrepreneur. But this is not the most typical reason for a deterioration of the probabilistic expectations when a portfolio is spread *too* thinly. Usually, the economies of scale to which the activities of a corporation are subject call merely for institutional arrangements by which enough investors are brought together, and in this case the investment of the *individual* investor in any one enterprise is not associated with economies of scale to him. Yet, even then, the stock exchange investor should not divide his eggs among *too many* baskets. After all, not all baskets are equally good.

The investor, even if he is interpreted as a purely probabilistic decision maker, may not always have separate probability judgments concerning various elementary events (such as would be analogous to heads or tails) and various odds on these events. His expectations may in some cases relate to highly compound events directly—say, to alternative payoffs with alternative probabilities. This is quite enough to give him a $G(x)$ and an $L(x)$ function. But we must not overlook the fact that for some securities, his expectations—his risk taker's ex ante surpluses—are almost certain to be more favorable than for others. As long as all the potential outcomes of the venture fall in a range of diminishing marginal utility, the following principle holds concerning the desirable degree of diversification.

The decision maker's expectations of utility gains—capable of being expressed numerically as risk taker's surpluses—are *more favorable* for a mix of assets to which he attributes some given mathematical expectations of money gains, and attributes some given dispersion around these mathematical expectations, then for any other mix of assets which is associated with the same (or worse) mathematical expectations of money gains and with greater dispersion *or* is associated with the same dispersion around lower mathematical expectations. The rational investor should exclude asset mixes which are inferior in the sense that by the foregoing principle, other available mixes are more favorable. Of the remaining admissible mixes, he should make his choice in view of how much mathematical expectation of money gains he is willing to trade for how much avoidance of dispersion.

Our conclusions are consistent with this principle, which plays a significant role in Harry Markowitz's and in James Tobin's[10] analysis of rational portfolio selection.

[10] Harry Markowitz, "Portfolio Selection," *Journal of Finance*, March, 1952; and *Portfolio Selection: Efficient Diversification of Investments* (**34**). James Tobin, "Liquidity Preference as Behavior Towards Risk," *Review of Economic Studies*, February, 1958 (**52**).

Both the advantages of reasonable diversification and the disadvantages of overdiversification are implicit in the principle we have just expressed. However, Tobin rightly called attention to the fact that only on specific simplifying assumptions concerning utility functions and/or concerning frequency distributions is it possible to arrive at definite conclusions about the relevant *measure* of dispersion in the sense in which the principle we have described requires measuring dispersion. A well-known article by Marcel K. Richter **(44)** added further clarity to this problem.[11]

Measuring dispersion in the relevant sense—in the sense in which investors with monotonically diminishing marginal utility want to reduce dispersion—creates a problem only if we are concerned with diversification among bets the probabilistic properties of which are *not* identical. We have seen that if our investor with his monotonically decreasing marginal utility were faced with bets which possess identical probabilistic characteristics and relate to uncorrelated events,[12] such as the outcome of random tosses of the same coin, then diversification would always reduce dispersion in the relevant sense. The desirable degree of diversification would have no limit other than that set by institutional costs. In the present analysis, differences between the probabilistic properties of the bets—differences between mathematical expectations of money gains and also between degrees of dispersion associated with the various projects—do set limits to the desirable degree of diversification. To find these limits, we must know not only the effect of the inclusion of additional securities on the mathematical expectations of money gains, but we must also be able to define precisely the concept of dispersion in the sense in which our investor is willing to trade some amount of mathematical expectation of money gains for some reduction of dispersion. This raises the question how dispersion should be measured for a portfolio including different types of bets. A useful answer requires the acceptance of simplifying assumptions. It can be shown that if the aggregate utility function is quadratic and/or the frequency distribution of the expected money gains is such that it can be fully described by the mean and the second moment about it, *then* the variance or the standard deviation will measure the dispersion adequately.

The basic principles discussed in these pages call for the maximum degree of diversification compatible with the avoidance of securities to

11 Marcel K. Richter, "Cardinal Utility, Portfolio Selection and Taxation," *Review of Economic Studies*, June, 1960 **(44)**.
12 Indeed, in this statement, it would be sufficient to exclude perfect correlation.

which either such a *low* mathematical expectation of yield or such a *high* expectation of dispersion is attached that their inclusion would lower the risk taker's ex ante surplus despite the *ceteris paribus surplus-raising effect of additional diversification.* The *ceteris paribus* surplus-raising effect of additional diversification results from the circumstance that if the mathematical expectations of money gain attached to an *additional* security are not appreciably lower than the expectations attached to the securities already held, and the expected yield dispersion for the additional security is not appreciably higher than the expected yield dispersion of the portfolio already acquired, then the inclusion of the additional security will raise the utility gain of an investor who operates in the range of diminishing marginal utility.

The smaller the covariance is for the yield of the additional security and the yield of the portfolio already held, the greater will be the *ceteris paribus* dispersion-diminishing effect, and thus the *ceteris paribus* surplus-raising effect, of the inclusion.[13] In our coin-tossing illustration the covariance was zero, since two independent tosses are entirely uncorrelated. This, of course, is rarely true of the movements of various securities. Indeed, in actual fact, high covariance between many pairs of securities considerably reduces the scope of efficient diversification.

Regardless of the specific assumption made concerning utility functions and probability appraisals, the problem remains a matter of maximizing an ex ante surplus which in a strictly probabilistic model is a cardinally measurable magnitude, analogous to the Marshallian consumer surplus. This final proposition of our analysis remains valid irrespective of the shape of the utility function and of the character of the probability distribution of expected money gains. Our $G(x)$ and $L(x)$ functions, and the risk taker's surpluses which can be derived with their aid, are generally applicable tools of any thoroughly probabilistic theory of profit.

(5) Further Considerations to Be Kept in Mind

When applying the propositions which can be derived with the aid of our G and L functions, it must always be remembered that profit theory of this kind is concerned with profits ex ante and with the amounts of investment determined by the objective of maximizing these in terms of utility. Given the amounts of investment, profits ex post depend on luck as well as on the factors considered in our analysis, although, as was said before, it is intuitively unconvincing to place the main emphasis on the element of luck when it comes to interpreting an *extended* record which

---

[13] See n. 9, p. 134.

is rather consistently one of success or of failure. Profits ex post may, of course, also be expressed in terms of utility as well as in terms of money.

As concerns the content of the concept of profits (ex ante *or* ex post), it is a matter of analytical convenience whether we wish to include capital gains as well as income proper from risky investments, or to include only income in the conventional sense. For our purpose in the present chapter, it was more convenient *not* to draw a distinction between income and capital gains; but for various other purposes, it is preferable to use this distinction.

Furthermore, it is a matter of analytical convenience whether the risky investments on which profits are earned, or on which negative profits are suffered, should be defined as including *all* assets other than money or whether some of these nonmoney assets should be classified as riskless. The riskless nonmoney assets might, for example, include time deposits and short-term government securities. Or if we are concerned only with income proper and not with capital gains, the riskless assets may even include the long-term securities of some governments. In our presentation, no distinction was drawn between risky and riskless income-yielding securities. All were regarded as risky, and all income derived from them was interpreted as profit. Whenever it seems convenient to distinguish between risky (profit-yielding) securities and riskless (merely pure interest-yielding) securities, one should not include in the concept of profit all the income from claims to wealth but merely that part which riskless securities of the identical market value do not earn.

The formal analysis of this chapter and the analysis of the preceding one were concerned with the theory of profits on purely probabilistic grounds. We now turn to a systematic discussion of semiprobabilistic allowances; subsequently, in Chapter 7, we shall develop various semiprobabilistic applications of our theory of profit to problems involving output and investment decisions.

Chapter 6

SEMIPROBABILISTIC THEORY
CONTRASTED WITH
RULE-OF-THUMB
SUBJECTIVISM

(1) The Rule-of-Thumb Subjectivism of the "Frequentist-Objectivists"

Looking at the matter for a moment with the preconceptions of a purely probabilistic decision theorist, one might say that the semiprobabilistic approach represents a deviation in the same direction as does the frequentist-objectivist approach. A semiprobabilistic theory recognizes that reasonable decision makers may use methods involving violations of the rules of probability to solve problems which do not qualify by frequentist standards. But the protagonists of the purely probabilistic-subjectivist movement should be willing to regard the semiprobabilistic position as merely somewhat heretical, or perhaps as a position advocating an undue lowering of formal standards because of an inclination to take account of unwieldly aspects of reality. On the other hand, the frequentist-objectivist deviation from the purely probabilistic line in decision theory is a much more serious business.

If a frequentist-objectivist faces a problem of risky prospects which does not qualify by his standards, he can take one of two positions. He can conclude that there exist *no* applicable rules, or he can conclude that there exist various rules of thumb with the aid of which the decision maker can bring his subjective judgment to bear on the problem. These rules of thumb do not recognize prior probabilities (probabilities other than frequency probabilities), at least not explicitly. Nor do they have a utility-theoretical character, at least not explicitly. The semiprobabilistic approach, on the other hand, regards all problems involving risky appraisals as problems in probability theory and in utility theory, although it recognizes that in some of the nonfrequentist situations the probabilities become distorted in a systematic fashion.

The frequentist-objectivists are empty-handed whenever they are faced with *any* decision problem which is not well behaved by Mises' criteria. Hence, they show a rather general inclination to combine rule-of-thumb subjectivism with their frequentist philosophy. By not being explicit, this kind of subjectivism often tends to give the impression of objectivity. Rule-of-thumb subjectivism may assume different forms, depending on whether it merely *supplements* a frequentist probability judgment or is applied to factual observations from which no frequentist probability judgment can be derived.

When it supplements a frequentist judgment, the rule of thumb typically guides the individual in playing safe against one possibility *to which a specific frequency probability (objective probability) can be assigned* more than against some other such possibility. Simple illustrations of such procedures, which are sometimes wrongly called "classical," were given in Chapter 2, Sections 5 and 6, and the problems will be considered again in Chapter 8. These procedures will not concern us in the present chapter, since the earlier passage to which we have just referred should make it clear to the reader what the general character of those procedures is.

When the rule of thumb is applied to factual observations from which *no* frequentist probability judgment can be derived, then the rule usually tells the decision maker how to play safe against one or the other objectively given possibility, *regardless of any probabilities assigned to these prospects.* Such rules will be discussed in the following sections of the present chapter. All these rules are deficient from the viewpoint of the purely probabilistic-subjectivist theory. They are deficient also from the semiprobabilistic-subjectivist point of view because the rules of thumb in question always circumvent the concept of subjective probability. Let us now consider some of these rules.

(2) Circumventing Probabilities: The Maximin of Gain

The maximin-of-gain[1] rule is one of the decision rules—rules of thumb—which by-pass the concepts of probability theory. A moderate amount of detective work is needed to discover what is implied in mechanical rules of this sort concerning subjective probability judgments. It will be shown that in essence, these rules imply complete suppression of the individual's degrees of belief by specific traits of his preference system. The decision suggested by such rules rests on the observation of objective data, and on a formula which expresses the way (or direction) in which the alleged traits of the individual's preference system should be allowed to suppress his subjective probabilities.

[1] Maximin stands for *maximum minimorum*.

For example, the maximin rule, as applied to *gain*—i.e., to gain in comparison with the decision maker's initial position—is identical with the minimax[2] rule as applied to *loss* (expressed also in comparison with the decision maker's initial position). The rule may be illustrated by the following monetary pay-off matrix for a situation, which is not one of a game of strategy because the decision maker is faced not with an individual playing against him (*or* in co-operation with him) but with "nature" alone. Being faced with nature alone—i.e., *not* being involved in a game of strategy—may here be defined as a condition such that the question of which state of nature will become established does not depend in the least on whether the decision maker does or does not make his moves public in advance.

The numbers in the matrix are the pay-offs, that is, they are gains in comparison with the initial situation. Let us first measure these gains in units of money.

The pay-off or gain (g) is the function g of the decision maker's act and of the state of nature. In symbols, $g = g(D, N)$, where the meaning of the symbols becomes self-explanatory after a glance at the matrix. It is guaranteed to the decision maker that N_1, N_2, and N_3 exhaust the possible states of nature, and that they carry the monetary rewards indicated in the matrix.

In Matrix 1 the maximin rule requires that the decision maker

MATRIX 1

A DECISION MAKER FACING NATURE
(NOT A GAME OF STRATEGY)

Acts of the Decision Maker	States of Nature		
	N_1	N_2	N_3
D_1	0	5	7
D_2	4	3	2

should choose action D_2, because the worst that can happen to him in that case is that he gains two units; this is better than the worst that can happen to him if he selects D_1 (i.e., better than zero). Hence:

$$\underset{D}{\text{max}} \quad \underset{N}{\text{min}} \quad g(D, N) = 2, \quad \text{for} \quad D = D_2, N = N_3$$

[2] Minimax stands for *minimum maximorum*.

In words, D_2 rather than D_1 will maximize g—i.e., will maximize $g(D, N)$— for that value of N which, for a given D, minimizes g. The rule focuses entirely on the worst that can happen to the decision maker, given the choice he has made.

In general, asymmetrical psychological weights of this sort could result from one of two reasons. One of these is that even when an attempt is made to measure the utility of wealth to the decision maker in a standard process, it may turn out that the utility of the goods he can obtain for the first units (in this case the first *two* units) of money gain is infinitely greater than the further utility embodied in the goods obtainable for additional units of money gain; the second possible reason is that in the particular process to which Matrix 1 relates, he slants downward to an extreme extent the subjective probabilities of all events which would yield him more than the minimum guaranteed pay-off. Only the second of these two reasons can be used for justifying the maximin-of-gain rule if Matrix 1 is interpreted as expressing pay-offs in *utility* (rather than in money), as is sometimes the case.

At any rate, very extreme assumptions are needed here. In exceptional cases, when such assumptions appear to be justified, they should be explained with reference to the utility function and/or the slanting tendencies of the individual rather than becoming incorporated in a mechanical decision rule.

An attempt to talk a customer into adopting the maximin of gain as a general decision rule would in almost all cases be an attempt to do great violence to his genuine preferences. There exists no excuse for such an attempt. Also, it would usually miscarry.

(3) Observation on the Special Problem of the Two-Person, Zero-Sum Game

The objections expressed in the foregoing section apply in this form to the maximin-of-gain (minimax-of-negative-income) rule only in cases where the decision maker is faced with nature alone. In particular, the objections do not apply in this form to cases where he is faced with another decision maker whose objectives are diametrically opposed to his own. The "two-person, zero-sum game" describes this latter situation, and this game has properties which make the maximin-of-gain rule much less implausible. When applied to the two-person, zero-sum game, a game of strategy in which one player's gain equals the other's loss, the implication of the rule merely is that each participant has perfect information about the states of nature and the pay-offs which correspond to all possible pairs of strategies (strategies of the two participants which thus *uniquely* determine the pay-offs without further uncertainties); and that each participant believes with certainty that the skills of the other participant are equal to his own, so that neither attempts to outwit the other. Considering that John von Neumann (**38**) has proved that there exist strategies—so-called "mixed" or "randomized" strategies—which will always make the maximin-of-gain (minimax-of-negative-income) solutions of the two participants coincide with one another in a "saddle point," the rule does indeed possess significance for these problems of conflict.

Even when it is used to solve the problem of the two-person, zero-sum game, the rule we are discussing still implies extreme assumptions about appraisals of a specific kind. But in this case the extreme assumptions are those frequently made in an effort to separate two sets of problems from one another. We mean the assumption of perfect information concerning the pay-offs for alternative pairs of strategies and the assumption of mutually recognized equal skills. Thus, where a subjective appraisal must be made, it is made with *certainty* as to its correctness; and in fact, the appraisal of each participant proves correct. By this extreme assumption the problems of subjective probability theory are eliminated, or rather, they become separated from the problem of locating a mutually consistent position. From the methodological point of view, resorting to such a separation of problems is a time-honored procedure. It is often a fruitful procedure.

However, when the same rule is applied to a decision maker faced with the uncertainties of neutral nature, then the implied extreme assumption does not have these defensible characteristics. In this event the maximin-of-gain (minimax-of-loss) rule implies complete lack of interest in what is more likely and what is less likely to happen in the world.

(4) Circumventing Probabilities: The Maximax of Gain

The maximax rule says that in Matrix 1 on page 141 the decision maker will select D_1 because, if the state of nature will be such that, given his decision, he will fare as well as possible, then D_1 will give him a higher reward than D_2. In this event, D_1 yields seven, while D_2 would yield only four. In symbols:

$$\overset{\text{max}}{D} \quad \overset{\text{max}}{N} \quad g(D, N) = 7, \quad \text{for} \quad D = D_1, N = N_3$$

With a self-evident *mutatis mutandis* clause the criticism to be made here is perfectly analogous to that expressed for the maximin rule in Section 2. Maximax has one of the following two implications: Either (*a*) the decision maker is assumed to show in his standard process a utility function which makes him appreciate additions to the goods available to him infinitely more *beyond* a certain addition than *up* to a certain addition (so that he is interested exclusively in getting seven money units' worth of additional goods but not at all interested in getting lesser additions); *or* (*b*) in the particular process to which the matrix applies, the decision maker slants upward his subjective probabilities by some system which has an extreme bias in favor of events carrying large monetary rewards. If Matrix 1 is interpreted as expressing pay-offs in utility (rather than money), then only the second of these two justifications can be used.

Persons whose needs happen to fit this rule must be exceedingly rare. At any rate, whenever the rule does accidentally fit, this should be explained by the characteristics of the individual's utility function or of his slanting tendencies.

Nor does it seem promising to construct a weighted maximax-maximin decision rule. It has been suggested that this could be done by the method of weighting for each act (D_1 and D_2) the *highest* and the *lowest* pay-off by fixed weights which reflect the inclination of the decision maker, and by then selecting the act for which the weighted pay-off is the highest. However, this is an unsatisfactory way of avoiding the extreme implications of maximax and of maximin, because it is quite arbitrary to disregard the intermediate items of the pay-off matrix.

(5) Circumventing Probabilities: The Minimax of Regret

How about a decision maker who "minimaxes regret"? Aside from a further elaboration, which will be presented in a moment, such a person may be said to select D_1 when faced with Matrix 1 on page 141. The reason is the following: Whatever action he takes (D_1 or D_2), it may turn out that, given the state of nature which actually emerges, another action would have benefited him more. This difference is called his "regret." For D_1, N_1, his potential regret is 4 because if N_1 should prove to be the true state of nature, then the pay-off which he *could have* earned *if the other decision had been made* exceeds $g(D_1, N_1)$ by 4; for D_1, N_2 the potential regret is 0; for D_1, N_3, it is 0; for D_2, N_1, it is 0; for D_2, N_2, it is 2; and for D_2, N_3, it is 5. Therefore, for D_1 the *maximum* possible regret is 4; while for D_2, it is 5. The minimaxer of regret chooses the action for which the maximum possible regret is the smallest. In our case, he chooses D_1. The minimax value of the regret is 4. In symbols:

$$\operatorname*{min}_{D} \operatorname*{max}_{N} \quad R(D, N) = 4, \quad \text{for} \quad D = D_1, N = N_1$$

By way of further elaboration, it is possible to argue, however, that the decision maker who wishes to follow the minimax regret rule should in most cases randomize his decision by some method. For example, we may define D_3 as "D_1 with probability $\frac{5}{9}$ and D_2 with probability $\frac{4}{9}$." Assuming this mixed decision, and using mathematical expectations, we obtain for N_1 the pay-off $1\frac{6}{9}$; for N_2 the pay-off $3\frac{7}{9}$; and for N_3 the pay-off $4\frac{3}{9}$. *Thus the maximum possible regret for D_3 is $2\frac{0}{9}$.* It is therefore possible to argue that once the pay-offs for D_3 are added to the matrix, the minimax value of the regret is reduced from 4 to $2\frac{0}{9}$, and the minimaxer of regret should select D_3. That is, with the allowance for randomization:

$$\min_{D} \quad \max_{N} \quad R(D, N) = 2\frac{0}{9}, \quad \text{for} \quad \left\{ \begin{array}{l} D_3 = \frac{5}{9}D_1 + \frac{4}{9}D_2 \\ N = N_1 \text{ or } N = N_3 \end{array} \right.$$

This latter interpretation of the rule is based on the idea that the minimaxer of regret is guided exclusively by the mathematical expectation of the outcome of the process used for randomizing his behavior. The randomized version of the minimax regret rule could be interpreted as implying that the decision maker relies fully on actuarial expectations in any situation that is frequency-probabilistic, even if he is faced with merely a single event (a single drawing from a deck containing red and black cards in say, the proportion *five* to *four*), and that at the same time he is completely unwilling to make guesses about the chances of his becoming faced with N_1 or N_2 or N_3 (to which frequency probabilities are not applicable). At any rate, if he wanted to minimax his regret for each individual outcome, he would always have to choose D_1 and would have to leave D_3 alone. In general, the minimax regret rule rests on assumptions which are so extreme that it is difficult to tell whether these assumptions do or do not stand the burden of the further implications needed for justifying the act of randomization, an act which, in our case, calls for using the probabilities $\frac{5}{9}$ and $\frac{4}{9}$.

While the assumptions underlying the minimax regret rule are indeed extreme, they are extreme in a somewhat different way from those underlying the maximax rule and the maximin or minimax-of-negative-income rule. We must interpret minimax regret as implying that the *disutility of regret* to the decision maker is so sweeping as to *swamp all his probabilistic appraisals.* Regardless of the likelihood of the alternative states of nature, he is entirely single-minded in playing safe against regret.

The approach used in the present volume recognizes the significance of a concept which has some traits in common with regret in the fore-going sense. Our version of the theory of subjective probability, unlike the de Finetti–Savage version, accepts the fact that reasonable decision makers may make allowances for the disappointment they will experience if, in retrospect, the subjective probability judgments concerning the events on which they have staked their fortunes will seem too optimistic to them and/or to others. We favor blending an element expressing this insight with a basically probabilistic approach. The minimax regret rule, on the other hand, magnifies this element to a point where it becomes the one and only principle of decision making. This is hardly defensible.

(6) Three Consistency Requirements of Semiprobabilistic Behavior

Since this volume does not postulate the general acceptability of purely probabilistic (all-around probabilistic) norms, the question arises as to what deviations from these norms are to be regarded as compatible with the standards of semiprobabilistic behavior. What are the intuitively acceptable rules of consistency which a semiprobabilistic subject must obey, lest his decision should lose its semiprobabilistic character and fall in the category of nonprobabilistic decisions?

I shall formulate three *behavioral* requirements which I consider to be very strong candidates for inclusion in a theory of consistent or rational slanting. A formal elaboration on the Second Requirement will be found in the Appendix to the present chapter.

First Requirement: Transitive Ordering. A subject must have a complete ordering of risky prospects when it comes to staking a prize of any given size on such prospects, i.e., when it comes to betting on risky prospects; and this ordering must be transitive. This must be true regardless of whether the prospects do or do not involve probability judgments which the individual has placed at a discount relative to other probability judgments. His choices must be transitive on the basis of the decision weights he actually uses.

Consider, for example, a semiprobabilistic individual who, on mature reflection, and after reasonable explanations, is equally willing to make a $100 prize contingent upon the nonstandard process event E' as on a standard process event whose probability is 0.6; and who also is equally willing to make a $100 prize contingent upon the complement of E' (i.e., on $\sim E'$) as on a standard process event whose probability is 0.3. The transitivity requirement then prescribes that he should be more willing to stake the prize in question on E' than on $\sim E'$, and that he should be more willing to stake a prize of \$100 on E' than a prize of \$100 on a standard process probability of 0.5, etc. It will be seen in Section 9 that such a semiprobabilistic ordering violates the Independence Axiom for nonstandard processes—i.e., the ordering of such a subject *would not* be complete and transitive *if* the Independence Axiom were to be upheld—but this is another question. The fact that the Independence Axiom is not upheld for slanting behavior in nonstandard processes becomes obvious if we consider that our individual must be assumed to assign unitary probability (not 0.9 probability) to the prospect "either E' or $\sim E'$ will happen."

We shall use the following notation: When tested with a \$100 prize, our individual will be said to attach to E' the *uncorrected probability* 0.6, and to $\sim E'$ the *uncorrected probability* 0.3. That is to say, to him, in this experiment, $P_u(E') = 0.6$, $P_u(\sim E') = 0.3$. The *corrected* probabilities—P_c terms—would have to add up to unity. In some cases, it is possible to reconstruct the numerical values of the P_c terms—for example, if $P_u(E') = P_u(\sim E')$, then $P_c(E') = P_c(\sim E') = 0.5$. In the general case, it is, however, not possible to derive operationally the precise values of the P_c terms from the P_u terms—that is, from the observed decision weights—without considerable arbitrariness. In the general case, knowledge of the P_u terms allows an observer to make a definite statement only concerning the *range* in which the P_c terms of a subject fall (see page 12). As was explained before, we shall, however, take it for granted that $P_u(E' \cup \sim E') = P_c(E' \cup \sim E') = 1$.

Second Requirement: Randomization Theorems. There exists a type of situation, capable of being established under experimental conditions, in which the distortion or slanting—i.e., the discrepancy between P_u and P_c—should diminish in relative terms and, indeed, should *tend* to zero, as the number of events to which the bet relates increases.

Take a semiprobabilistic subject to whom $P_u(E') = P_u(\sim E')$. We could also assume that this person is faced with three or more possibilities, all of which are subjectively equiprobable to him. Furthermore, we could consider a subject who is indifferent as between two, three, or more prospects *not* because these are subjectively equiprobable to him but because asymmetries between the subjective probabilities are precisely compensated by contrary asymmetries of the pay-offs. Precise compensation requires that if, for example, one of two prospects is subjectively twice as probable as a second prospect, then, in terms of utility, the prize set on the second prospect should be twice as high as the prize set on the first. In other words, *indifference* between betting on two or more prospects *is* an essential condition for describing and testing the Second Requirement, and it is simplest to argue the case for two equiprobable prospects. We shall describe the problem as if the nonstandard event E' were the drawing from an urn of a ball possessing the color of the subject's choice, where the urn contains only red and/or black balls but with no guarantee concerning the red-black ratio. This situation, as symbolized by the "uncertain urn," merely *stands* for situations in which the decision maker has unstable and controversial hunches which tend to neutralize each other at the present moment, so that he has no preference for betting on one event rather than on the other. A bet on "Dow Jones will rise" (E') or "Dow Jones will not rise" ($\sim E'$) belongs among those which may *occasionally* create this type of problem. All problems of this sort are subsumed under our problem of the uncertain urn.

Let us now imagine that E' carries a prize of \$100, while $\sim E'$ is associated with no gain or loss. We assume also that for this particular semiprobabilistic individual, $P_u(E') = P_u(\sim E') = 0.4$. That is to say, he is less willing to make a given prize contingent on his drawing the color of his choice from the uncertain urn than on his drawing from a *guaranteed* urn in which the proportion of red balls and also of black balls is 50 per cent.

Say that our individual has been made aware of the fact that if he decides to draw from the uncertain urn, he could, just before drawing, use an objective chance device—e.g., the flipping of a fair coin—to decide whether he should guess red or black for the ball he is about to draw. It may have been suggested to our individual that by using an objective *randomization device* of this sort, he can make *even a single bet* on the uncertain urn equivalent to a bet on a fair coin (therefore also to a bet on a guaranteed 50–50 urn): If he loses on his guess concerning the next drawing from the uncertain urn, he can always tell himself that essentially he lost on the objective chance device, which he was using as a randomization device. If the coin had fallen differently, he would have *won* his bet on the uncertain urn (or on a stock exchange prospect, etc.). In cases of indifference between betting on two or more prospects from uncertain urns, this randomization argument may seem convincing even to semiprobabilistic subjects; and in such cases of indifference, some semiprobabilistic individuals may therefore cease to place their subjective probabilities at a discount relative to their standard process probabilities.

However, when a semiprobabilistic subject is faced with a single bet, or with a small number of bets, he *may* consider the foregoing randomization argument inconclusive. If he draws a ball from the uncertain urn and misses, then he may be $100 worse off than if he had drawn from the guaranteed urn; the initial subjective equiprobability concerning the uncertain urn, and hence his decision to hold himself to that judgment by means of randomization, may subsequently seem quite implausible to him and to most other people (the chance device may have led him to bet on red or on "Dow Jones will rise," and he may discover that for reasons which he had dimly suspected, all balls in the urn are black; or *mutatis mutandis*, that a rather widely expected fall in stock prices has occurred). He may feel that the loss relative to the standard process bet has resulted not exclusively from the workings of the objective chance device but *also* from a wrong probability judgment concerning the uncertain urn, a judgment which induced him to employ the chance device for randomization. To suffer an opportunity loss of $100 in such circumstances may be particularly painful to him, more so than to suffer an opportunity loss of $100 on a correctly estimated standard process probability and on *not* having followed a vague, oscillating, and controversial hunch concerning the uncertain urn. In cases where his hunches are highly unstable and controversial, he may react differently to an opportunity loss suffered by forcing himself to bet on some average level of these hunches than he reacts to an opportunity loss suffered by disregarding the availability of a bet on such uninformed hunches.

"Never mind that you acted on a flimsy judgment (suspect even to yourself) concerning the composition of the uncertain urn"—this need not be a compelling admonition, unless it is possible to add that "reliance on that judgment cost you nothing as compared to the alternative which was open to you (namely, as compared to a bet on the guaranteed half-and-half urn)." While the second part of the statement becomes valid, with an arbitrarily close approximation to certainty, when the number of trials from the uncertain urn is made ever larger, this second part may prove to be quite wrong for a single trial or for a small sample. This is why I do not consider it, strictly speaking, a consistency requirement of semiprobabilistic behavior that a person who happens to be indifferent between the prospects "Dow Jones will rise" and "Dow Jones will not rise" should be at least as willing to place a small number of randomized bets on these prospects—i.e., on prospects offered by the uncertain urn—as on red or black from a guaranteed half-and-half urn. An individual who in these circumstances acquires the prospect of a $100 prize contingent on red from the guaranteed urn by giving in exchange for this prospect that of a \$110 prize contingent on red from the uncertain urn does not thereby violate the principle of *coherence* in the usual decision-theoretical sense (where this principle prescribes avoidance of bets which must lead to loss regardless of which state of nature becomes established).[3] Most of us might not share such a person's preferences, but this question needs to be distinguished from that of consistency.

Yet, *in these particular cases of symmetry* (indifference between betting on red or black from the uncertain urn) the semiprobabilistic objections against the randomization argument *lose in weight as the number of drawings from the uncertain urn is increased.* Assume, for example, that the subject—instead of being promised \$100 if, from the uncertain urn, he draws one ball of the color of his choice—is promised \$1.00 for each of one hundred drawings, and that he will indicate in advance, with reliance on an objective chance device, in which of these drawings he will be trying for red and in which for black. Even if he is the kind of person who does slant when faced with a single bet, he should in these circumstances slant *very much less* in relative or percentage terms —that is to say, he should bring $P_u(E') + P_u(\sim E')$ very much closer to unity than in the case of a single drawing. The reason for this is that for an unlimited increase in the number of events (trials) the *success ratio* for the uncertain urn almost always[4] tends to 0.5, *regardless of the composition of the urn.* This success ratio can (almost always) be assured, for example, by betting on red whenever a fair coin falls heads and on black whenever it falls tails—and we are now comparing this success ratio of 0.5 with the success ratio for a direct bet on coin flipping, or with the success ratio for a bet on the guaranteed urn, which (almost always)*also* tends to 0.5. Consequently, in the special case of *indifference* between betting on red or on black from the uncertain urn, the slanting can be justified for a small number of trials only because the *deviations* from 0.5 will usually come out differently for the uncertain urn than they come out for the guaranteed urn, even if the bet on the uncertain urn is randomized. While, for some individuals, this may be disturbing for a single drawing (or for a small number of drawings), the percentage deviations diminish sharply with an increase in the number of drawings, and the slanting becomes increasingly less justified. Hence, if for one drawing from the uncertain urn, we observe $P_u(E') = P_u(\sim E') = 0.4$, we should be able

---

[3] Nor is even the principle of *strict coherence* violated. This principle prescribes the avoidance of bets which must lead either to loss or to zero gain, depending on which state of nature becomes established, but cannot lead to positive gain.

[4] For the meaning of the "almost always" clause and its unimportance for the present purpose, see page 17.

to observe operationally a gradual and continuous approach to $P_u(E') = P_u(\sim E') = 0.5$ as the number of drawings, on which the bet is placed in advance, gets larger. In other words, *in the case of symmetrical bets in the foregoing sense the consistent semiprobabilistic subject either should not slant even for a small number of drawings; or if he does, then with an increasing number of drawings the slant should tend to disappear, i.e., the uncorrected probabilities should approach the corrected ones, and the condition $P_u(E') + P_u(\sim E') = 1$ should become approximated. This is our Second Requirement of consistency for semiprobabilistic behavior.*

Strictly speaking, even a person violating our Second Requirement cannot be said to violate the decision-theoretical principle of coherence, as this principle was defined on page 150, because the result of a standard process experiment does not become literally *certain* when the number of trials is increased further and further. Hence, with a higher prize set on the uncertain urn than on the guaranteed urn, it cannot be said that a large-sample bet on the guaranteed urn literally *must* come out worse (or even literally *cannot* come out better) than a randomized bet on the uncertain urn. But in these circumstances, a bet on the guaranteed urn should be expected to come out worse than a randomized bet on the uncertain urn with *an arbitrarily close approximation to unitary probability*. Hence a person violating our Second Requirement comes arbitrarily close to violating the decision-theoretical principle of coherence. This, I submit, is bad enough to be considered a piece of inconsistency.

The Second Requirement can be formulated rigorously only for those nonstandard events which evoke a judgment of indifference between staking one's fortunes on any one of two or more nonstandard events. The argument fails for situations which lack this trait of symmetry. The reason is that if, for example, $P_u(E') = 0.75$, $P_u(\sim E') = 0.15$, and if the same prize can be made contingent on E' as on $\sim E'$, then, on the basis of these appraisals, our individual has a clear-cut preference for betting on E'. Yet, if he vaguely expects a very high success ratio, there exists no objective chance device with the aid of which he could make sure that his success ratio for the uncertain urn should (almost always) tend to the expected limit regardless of the composition of the urn. For a large set of events, as for a single event, the purely probabilistic adviser could try to preach to the subject that once he has decided to regard E' five times as likely as $\sim E'$, he should not worry about the possibility that this judgment will seem absurd to him in retrospect; or the purely probabilistic adviser could try to persuade the subject that in the long run, his subjective appraisals relating to various types of events will presumably tend to come out right. But such statements are inconclusive. They are no more cogent for a large set of events than for a single event. They cannot be substantiated by any theorem in a fashion analogous to that in which for the special case of indifference between betting on red or black from the uncertain urn the equivalence of such a bet with a bet on the guaranteed urn *can* be substantiated in a model involving an infinitely long sequence of events. This is the reason why the Second Requirement can be defined only for symmetrical situations, involving subjective *indifference* between staking one's fortunes on one of two or more nonstandard events.

To summarize, and to amplify in the operational direction: If red and black from the uncertain urn are subjectively equiprobable, and if they carry equal prizes, then, according to the Second Requirement, a semiprobabilistic individual must disclose awareness of the (practical) equivalence of such an option with a standard process option for a long sequence of bets; he must be aware of the proposition that betting on red whenever a fair coin falls (say) heads, and betting on black whenever a fair coin falls (say) tails, will almost always tend to give him one half of the prize per bet, regardless of the composition of the uncertain urn. In this sense the individual's firm expectation, based on standard process probabilities, can be made identical with his expectation based on his thoroughly unstable and controversial hunches concerning the uncertain urn. Also, if red from the uncertain urn (or "Dow Jones will rise") seems to the individual five times as likely as black from the uncertain urn (or "Dow Jones will not rise"), and if the less likely prospect carries a prize which is worth to the individual five times as much as the prize set on the more likely prospect, then symmetry in our sense is restored: The individual can still establish practical equivalence with standard process expectations by betting on the more likely prospect whenever a fair die falls with a nonace up and betting on the other prospect whenever the die falls with the ace up. Such behavior will almost always tend to lead to winning, on the average bet of the long sequence, five sixths of the low prize set on the more likely prospect—i.e., one sixth of the high prize set on the less likely prospect. On the other hand, if the condition of indifference or of *symmetry is not satisfied*—say, if he has a 5 ÷ 1 hunch in favor of "Dow Jones will rise" and the prize set on "rise" is the same as that set on "no rise"—*then, on the basis of these vacillating hunches, he should (if he trusts his hunches) always bet on "rise," and he should expect to win on the average bet five sixths of the prize; but no randomization de-*

vice will give him a secure fair-die probability of winning five sixths of the prize regardless of what happens on the stock exchange.

Even in the last of these cases—the case of *asymmetrical* subjective probabilities which are not compensated by asymmetrical pay-offs—the Second Requirement of consistency sets a *limit* to the rationally permissible extent of slanting downward the five-sixths probability attached to the stock exchange event. The reason is that a randomization device will in this case (practically) guarantee to the individual *one half* of the prize for a long sequence of bets. This follows simply from the fact that if the individual had considered "rise" and "no rise" equally probable, then, given the equal pay-offs for "rise" and "no rise," the bet would indeed have possessed the required traits of symmetry. The observance of these limits of slanting is operationally testable because the prizes set on alternative events can be adjusted experimentally, and in a long sequence of trials a subject satisfying the Second Requirement must not assign lower decision weights to red from the uncertain urn than the weights at which the bet becomes symmetrical. He may assign a lower weight to the prospect "red from the uncertain urn" than to the prospect "black from the uncertain urn"; but if the prize set on red is worth to him n times the prize set on black, then the uncorrected probability he assigns to red must in a long sequence of trials approach a value not falling short of $\frac{1}{n}$ times the uncorrected probability he assigns to black. This is because at this level of the uncorrected probabilities, these *are* convertible into standard process probabilities.

If an individual satisfies the Second Requirement, including this corollary concerning the limits of slanting, then he thereby gives strong indications of his desire to maximize the genuinely probabilistic expectations of utility even for uncertain urns, except for allowances he makes in situations where he is disturbed by doubts about the shakiness of a nonstandard judgment. The indications he gives are very strong indeed, because he observably does maximize his probabilistic utility expectations even for uncertain urns in all circumstances in which he can dispel his doubts by randomization.

I believe that the Second Requirement has been explained here in a generally understandable way. But formal discussion is needed to make the argument rigorous. The reader will find a formal analysis in the Appendix to the present chapter. It should be pointed out that while our two other consistency requirements—the first and the third—apply to individuals who slant *up* the subjective probabilities of the events on which they place a bet as well as to downward-slanting individuals, the limits to rational slanting expressed by the Second Requirement apply only to those who slant downward. However, I believe that most semiprobabilistic persons show a downward-slanting tendency, and that practically all persons with semiprobabilistic inclinations slant downward (relative to standard processes) for a good many nonstandard sets of events, even if they slant upward for *some* such events.

Third Requirement: Common Subranges. Say that when a $100 prize is made contingent on the nonstandard process event E' (such as "Dow Jones will rise"), then our individual assigns the decision weight 0.6 to E'; and when the same prize is set on $\sim E'$, then he assigns the decision weight 0.2 to $\sim E'$. In other words, when tested with a $100 prize, he is equally willing to bet on E' as on a standard process probability of 0.6, and equally willing to bet on $\sim E'$ as on a standard process probability of 0.2. In accordance with our definition of uncorrected probabilities, we conclude: $P_u(E') = 0.6$, $P_u(\sim E') = 0.2$. We conclude also that the true or corrected probability of E' to our individual must then lie *in the range 0.6 to 0.8*, where the upper limit of the range is derived from the observation that when the individual bets on $\sim E'$ then, by implication, he assigns the decision weight 0.8 to E'.[5] *Our Third Requirement says that while the value of the* P_u *terms (i.e., of 0.6 and of 0.2) may change if the magnitude of the prize is changed from $100 to some other amount, the range identified as that in which the corrected probabilities lie when the prize is $100 must have a common element with the range so identified when the prize is any other amount.* (For example, the range must not be 0.6 to 0.8 with one prize and 0.45 to 0.55 with another prize.)

The Third Requirement is justified for the following reason: While, depending on the magnitude of the prize, the reluctance to bet on a shaky judgment may create different degrees of uneasiness (or of eagerness), and hence may lead to different degrees of slanting, the genuine ("true" or "corrected") probability of an event to the individual must stay uninfluenced by the magnitude of the prize.

The reader can convince himself easily of the fact that the Third Requirement must necessarily be satisfied if a somewhat more severe requirement is, and even this more severe requirement has great intuitive appeal. The more severe requirement is that a change in the prize which

---

[5] This latter decision weight we do not call an uncorrected probability.

lowers $P_u(E')$, as tested when the individual bets on E', must also lower $P_u(\sim E')$, as tested when the individual bets on $\sim E'$; and that a change in the prize which raises $P_u(E')$, as tested when the individual bets on E', must also raise $P_u(\sim E')$, as tested when the individual bets on $\sim E'$. This more severe requirement has considerable intuitive appeal because if changing the prize makes the individual react more intensely to the vagueness of his probability judgment (i.e., makes him slant more), then this should show in his behavior when he bets on $\sim E'$ as well as in his behavior when he bets on E'. After all, in these two bets, his judgment results from one and the same type of appraisal. If this more severe requirement is met, then the Third Requirement must be satisfied, because the more severe requirement implies that if changing the prize lowers the lower limit of the range in which the true probability of E' lies, then it raises the upper limit of that range; and the more severe requirement implies also that if the change raises the lower limit of the range in which the true probability is located, then it lowers the upper limit, which means that *the range identified by the $100 experiment and the range identified by the $1,000 experiment must have a common element (a common subrange)*.[6]

But while the more severe requirement is indeed appealing, the Third Requirement postulates merely the existence of common subranges, and this requirement *may* be satisfied even if the more severe requirement is not satisfied. The Third Requirement—i.e., the milder requirement of common subranges—obviously needs to be postulated because the true probability which is being slanted by the semiprobabilistic individual must be the same to him regardless of the magnitude of the prize.

(7) How to Estimate the Corrected Probabilities from the Directly Observable (Slanted) Decision Weights

Let us exclude betting situations in which a subject may be expected to behave nonprobabilistically, either because he has ethical misgivings about winning on one or the other event or because he attributes negli-

---

[6] Say that when tested with a $100 prize, the individual in a bet on E', attaches to this event the decision weight 0.6; and in a bet on $\sim E$, he attaches to *this* event the decision weight 0.2. It follows that the range 0.6 to 0.8 becomes identified as that in which the true probability of E' to this individual is located (where the upper limit of the range is defined as one minus 0.2). Now, if—when tested with a $1,000 prize—this individual lowers the 0.6 to 0.55, and lowers the 0.2 to 0.15, then the range in which the true probability of E' is located gets to be bounded by 0.55 and 0.85, and this range includes the entire range of 0.6 to 0.8. The reasoning illustrates the proposition that the more severe requirement, which in this example is satisfied, does imply the Third Requirement.

gible importance to the problem. Let us assume that in betting situations which do not have these traits, he either behaves purely probabilistically (as in a standard process) or satisfies our three consistency requirements of semiprobabilistic behavior. Does it follow that we can *generally* reconstruct the corrected (genuine) subjective probabilities of such individuals from their observable slanted probabilities (decision weights)? Does this follow for all situations in which these individuals behave semiprobabilistically?

The answer is that a convincing method for reconstructing the precise numerical value of the corrected probabilities (P_c) exists only if some rather far-reaching simplifying assumptions are satisfied.

Take, for example, the case in which the uncorrected probabilities $(P_u$ terms) of all events belonging in a set are found to be equal. This, of course, is a very special case. Say that, for a prize of $100, all uncorrected probabilities are found to be 0.2. Then it is to be expected that the uncorrected probabilities will be found equal also for any other prize, although possibly not at the value 0.2, and the corrected probabilities should also be assumed to be equal. For example, if we find that $P_u(E') = P_u(\sim E')$, then it seems convincing to conclude that $P_c(E') = 0.5$, and $P_c(\sim E') = 0.5$. This seems convincing because if, when tested with a prize of given magnitude, the individual shows identical uncorrected probabilities for two events, then all circumstances which increase or decrease his willingness to bet on the kind of judgment he has made must be assumed to have the identical effect on each of the two uncorrected probabilities.

Thus, there do exist special situations in which the precise numerical values of the corrected probabilities can be reconstructed from the semiprobabilistically slanted P_u terms by a rather convincing method. Yet, it is not necessary to formulate the validity of this method as a postulate, since in the general case it is not possible to estimate the precise numerical values of the corrected probabilities from the observed, semiprobabilistically slanted P_u terms of a subject.

Say that when a subject is tested with a given prize, we observe that for him, $P_u(E') = 0.6$, and $P_u(\sim E') = 0.2$. Then, all we are entitled to conclude is that a reasonable estimate puts this subject's $P_c(E')$ between 0.6 and 0.8, and puts his $P_c(\sim E')$ between 0.2 and 0.4. As we have seen, the P_u term attached to E' and the P_u terms attached to $\sim E'$, and therefore also the widths of the observed ranges, may be found different for prizes of different magnitudes; but if the individual behaves consistently, all observations must be compatible with the proposition that the P_c terms lie in these ranges (all of which must have common elements according to the Third Requirement). The reason why—for $P_u(E') \neq P_u(\sim E')$—it is not, in general, possible to describe a convincing method for reconstructing the unique numerical values of the P_c terms from our observations is that if the probabilistic appraisals of our subject were made "firm" this might influence the higher and the lower P_u term in different proportions. On the other hand, there exist cases in which the investigator may want to make the explicit assumption that the uncorrected probabilities *have* resulted from equiproportionate slanting of all relevant genuine probabilities, and this assumption (or some similar assumption) *would* enable us to reconstruct the genuine values by a process of correction. Note, however, that if $P_u(E')$ results from slanting in the identical proportion as $P_u(\sim E')$, then *unless* $P_u(E') = P_u(\sim E')$, this equiproportionality of slanting implies that $1 - P_u(E')$ does *not* result from slanting in the identical proportion as $1 - P_u(\sim E')$. What do these $1 - P_u$ terms mean?

Throughout this analysis, we have taken it for granted that the uncorrected probability of an event E' for a given prize is measured by the probability of the standard process event E on which the individual is as willing to stake a prize as on E'. This is how we obtained our P_u terms. In other words, we took it for granted that the uncorrected probability of E' is an indifference value relative to a standard process probability when the individual has acquired an interest in the occurrence of E' rather than in its nonoccurrence. Such an individual obviously slants the probability of E' in the opposite direction when the prize is staked on $\sim E'$ rather than on E'. Therefore, it would have been possible to introduce also another concept of uncorrected probabilities. While our uncorrected probabilities, as defined above, are hope-of-gain indifference values relative to standard process probabilities, this other concept would have to be measured by fear-of-no-gain (or fear-of-loss) indifference values relative to standard process probabilities. These other indifference values—$1 - P_u$ terms— one could also call uncorrected probabilities, in a different sense of the word. If the subject slants down the probabilities of events on which he hopes to gain, he obviously slants up the probabilities of the complements of these events, that is, of the events he fears. We shall not call this other set of slanted weights uncorrected probabilities, but it is necessary to stay aware of their importance because they set one of the two limits of the range in which the true probabilities are located.

(8) What Significance Can Be Attached to the Corrected Probabilities?

Since, in the general case, operational methods can detect only ranges in which the true (corrected) probabilities of a slanting individual lie, a strictly operational semiprobabilistic theory would have to arrive at the conclusion that for events generated by nonstandard processes, only these ranges of corrected probabilities are generally meaningful. Of course, the specific numerical values of the *slanted* probabilities—of the observable decision weights—are also generally meaningful, even from a strictly operational point of view.

While recognizing this, I am inclined to stress the intuitive significance of the specific numerical values of the true probabilities, even where an observer cannot reconstruct these values from the subject's behavior. The reason for stressing the intuitive importance of these values even in such cases is that the way of thinking of an individual is logically deficient if he does not understand that his semiprobabilistic range of values results from the slanting of a specific value, i.e., of its slanting in different directions in different circumstances.

Say that his behavior discloses that to an event E' he assigns the probability range 0.6 to 0.8 when a specific prize is at stake, and say that he is honestly convinced that there exists no basis on which he would give any value within this range preference over any other value. In this case, he has so far tentatively stated that the probability of E' is 0.7. If he is willing to give some values within the range preference over others, then he has tentatively made another specific numerical statement. But say that we now observe that (on reflection) he assigns the decision weight 0.6 to E' when he bets on E', and the decision weight 0.8 to E' when he bets on $\sim E'$. Logically, he must accept the proposition that he is slanting a specific numerical value—a tentative value—in one direction or the other, and that he is doing this because he considers it more painful to suffer an opportunity loss by staking his fortunes on this tentative value than to suffer an opportunity loss by refusing to base an act on it. Hence, it seems quite reasonable to infer that he has in his mind the numerical value of a tentative "true" probability which he is slanting. The argument implies that it is reasonable to interpret the observed range 0.6 to 0.8 as a *probability* range. It is reasonable to do so if the subject satisfies all three consistency requirements of semiprobabilistic behavior. Indeed, the content of the Second and the Third Requirements essentially is that an individual satisfying these requirements has in himself a numerical probability judgment at a value falling in the observed range, and that he slants this value merely because of the doubts he has about the validity of the judgment.

(9) Savage's System: How to Bridge the Gap

In the present analysis, we defined purely probabilistic, semiprobabilistic, and nonprobabilistic behavior with reliance on the Standard Process Postulate. This enabled us to say: (*a*) Let us find an individual's decision weights for a nonstandard process prospect by observing the numerically known probability of the heads-or-tails prospect which he considers equal to the nonstandard process prospect when he has a choice between betting on one or the other. (*b*) With respect to choices in which the nonstandard decision weights (so discovered) obey the rules of probability theory, we conclude that the individual satisfies the Postulate of Equivalent Degrees of Belief (page 97), i.e., that he behaves purely probabilistically. (*c*) With respect to choices in which the rules of purely probabilistic choices are violated but the three consistency requirements of *semiprobabilistic* behavior are satisfied, we conclude that the violations merely express allowances for the psychological instability and the interpersonally controversial character of the nonstandard process probabilities; and hence, we regard the behavior in question as consistent behavior of the semiprobabilistic kind. (*d*) With respect to choices in which the violations of purely probabilistic behavior do not satisfy our consistency requirements, we conclude that the violations are too unsystematic for our purpose, and we therefore regard the behavior as nonprobabilistic. It should be repeated here that these Version 1 statements are proxies for a Version 2 presentation.[7] While it may sometimes be appropriate to visualize these matters in terms of Version 2, I feel convinced that a fruitful approach to most problems of economics requires Version 1.

I suggest that this is a useful way of looking at the problem, but it is undeniable that the aesthetic qualities of L. J. Savage's all-around purely probabilistic theory are superior (**45**). Savage does not rely on any postulate that would take the existence of standard processes for granted. Instead, he describes a system of postulates for the *preference ranking (ordering) of acts;* among these acts, he of course includes acts of making rewards of various sizes contingent on this or that prospect. The choice postulates relating to acts are formulated in such a way that an individual complying with them discloses, in all his choices, decision weights which obey the rules of probability theory, and discloses also his

---

[7] This was explained in the Introduction to this volume (and *passim*).

utility assignments which are measurable up to a linear transformation. A brief verbal summary of the Savage postulates is given in the footnote below.[8]

Savage would, of course, not deny that in some of their choices, reasonable individuals violate these postulates and that this may in some cases result from causes other than confusion. About the existence of an area of nonprobabilistic behavior, there can be no disagreement. One cannot call an individual unreasonable if he regards it as repulsive to acquire the prospect of making a net gain in the event that New York is destroyed in a nuclear war.

I think there may even be essential agreement on the fact that some people who are not victims of confusion tend to behave in the fashion which I call semiprobabilistic (or tend to behave in some similar fashion). But the protagonists of purely probabilistic decision theory are inclined to attribute such behavior to imperfections, that is, to the fact that no mathematical theory can be expected to fit perfectly when it comes to physical applications.

The semiprobabilistic deviations require more attention than the phenomena which can be lumped together as imperfections in a useful theory. A useful normative theory must describe *consistent* behavior of a kind which to reasonable individuals seems desirable when they reach decisions about important matters. Hence, such a theory acquires positive, empirical content in addition to being normative. A useful theory should not disregard the distinction between firm and shaky judgments, because even on mature reflection, many reasonable individuals do not wish to disregard this distinction, and because, in retrospect, they would regret having disregarded it.

The easiest way of demonstrating that our semiprobabilistic individuals violate Savage's postulates is to stress the fact that these postulates include the Independence Axiom which was described in Chapter 3, Sec-

---

[8] P1 is the postulate requiring a complete, transitive ordering of preferences among acts (for the concept of acts, see p. 11, above). P2 expresses the "sure-thing" principle, which is Savage's formulation of the Independence Axiom (see p. 82; and see also the immediately following passages of the text, above). P3 requires that knowledge of an event should never change the preference or indifference relation among any two consequences (this may also be interpreted as part of the sure-thing principle). P4 postulates that a preference for staking a given prize on this or on that event must not depend on the size of the prize. P5 says that there exists a worth-while prize. P6 is an extension of P6′, that is, of a postulate which was briefly explained in n. 11, p. 99. P7 requires that if every one of the consequences which one act may conceivably have is preferred to the privilege of engaging in another act, then the first-mentioned act should be preferred to the other act.

For a precise formulation of the seven postulates, see L. J. Savage, *The Foundations of Statistics* (**45**), pp. 18, 23, 24, 31, 39, and 77.

tion 5, or, rather, that they include an equivalent of this axiom. An essentially equivalent formulation appears in Savage's work as the "sure-thing" principle (compare his Postulate 2; see note 8, above). In Chapter 3, above, we limited the Independence Axiom to mutually exclusive events generated by standard processes; but in Savage's conception, it is of general validity. In his conception the axiom applies also to mutually exclusive events generated by nonstandard processes. This extension involves postulating the type of behavior which in the present volume is called purely probabilistic. To semiprobabilistic subjects the extended postulate must seem unconvincing.

In its extended form the postulate implies that if the individual prefers to make a prize contingent on standard process event E_1 rather than on nonstandard process event E'_1, and also prefers to make the same prize contingent on standard process event E_2 rather than on nonstandard process event E'_2, where E_1 and E_2 are mutually exclusive and E'_1 and E'_2 also are, then he should prefer an option which gives him the foregoing prize if E_1 happens and *also* gives him some specific amount x if E_2 happens, to an option which gives him the foregoing prize if E'_1 happens and *also* gives him the amount x if E'_2 happens. This clearly follows from the independence (noncomplementarity) requirement for mutually exclusive events. A purely probabilistic subject satisfies this postulate, but a semiprobabilistic subject is apt to violate it. To demonstrate this, make E_2 the complement of E_1, and E'_2 the complement of E'_1. Now, a semiprobabilistic subject *may* have a preference for a bet on E_1 rather than on E'_1, and also a preference for a bet on $\sim E_1$ rather than on $\sim E'_1$, but this would have to result from the shakiness of his judgment concerning the prospect of nonstandard events such as E'_1 or $\sim E'_1$. On the other hand, his judgment about "either E'_1 or $\sim E'_1$ will happen" must be absolutely firm, since this is a judgment concerning a logical certainty. To take an illustration: He may have a very shaky (unstable) judgment about "Dow Jones will rise" and also about "Dow Jones will not rise" when he bets on just one of these prospects, but his judgment concerning "Dow Jones either will rise or will not rise" will be just as firm as his judgment concerning "this coin either will fall heads or will fall tails." Hence, he *may* prefer a bet on heads to a bet on "Dow Jones will rise," and also a bet on tails to a bet on "Dow Jones will not rise," but he will not prefer a bet on the union of the two coin events to a bet on the union of the two stock exchange events. We have here something akin to a complementarity effect: a violation of the Independence Axiom, or of Savage's "sure-thing" principle (Postulate 2; see note 8, above).[9] Individuals of this kind would have to be said to violate this axiom even if their behavior were interpreted in terms of Version 2, as defined in the Introduction.

As was said a moment ago, the purely probabilistic theory has an impressive, unified structure; but it is forced to regard behavior of this sort as resulting from imperfections the analysis of which lies outside the realm of the theory. If one is willing to attribute a strategic role to the Standard Process Postulate and to distinguish between (*a*) standard processes and (*b*) various types of nonstandard sets of events, and if one recognizes that the nonstandard decision weights of many reasonable individuals are at a discount or at a premium relative to their standard process probabilities, then it is possible to pay attention to the difference between firm and shaky probability judgments. But since this goes at the expense of the simplicity of the basic logical construction, it is advisable to ask oneself the question: If Savage's system were used as a point of departure, what complications would have to be introduced to make room for semiprobabilistic and nonprobabilistic behavior?

Let us use as our point of departure Savage's preference ordering of acts, an ordering which obeys all seven Savage postulates and which implies that the individual uses in all his choices decision weights (expectation weights) possessing the properties of genuine probabilities. In other words, no probabilities are at a discount or at a premium relative to others (no probabilities are slanted). According to the purely probabilistic decision theory, this ordering of acts should be directly disclosed by the choices of a reasonable individual; hence, *this* is his directly observable preference ordering. We shall call such a ranking of acts a Savage Ordering; and to arrive at our semiprobabilistic construction, we shall add the following:

a) If the choices of the individual are limited to a specific subset of acts—call it Subset I—then a Savage Ordering is indeed his directly observable preference ordering of acts. In the limiting case in which an individual becomes wholly converted to the purely probabilistic norms, all acts fall in this category. However, as concerns acts of betting, many individuals behave in such a way that mainly their bets on standard processes, and on various sets of events generated by processes with simi-

---

[9] It is obvious from the foregoing that the Independence Axiom is violated. Decision makers with the inclinations here considered violate also that specific version of essentially the same postulate which Savage has formulated on page 23 of his *Foundations of Statistics* (**45**), i.e., the "sure-thing" principle. See Daniel Ellsberg's contribution to "Symposium: Decisions under Uncertainty" in the November, 1961, issue of the *Quarterly Journal of Economics* (**16**) (and cf. Savage's specific formulation in *loc. cit.*).

lar properties, belong in Subset I, while most of their other acts of betting belong in Subset II or Subset III.

b) Subset II comprises the acts which have a very unstable place in the individual's Savage Ordering. It is convincing to postulate that at any moment of time a reasonable individual should be able to make himself aware of the rank he would assign to any of the available acts in a Savage Ordering, but the individual is aware also of the fact that the rank of these acts is apt to change rapidly and that the present rank of the act will soon seem very unconvincing to him. Hence, many reasonable individuals—semiprobabilistic decision makers—move from a Savage Ordering to a directly observable preference ordering by changing the rank of these acts. Those who lower the rank of acts belonging in Subset II—the downward-slanting individuals—do so because they consider it more painful to suffer an opportunity loss by assigning a definite rank to acts that are highly controversial and show a high degree of instability in their Savage Ordering than to suffer an opportunity loss by excluding these acts from the decision process (as if the acts were not available). If this is the reason for the violation—i.e., the reason for the difference between the place of an act in a Savage Ordering and in the directly observable preference ordering of the individual—then the three behavioral consistency requirements formulated in Section 6, above, apply to the operationally observable preference ordering. This means that the observable preference ordering remains complete and transitive; and that the size of any discount at which some decision weights are placed relative to the standard process probabilities is subject to a limit set by opportunities to randomize; and when the individual is tested with different prizes, the observable ranges of decision weights for any event possess common subranges. Especially in view of the Second and the Third Consistency Requirements, it is convincing to *infer* that the range of slanted decision weights which is observable in the behavior of such subjects is a probability range.

c) Subset III is made up of acts the place of which in the observable preference ordering is different from their place in a Savage Ordering because of misgivings connected with making a gain on the occurrence of certain kinds of events. In Frank Ramsey's terminology (**43**), these are acts of betting on events which do not satisfy the criterion of "ethical neutrality." In such acts of betting, individuals cannot be expected to satisfy our three requirements of semiprobabilistic behavior, and we have not tried to formulate consistency requirements for those deviations from the purely probabilistic norms which fall in this category. As concerns these deviations, people behave nonprobabilistically rather than semi-probabilistically. Nor have we tried to make normative or empirical statements about individuals facing a decision problem which they consider insignificant.

d) Our way of bridging the gap between Savage's system and the semiprobabilistic theory of this volume admittedly suffers from a weakness, but it would seem far-fetched to neglect the essential difference between firm and shaky probability judgments merely in order to avoid this weakness and to obtain greater simplicity of the theoretical structure. The weakness in question expresses itself in the fact that while it is intuitively convincing to postulate for a reasonable individual the introspective existence of an ordering which is well behaved by Savage's criteria, it is not generally possible to reconstruct this ordering operaitonally from the directly observable preference ordering of a semiprobabilistic subject. This statement is identical with our previous statement that only in special cases is it possible to discover operationally the numerical values of the corrected (true) probabilities; *generally*, only the ranges in which the corrected probabilities lie can be identified operationally (see Section 7, above). For the same reason, in the general case, only the *range* in which the rank of a Subset II act lies in Savage's Ordering can be identified operationally. We must therefore conclude that while the directly observable preference ordering we have described is complete and transitive even if the acts of Subset II are included,[10] the statement that behind this ordering there is a genuinely *probabilistic* complete ordering—i.e., a Savage Ordering—is not, strictly speaking, operationally meaningful. For individuals satisfying our three consistency requirements of semiprobabilistic behavior, the existence of definite ranks in a Savage Ordering—and thus the existence of true numerical probabilities—can be strongly supported by logical argument but not by operational procedure.

e) If choices were limited to acts belonging in Subset I, then numerical subjective probabilities and cardinally measurable utilities could be made to emerge simultaneously from the individual's behavior. In Savage's analysis, they generally emerge as two aspects of the same thing. In a semiprobabilistic theory, one must choose between two conceptions. We have implied that the standard process utility function (Subset I utility function) is of general validity—i.e., applies also to monetary wealth acquired in nonstandard processes—and that the Subset II prob-

---

[10] This follows from our First Requirement of consistency of semiprobabilistic behavior.

abilities become slanted in a systematic fashion. The reason for choosing this presentation—Version 1 presentation—was explained in the Introduction to the volume, and again in Sections 7 and 8, above. Here, we may add that if we had presented the problem along the lines of Version 2 rather than of Version 1, it still would have to be recognized that the observable behavior of an individual whom (in the terminology of Version 1) we call semiprobabilistic violates the Savage axioms. It would therefore at any event be necessary to bridge the gap between a Savage Ordering in the mind of such a decision maker and his directly observable ordering of acts.

APPENDIX TO CHAPTER 6

Randomization Theorems

The proofs contained in this Appendix tie in with our discussion of the Second Requirement of consistency of semiprobabilistic behavior. Here, we shall further explore the circumstances in which randomization makes it possible for an individual to rely on firmly held standard process probabilities instead of trusting his unstable and controversial degrees of belief. It will be shown that if the number of bets is large enough to justify practically exclusive concern with actuarial expectations, then randomization enables an individual who is faced with symmetrical bets to convert his subjective degrees of belief into firmly held standard process probabilities. That is to say, the more the conditions described in the preceding sentence are approximated, the more will the slanting inclinations of a rational individual decline (and gradually vanish). It will be shown also that the randomization argument fails for bets involving uncompensated asymmetries. Yet the validity of the argument for symmetrical bets sets limits to the extent of rationally justifiable downward slanting even in cases where the bet does involve uncompensated asymmetries. The relevant concept of symmetry was briefly explained on pages 150–51, above, and a formal definition of the concept will be given on page 167.

A. *The Symbols*

E_x means an event generated by a nonstandard process (e.g., stock exchange event, the drawing of red or black from an urn of uncertain composition, etc.).

$\sim E_x$ means the complement of E_x.

E_s means a standard process event (e.g., heads or tails with a practically fair coin).

$\sim E_s$ means the complement of E_s.

$P(E_x)$, $P(E_s)$, etc., mean the true or genuine probabilities (degrees of belief) assigned to these events.

M_r means the mathematical expectation of utility from a randomized bet on E_x or $\sim E_x$.

B. The Concept of Successful Randomization

You are given a choice between acquiring the utility gain $U(E_x)$ if E_x happens or acquiring $U(\sim E_x)$ if $\sim E_x$ happens. That is to say, you may opt either for a prize which is contingent on E_x or for one that is contingent on $\sim E_x$. In this sense, you may "bet" on one of these two events. The argument of the Appendix will relate to such binary choices, but extension of the argument to problems of multiple choice presents no difficulty.

You will be offered many options (prizes), but each of these will relate to a different instance in which E_x or $\sim E_x$ happens. In other words, in our discussion of randomization, we assume the existence of classes of events, each member of which is designated by E_x or $\sim E_x$, respectively.

On the basis of your probabilities, your mathematical expectation of utility gain would be:

$$P(E_x)\, U(E_x) \quad \text{or} \quad P(\sim E_x)\, U(\sim E_x)$$

whichever of the two expressions is greater; or if the two expressions are equal, either of the two defines your expected utility gain, i.e., your mathematical expectation of the utility gain for a single option.

You are worried about the possibility that in retrospect, after you have committed yourself to a bet, $P(E_x)$ and $P(\sim E_x)$ will not seem to be the plausible probabilities of E_x and $\sim E_x$. Even now, these probabilities seem unconvincing to others. After having acquired further information, you may arrive at the conclusion that events such as E_x tend to happen with a probability of $P(E_x) + l$, and events such as $\sim E_x$ with a probability of $P(\sim E_x) - l$, where l could turn out to be *positive or negative*. In retrospect, your probabilistic expectation of the utility gain will then seem wrong to you. If you should be unable to overcome these misgivings, then your decision weights for E_x and $\sim E_x$ will not be $P(E_x)$ and $P(\sim E_x)$, but will be derived from these probabilities by slanting. But you wish to explore whether your misgivings could not be overcome by randomization. In an attempt to randomize, it is your objective to generate E_s and $\sim E_s$ events with probabilities such that $P(E_s) = P(E_x)$ and $P(\sim E_s) = P(\sim E_x)$, and to adopt a randomization rule for deciding whether to bet on E_x or on $\sim E_x$ such that your mathematical expectation of the utility gain for each option should be

$$P(E_s)\, U(E_x) \quad \text{or} \quad P(\sim E_s)\, U(\sim E_x)$$

whichever is greater; or if the two expressions are equal, either of the two foregoing magnitudes should be the value of the mathematical expectation of your utility gain, an expectation which should at any event remain unchanged (convincing) in retrospect even if you arrive at the conclusion that the probability of the occurrence of E_x and that of the occurrence of $\sim E_x$ are different from $P(E_x)$ and $P(\sim E_x)$, respectively. Your randomization will be considered successful if you achieve this objective.

The foregoing implies that for no option can a randomization rule raise your expected utility gain beyond what that gain would be on the basis of your $P(E_x)$ and $P(\sim E_x)$, except that randomization substitutes firmly held standard process probabilites for the unstable $P(E_x)$ and $P(\sim E_x)$ terms. Aside from this substitution, randomization can give you for each option *at best* the same expected utility gain (M_r) which you have on the basis of your unstable subjective probabilities. This, I think, is self-evident, but you may convince yourself of the proposition by looking at equation 1, below, and by recalling what your expected utility gain would be for a single option without randomization (see above). Successful randomization performs for you the service of giving you for each option the same expected utility gain which you would have without randomization, and of giving you this expected utility gain on the basis of firmly held standard process probabilities. Your objective is to randomize successfully in this particular sense.

C. The Proposition and Its Proof

Proposition. You cannot achieve your objective unless the symmetry condition $P(E_x)\, U(E_x) = P(\sim E_x)\, U(\sim E_x)$ is satisfied. The proof is the following.

We shall first take it for granted that if you can find a successful rule of randomization, then—given $P(E_x) = P(E_s), P(\sim E_x) = P(\sim E_s)$ —this rule will prescribe to you betting on E_x with probability $P(E_s)$, and on $\sim E_x$ with probability $P(\sim E_s)$. This proposition sounds convincing, but it may not be entirely self-explanatory; hence, its validity, too, will be proved in what follows. On the assumption concerning probabilities of betting on E_x and on $\sim E_x$, we obtain for your expected utility of the randomized prospect of each option

$$M_r = P(E_s) \cdot P(E_x) \cdot U(E_x) + P(\sim E_s) \cdot P(\sim E_x) \, U(\sim E_x) \qquad (1)$$

It is a necessary condition of successful randomization that if in the first term of the sum appearing in equation 1, you change $P(E_x)$ to $P(E_x) + l$, and in the second term of that sum you change $P(\sim E_x)$ to $P(\sim E_x) - l$, then M_r should remain unchanged. This necessary condition is satisfied if and only if

$$P(E_s) \, U(E_x) = P(\sim E_s) \, U(\sim E_x) \qquad (2)$$

This latter necessary condition is identical with the symmetry condition which we proposed to prove, namely, with

$$P(E_x) \, U(E_x) = P(\sim E_x) \, U(\sim E_x) \qquad (3)$$

If equations 2 and 3 are satisfied, then, through randomization, you satisfy also the sufficient condition expressed in the final sentence of Section B above, namely:

$$M_r = P(E_s) \, U(E_x) = P(\sim E_s) \, U(\sim E_x) \qquad (4)$$

Equation 3 expresses the absence of uncompensated (or of essential) asymmetries. Any possible asymmetry between $P(E_x)$ and $P(\sim E_x)$ must be compensated by the reverse asymmetry between $U(E_x)$ and $U(\sim E_x)$. Otherwise the randomization cannot be successful.

Two remarks need to be added. Equation 4 expresses successful randomization if and only if $P(E_s) = P(E_x)$, and $P(\sim E_s) = P(\sim E_x)$, as was assumed. If you had bet on E_x with a probability other than $P(E_s)$, and on $\sim E_x$ with a probability other than $P(\sim E_s)$, then, in equations 1 and 2, these other probabilities would have appeared instead of $P(E_s)$ and $P(\sim E_s)$. In this case, equation 3 would not have followed from equation 2, and equation 4 would not imply the essential conclusion that the randomized bet gives the same mathematical expectations as would have been obtained with $P(E_x)$ and $P(\sim E_x)$. Successful randomization requires that in equation 1 the terms $P(E_s)$ and $P(\sim E_s)$ should not be replaced by other terms. Therefore, it requires those probabilities of betting on E_x and $\sim E_x$ which we have assumed.

The second reminder that needs to be added is the following: In Chapter 6, it was argued that in the circumstances in which successful randomization (as defined in this Appendix) is possible, failure to randomize—i.e., slanting instead of randomization—clearly violates a requirement of consistency *if and only if* the decision maker bets on a long sequence of events of the E_x type. Only in this case can he be said to come arbitrarily close to incoherence if he slants, instead of relying on his genuine subjective probabilities and randomizing (pages 148–51, above).

We may summarize the content of our four equations in a simple sentence: In any option, bet on E_x when E_s happens, and bet on $\sim E_x$ when $\sim E_s$ happens, making $P(E_s) = P(E_x)$ and $P(\sim E_s) = P(\sim E_x)$; *if* you observe this rule, and *if* the symmetry condition $P(E_x) \, U(E_x) = P(\sim E_x) \, U(\sim E_x)$ is satisfied, then and only then will your randomization be successful. Given these assumptions, the necessary and sufficient conditions of Section B, above are met. You may want to make use of *any* randomization opportunities which satisfy these conditions; and you come arbitrarily close to incoherence in the decision—theoretical sense if *in a sufficiently long sequence of trials* you slant instead of making use of such opportunities (provided they are available).

D. *Limits of Rational Slanting in Asymmetrical Situations*

You are faced with given monetary pay-offs for E_x and $\sim E_x$. The utility pay-offs $U(E_x)$ and $U(\sim E_x)$ correspond to these monetary pay-offs. Your subjective probabilities are $P(E_x)$ and $P(\sim E_x)$. Assume that $P(E_x) \, U(E_x) > P(\sim E_x) \, U(\sim E_x)$, from which it follows that the ratio of $P(E_x)$ to $P(\sim E_x)$ *exceeds* the ratio of $U(\sim E_x)$ to $U(E_x)$. For asymmetrical bets the inequality can be postulated in this form without loss of generality because it clearly does not matter whether the favored alternative is called E_x or $\sim E_x$.

Were it not for your feelings of discomfort caused by the instability of your $P(E_x)$ and $P(\sim E_x)$ appraisals, you would surely bet on E_x. However, you may not be able to get rid of these feelings of uneasiness, and the postulated asymmetry prevents you from randomizing successfully in the sense of substituting standard process probabilities for your subjective probabilities without reducing your expected utility below $P(E_x) \, U(E_x)$.

Say that

$$\frac{P(E_x)}{P(\sim E_x)} = r_1, \quad \frac{U(\sim E_x)}{U(E_x)} = r_2, \text{ where } r_1 > r_2$$

so that you *could* randomize successfully if the ratio of your $P(E_x)$ to your $P(\sim E_x)$ were r_2 rather than r_1. Note that actually to you

$$P(E_x) = \frac{r_1}{r_1 + 1}, \quad P(\sim E_x) = \frac{1}{r_1 + 1}$$

Note also that if you made the concession of reducing the subjective probability of E_x on which you would be betting, and of raising the subjective probability of $\sim E_x$ against which you would be betting, to the following *modified* terms:

$$P_m(E_x) = \frac{r_2}{r_2 + 1}, P_m(\sim E_x) = \frac{1}{r_2 + 1}$$

then, through randomization, you *could* indeed substitute standard process probabilities for these P_m terms without further loss of expected utility. This is because

$$\frac{P_m(E_x)}{P_m(\sim E_x)} = \frac{U(\sim E_x)}{U(E_x)} = r_2$$

and hence

$$P_m(E_x)\, U(E_x) = P_m(\sim E_x)\, U(\sim E_x)$$

You can now generate E_s and $\sim E_s$ with the proviso that $P(E_s) = P_m(E_x)$ and $P_m(\sim E_s) = P_m(\sim E_x)$, and you can bet on E_x when E_s happens and on $\sim E_x$ when $\sim E_s$ happens. This will give you for each bet an expected utility equal to that which you would have on the basis of $P_m(E_x)$ and $P_m(\sim E_x)$, and randomization will give you this expected utility on the basis of equivalent standard process probabilities. You can randomize successfully if you talk yourself into the appraisals $P_m(E_x)$ and $P_m(\sim E_x)$, although—given the pay-offs with which you are confronted—you cannot randomize successfully for your $P(E_x)$ and $P(\sim E_x)$.

It follows that aside from the small-sample qualification developed on pages 148–51, above, you should not slant your $P(E_x)$ below $P_m(E_x)$. Slanting down to $P_m(E_x)$ would involve a reduction of your $P(E_x)$ in the following proportion: $\dfrac{r_2(r_1 + 1)}{r_1(r_2 + 1)}$, i.e., *to* this expression times your original $P(E_x)$.

If your feelings of uneasiness about $P(E_x)$ are not so great as to warrant downward-slanting fully in this proportion, then you will not randomize but will be sure to bet on E_x. If, however, the possibility of randomization sets for you the effective limit of the downward slanting applied to the probability of the event on which you consider placing your bet, then the foregoing considerations should determine the extent of your slanting. Given your downward-slanting inclinations for the events on which you stake your fortunes, you, of course, slant up the probability of the event $\sim E_x$ *against* which you would be betting aside from your randomization; but if you slant fully to the point where randomization would make further slanting irrational, then you will bet either on E_x or on $\sim E_x$, depending in each instance on what the randomization device tells you to do—and in this case, given the assumptions of large-sample models, you cannot be said to bet on one of the two events or against the other event, although even in this case you do act as if you had slanted down your $P(E_x)$ and had slanted up your $P(\sim E_x)$.

Assume that you do slant your $P(E_x)$ to $P_m(E_x)$ and that you do then randomize. Considering that $P_m(E_x) + P_m(\sim E_x) = 1$, the question might be asked how we can tell at all that your P_m terms are *slanted* probabilities. One way of making you disclose this is to face you with alternative pay-off ratios and to observe how, within certain limits (possibly wide ones), you adjust your modified $P(E_x)$ and $P(\sim E_x)$ to the given pay-off ratios in order to acquire the safety provided by randomization. If, on the other hand, you slant down and do not randomize, then the standard process probability equivalent of the decision weight you attach to E_x when you bet on E_x, and the standard process probability equivalent of the decision weight you attach to $\sim E_x$ when you bet on $\sim E_x$, will add up to less than unity. (These decision weights are P_u terms, as defined on page 147.)

A downward-slanting individual may be said to slant *up* the probabilities of the events *against which* he bets; but when we speak of upward-slanting behavior, then we mean the behavior of individuals who slant up the probabilities of the events *on which* they stake their fortunes. In the foregoing discussion, "you" were not such an individual, but such individuals do exist. These individuals prefer nonstandard process probabilities to standard process probabilities. They will not randomize; hence, randomization possibilities do not set a limit to the extent of such upward slanting. However, I believe that downward-slanting tendencies are much more common. Furthermore, there exist many individuals who, in the circumstances in which they were observed, do not seem to slant either way.

Chapter 7

APPLICATION TO
SPECIFIC PROBLEMS OF
ECONOMIC THEORY

(1) *Simple and Complex Judgments*

The slanting tendencies discussed in the preceding chapters can be taken into account in a general way by making allowances for the fact that the magnitude of the risk taker's surplus—a magnitude defined in Chapters 4 and 5—needs to be corrected for the character of the probability judgment from which the surplus was derived. In Chapters 4 and 5 the surplus was defined on purely probabilistic assumptions. As compared to positions contemplated in those chapters, a downward-slanting subject will lower the function of the weighted marginal utility of potential gain for various prospects, and he will raise the function of the weighted marginal utility of potential loss for these same prospects. Consequently, the equilibrium-determining functions of traditional economic theory will also be shifted. But the nature of these shifts will depend in each case on *which* of a great number of specific probability judgments is mainly responsible for the tenuousness of the over-all judgment. At this point, it is necessary to recognize that a probability judgment concerning the outcome of an economic process—say, of an investment that is being planned—is a complex judgment which reflects the sum total of a great many simple judgments. Differently expressed, the compound event to which the over-all judgment relates—say, the realized return's falling in any specified numerical range—results from a large number of events which need to be distinguished.

A person who believes that an act of investment should be associated with the prospect of alternative potential gains and losses carrying specific probabilities knows that he is implying various probabilities for many simple events which he is not even capable of listing completely. However, he can go some way toward decomposing the compound event. He can pose to himself the question what probabilities he wishes to assign to various input prices and product prices, to the competence and the efficiency of various individuals, perhaps to the characteristics of various kinds of equipment, etc. No individual can go to the extreme limit of such decomposition; and all reasonable individuals must be aware of the fact that whenever they go one step further, they are likely to discover that the previous, more aggregative judgment needs to be revised in order to assure consistency of the whole system of judgments. Therefore the slanting inclinations of a semiprobabilistic subject are likely to be stronger in circumstances involving complex rather than simple judgments.

The conventional equilibrium-determining functions of economic theory invariably imply judgments about highly compound events. The question of why and how an individual slants his expectations concerning these functions calls for examining some of the simpler appraisals of which the complex appraisal is made up. The question calls for distinguishing between uncertainties attaching to different kinds of simple judgments.

We shall use three well-known problems of economic theory for illustration.

(2) *Profit Maximization and Average Cost Pricing*

In the theory of the firm the conventional MR-MC[1] intersection marks the maximization of money profits. However, the analytical framework we are developing in the present volume strongly suggests that the maximization of the mathematical expectations of money profits does not usually involve the maximization of the mathematical expectations of utility. This is because decision makers ordinarily do not act as if they had linear utility functions. I am implying here that even if the financial consequences of the decision are borne largely by others, the decision maker may still be viewed as assigning utilities to alternative potential outcomes. As long as he behaves in accordance with some utility function, it is a matter of no importance whether we interpret his behavior as being guided by his own utility function of gains that go largely to others, or as being based on his appraisal of the utility functions of the beneficiaries. We prefer the former to the latter way of looking at the matter. But at any event, the concept of the utility function remains significant, even if ownership is separated from management. The utility function is very unlikely to be linear.

Therefore the profit-maximization principle should not be interpreted as applying to the maximization of *money* profits. As was argued

---

[1] *MR* stands for marginal revenue, *MC* for marginal cost.

in Chapters 4 and 5, a purely probabilistic subject maximizes expected utility, i.e., he maximizes his risk taker's surplus, and the algebraic treatment on pages 120–23 makes it clear in what way the maximization of this magnitude differs from the maximization of money profits. Semiprobabilistic subjects will deviate from the principles developed in Chapters 4 and 5, since they will slant some of their probabilities. Yet, we shall begin by illustrating graphically the difference between the *MR-MC* intersection and the point of execpted utility maximization for *purely probabilistic* decision makers.

Figure 7 relates to an enterprise. The average cost curve of the enterprise is exceedingly unlikely to be horizontal in all ranges. For the long run, this is a consequence of scale effects, and for the short run a consequence of the hyperbolic shape of the function of average fixed costs (and sometimes a consequence also of other factors). Even if the individual shareholder in the enterprise is faced with constant money returns to the scale *of his individual investment*, the management of the enterprise must not disregard the slope of the average cost curve because, by setting the level of operations appropriately, it can shift up the level of the constant money returns for the individual shareholder to the maximum possible extent (see page 135). Figure 7 shows a U-shaped average total cost curve for the enterprise (ATC). This curve, as here interpreted, expresses the decision maker's mathematical expectation of the average total cost for each potential output level. For the present purpose, it is convenient to use a short-run analytical apparatus, in the sense of interpreting costs as the sum of fixed and variable costs.

Figure 7 includes also a downward-sloping demand curve for the product of the enterprise (DD'). This is here to be conceived of as the mathematical expectation of average revenue for each potential output level, i.e., as the sum of the probabilistically weighted potential values of the average revenue for each output. The MR curve shows the first derivative, with respect to output, of the mathematical expectation of aggregate revenue; and the MC curve shows the first derivative, with respect to output, of the mathematical expectation of aggregate cost.

Furthermore, Figure 7 includes a curve defined as the marginal utility surplus (MUS). This latter marginal function is derived for any potential output level in the following way.

Express for any given output the algebraic sum of the probabilistically weighted utility gains which may accrue at each output level, and differentiate this "risk taker's ex ante surplus" (as defined in Chapters 4 and 5) with respect to output. The implied functional relations are (a) the von Neumann–Morgenstern utility function, with the aid of which all potential money gains and losses at each output level are transformed into their utility equivalents; and (b) the probability of realizing each of these utilities at any output level (so that we can sum these probabilistically weighted utilities for each output and differentiate the sum with respect to ouput).

The equilibrium output is determined by the intersection of the *MUS* curve with the abscissa, that is, by the condition that $MUS = 0$.[2]

[2] The following is suggested as a method for locating the output at which the *MUS* curve assumes the value zero (i.e., intersects with the abscissa). Let us make the simplifying assumption that it is possible to associate with each potential output an amount x, to be regarded as the stake. The meaning of this is that x is the maximum amount which the enterprise could conceivably lose at that output level. A different x corresponds to each potential output. Any amount the firm might potentially lose at output x may be expressed as mx, where $0 \leq m \leq 1$. Any amount the firm might potentially gain can be expressed as nx, where $n \geq 0$. The firm will either gain nx or lose mx. If, now, the probability distribution of the random variables n and m were regarded as independent of x, then the problem would become identical with that described for continuous distributions in n. 2, p. 121, and in n. 4, p. 122. The condition $MUS = 0$ could then be defined by the equality of the two *marginal* functions formulated in those footnotes. We shall, indeed, define $MUS = 0$ by the equality of two marginal functions—the equality of the weighted marginal utility of potential gains with the weighted marginal disutility of potential losses—but these functions will be formulated somewhat differently than they were in the footnotes to which we have referred, because in the present context we need to take account of the fact that the probability of any gain factor n becoming the relevant one, and of any loss factor m becoming the relevant one, depends not only on the magnitude of n and of m but also on the magnitude of x. Hence the probability distributions in question are not $f_g(n)$ and $f_l(m)$, as was the case in the two footnotes, but $f_g(n|x)$ and $f_l(m|x)$; both f_g and f_l will be assumed differentiable with respect to x.

The weighted aggregate utility of the potential gains then becomes:

$$\int_0^\infty U(nx) \; f_g \; (n|x) \; dn \quad . \; . \; . \; . \; . \; . \; . \; . \; . \; . \; . \; . \; . \quad (1)$$

and the weighted aggregate disutility of the potential losses becomes:

$$\int_0^1 - U \; (-mx) \; f_l \; (m|x) \; dm \quad . \; . \; . \; . \; . \; . \; . \; . \; . \; . \; . \quad (2)$$

Maximization of the difference between equation 1 and equation 2 requires the equality of two marginal functions (derivatives with respect to x). That is to say, the marginal condition is:

$$\int_0^\infty [nU'(nx)f_g(n|x) + U(nx)\frac{\partial f_g}{\partial x}]dn = \int_0^1 [mU'(-mx)f_l(m|x) - U(-mx)\frac{\partial f_l}{\partial x}]dm$$

At the margin of the investment, there is no additional net utility gain, but the intramarginal region does carry a net utility gain (which would be zero only in the limiting case of the decision maker's indifference between producing the utility-maximizing output and not producing any output at all).

The problem is to solve for the value of x (and indirectly for that of output) which satisfies the marginal equality. In the graph in Figure 7, there is only one such value. In the case of multiple equilibria (Chapter 5), there are several such values because *MUS*, after having descended in the negative range, could become positive again, and then negative again, etc. The second-order condition is satisfied only where *MUS* intersects with the abscissa from above. The global maximum is at that intersection where the aggregate utility surplus is the greatest.

FIGURE 7

EQUILIBRIUM OF THE FIRM

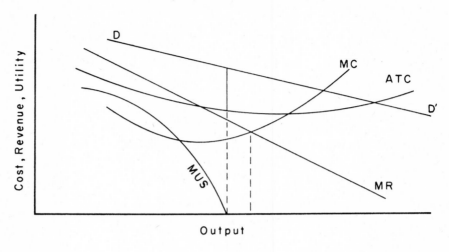

For a decision maker with monotonically decreasing von Neumann–Morgenstern marginal utility, this output is smaller than that corresponding to the *MR-MC* intersection. The graph in Figure 7 was drawn for such an individual. Since for any output the firm expects to charge the price indicated by the *DD'* curve, the expected monetary profit margin per unit of output of this particular firm is measured by the vertical stretch shown in Figure 7—a stretch connecting *DD'* with *ATC*.

Say that the graph is drawn so as to apply to a purely probabilistic decision maker. If, now, the identical decision maker should acquire *downward-slanting* (semiprobabilistic) inclinations, and if he therefore should weight his potential revenues and costs by correspondingly slanted decision weights, then the intersection of the so-weighted *MR* and *MC* curves will shift to the left. The intersection of *MUS* with the abscissa will also shift to the left.

The way in which semiprobabilistic behavior shifts these points depends on which elements of the complex probability judgment concerning net revenue are particularly strongly slanted. It is, for example, obvious that the leftward shift of the *MR-MC* intersection and of the intersection of *MUS* with the abscissa will usually be different, depending on (*a*) whether the slant expresses itself in a habit of acting as if for *each* potential output the expected price were *x* per cent lower than mathematical expectations or (*b*) whether the slant expresses itself in a habit of acting as if for *some* potential outputs (about which expectations are rather confident) the expected price were merely x per cent lower and as if for other outputs the expected price were lower by a greater margin. This, in turn, depends on which of his hypotheses the decision maker regards as straightforward and which as elusive in various degrees. Other things equal, downward slanting of any kind reduces, of course, the amount of investment, as indeed decreasing marginal utility also does. But pooling arrangements and diversification in general may and do weaken this effect very considerably (see Chapter 5).

Operational tests for discovering the presence of slanting were discussed earlier in this volume. Here, I should like to call attention to the fact that the usual description of industrial and commercial pricing practices possesses certain implications with respect to the problem just discussed.

In the late 1930's and thereafter, several economists expressed the view that it is rather usual for business management to describe its price policies as policies of "average cost pricing." It was maintained that business typically interprets the price it charges as made up of average total cost—or of average variable cost—*and* of a profit margin per unit of output. This was said to be a rather usual description of pricing practices not only in public-relations-minded statements of corporate management but also in internal deliberations of firms. More recently, some students of this problem—James S. Earley (**12**) of the University of Wisconsin is a prominent illustration[3]—have argued that in the thirties and the forties, economists discussing business policies overstressed this point, in that business policies seem to be influenced quite a bit by the *marginalist* outlook, which our profession rightly considers convincing. This is very likely true. Nevertheless, it is very difficult to avoid the conclusion that businessmen are mixing some degree of the *average* cost pricing attitude into their profit-maximizing (i.e., essentially marginalist) considerations. One is apt to arrive at this conclusion, because *per unit margins*, i.e., differences between prices and average costs, clearly belong among the relationships which play a large role in business thinking, and in statements about prospective business results. Formulas pointing to average cost pricing do not by any means give a good *general* description of business practices, but these formulas do appear to describe an aspect of reality. How should this aspect be interpreted?

There has existed a tendency among economic theorists to make sense of the "average cost plus profit margin" principle by toying with the

---

[3] See his articles in the June, 1955, issue of the *Journal of Political Economy*, and in the March, 1956, issue of the *American Economic Review*.

assumption that cost conditions and demand elasticity assumptions are frequently such as to make a *constant* percentage profit margin per unit of output consistent with the maximization of aggregate profits. This kind of reasoning does not rely on probability theory but proceeds through the following steps: It can be shown that if in each period the average variable cost is the same for all outputs (even though the level of the horizontal line in question may change), *and* if the demand curves of successive periods are assumed to have the same elasticity in the neighborhood of the equilibrium point (even though the demand curves may shift), then the maximization of aggregate profits requires adding to average variable cost a profit margin per unit of output which is uniquely determined by the assumed demand elasticity. This follows from the fact that if AR stands for average revenue (i.e., for the price buyers are willing to pay), and MR stands for marginal revenue, and ϵ for the elasticity of demand, then $MR = AR\left(1 - \dfrac{1}{\epsilon}\right)$; *and* if the conventional profit-maximization postulate is now satisfied, so that $MR = MC$, where MC stands for marginal cost, then we may also write $MC = AR\left(1 - \dfrac{1}{\epsilon}\right)$; *and* if the assumption concerning horizontal average variable cost curves is satisfied, so that $MC = AVC$, where AVC stands for average variable cost, then we may *also* write $AVC = AR\left(1 - \dfrac{1}{\epsilon}\right)$. The last of these equations gives us the ratio of price (AR) to AVC as a magnitude equal to $\dfrac{\epsilon}{\epsilon - 1}$ for the maximizer of aggregate profits.

On these particular assumptions the statement "I am going to charge AVC plus a profit margin" *may* acquire the meaning "I am a conventional profit maximizer; and as such, I am going to charge AVC plus a percentage markup the size of which will stay unchanged as long as my estimate of the demand elasticity in the relevant range does not change much."

This kind of reconciliation of average cost pricing with profit maximization requires further assumptions if the practice is described as one of adding the profit margin onto average *total* cost (ATC) rather than onto average variable cost (AVC). This is because the foregoing reconciliation relies heavily on the assumption that AVC is the same for all outputs and that therefore $AVC = MC$, so that constancy of the percentage margin over MC is equivalent to constancy of the percentage margin over AVC. But in the circumstances in which the AVC function is a horizontal line, the *ATC* function, as usually interpreted, has a downward slope, and the margin over *ATC* is not a constant. Hence the assumption on which the foregoing reasoning relied to reconcile average cost pricing with profit maximization serves distinctly less well if by average cost we mean average *total* cost (*ATC*) rather than average *variable* cost (*AVC*). On the other hand, it may be argued that some firms seem to have the habit of treating various constituents of their fixed costs as if these were variable—this is sometimes done by charging more or less of these fixed costs to one period or to another (or to one activity or another) roughly in proportiton to the output of that period (or of that activity)—and the difference between charging markup over *AVC* and charging markup over *ATC* is, of course, reduced if important constituents of fixed costs are treated as if they were variable.

In an attempt to appraise the pros and cons, I should say that the whole line of reasoning which reconciles average cost pricing with the maximization of aggregate profits by assuming horizontal cost curves and constant demand elasticity is at best *moderately* convincing. I do believe that the reasoning throws some light on what goes on in the minds of decision makers in specific situations. But the assumptions on which the reasoning is based are *much less generally valid* than is the proposition that in the thinking of the business community, some considerable degree of average cost analysis (emphasis on per unit margins) gets mixed in with considerations of marginalist character.

I should like to suggest that this combination of average cost and marginalist thinking can be interpreted as resulting from a downward-slanting tendency. The per unit margin may be said to measure the maximum extent of the downward shift of the demand function, as compared to mathematical expectations, which could occur in the neighborhood of the actual output *without* causing profits to be negative; alternatively, the same margin may be said to express the maximum extent of the upward shift of the average cost function which could occur without causing profits to be negative; or the margin may be said to express some combination of these two barely tolerable shifts. Any management with a downward-slanting tendency is likely to have unfavorable deviations from mathematical expectations in mind, most of which are capable of being expressed as such shifts of the demand and cost functions. Any pronounced downward-slanting tendency will therefore lead to emphasizing the need for adequate per unit margins—i.e., for per unit margins that are sufficient in view of the existing risks—in addition to acknowledging the obvious interest of the decision maker in high aggregate profits. Or to express the same proposition differently, the mere fact of downward slanting makes a management *deviate* from purely probabilistic profit maximization *in the direction* of higher per unit margins, and this inclination may well tend to be expressed by stressing the need for adding an adequate per unit margin onto average total cost. Even aside from diminishing marginal utility, such policies would make the firm land somewhere between what in a purely probabilistic construction would be aggregate money profit maximization and per unit margin maximization. Diminishing marginal utility may frequently cause a deviation from aggregate money profit maximization in the same direction. (Note that the point of per unit profit maximization can never be located to the right of aggregate money profit maximization.)

(3) *Joint Maximization and Reformulated Cournotesque Results in Oligopoly*

In his significant contribution of 1838, Augustin Cournot **(8)** described an oligopoly equilibrium which is based on the assumption that each oligopolist takes the quantity of output of all his rivals as given— i.e., as given independently of the quantity *he* will decide to produce— and then produces the output which maximizes his own aggregate profits for these *given* outputs of his rivals. Assuming such behavior, Cournot gave a demonstration of a tendency toward oligopoly equilibrium and of the stability of that equilibrium: On Cournot's assumptions the outputs of the firms return to the equilibrium level if some accidental disturbance leads one or the other producer to place an output of different size on the market. The equilibrium level which establishes itself is such that the quantity of output produced by any firm A, given the actual output of any firm B, is that quantity which B took as given when deciding to produce its output.

On Cournot's assumptions the equilibrium so described *is* stable, but it is not clear why Cournot's firms should want to establish this equilibrium. After all, it should be perfectly obvious to each producer that the output his rivals will produce is not independent of the output *he* will produce. He himself adjusts the quantity of his own output in a profit-maximizing fashion to the output of the others. Why should he be unaware of the fact that others do likewise?

By making unrealistic assumptions about their rivals, Cournot's oligopolists appear to be moving into a position which is inferior for all concerned to the position they could attain by maximizing the joint profit and by sharing the maximized net gains. Various institutional obstacles might, of course, stand in the way of joint maximization; and therefore, reasonable theories of joint maximization would have to recognize the existence of constraints and of qualifications. But even a theory of qualified joint maximization would have to rest on the assumption that all firms recognize the mutual interdependence of their output decisions. In Cournot's presentation the oligopolists show no awareness of this.

Still, Cournotesque tendencies have been observed in the real world. The details of Cournot's model are, of course, unrealistic; but if, by *Cournotesque results*, we mean results developing from a tendency of oligopolists to take as given (i.e., to regard as parameters) the values of certain variables which are controlled by rival producers, then, in realistic analysis, we must surely not rule out such Cournotesque results. Especially the behavior of oligopolists *with respect to significant nonprice variables* (product variation, advertising, etc.) often appears to have Cournotesque characteristics rather than those of joint maximization. This statement is based on general, common-sense observation; but one might also refer to game experimental results which point to Cournotesque behavior in certain circumstances and to joint maximizing behavior in others.

Cournotesque tendencies can be explained satisfactorily only in a model in which the oligopolists do not misjudge each others' intentions—as they appear to do in the original Cournot analysis—i.e., in which each oligopolist can tell himself, in effect: "I assign a high probability to its being reasonable for me to act *as if* I believed that the values of the variables of my rivals are given magnitudes (regardless of how I adjust to these values), because the equilibrium which establishes itself in the event of such behavior is likely to be more favorable from my point of view than are the conditions which will exist in the market if I try to earn higher profits." To be suitable for such analysis, a model must allow for more strategies than one—i.e., for more than the Cournotesque strategy of individual maximization given the values of the rivals' variables—*and*, at least at some point, the model must make room for probabilistic considerations (risk). I shall present a simple piece of analysis which takes account of two strategies for a duopoly, and in which Cournotesque results become possible if and only if we go beyond a first approximation by introducing subjective-probabilistic considerations.

As my point of departure, I shall use Matrix 2, which is taken from Martin Shubik's *Strategy and Market Structure* (**50**), and the like of which was used extensively also in R. Duncan Luce and Howard Raiffa's *Games and Decisions* (**33**). Matrix 2 was originally constructed for the discussion of the special game theoretical problem called the "prisoner's dilemma," but the model is of much wider applicability.[4]

MATRIX 2

DUOPOLISTIC PAY-OFF MATRIX:
A TWO-PERSON, NONZERO-SUM GAME OF STRATEGY

	B Uses Strategy I	*B Uses Strategy II*
A uses Strategy I	*A* earns 3 *B* earns 3	*A* earns —1 *B* earns 4
A uses Strategy II	*A* earns 4 *B* earns —1	*A* earns 1 *B* earns 1

LEGEND: The meaning of Matrix 2 can be illustrated by the statement that if, for example, participant *A* uses Strategy II and participant *B* uses Strategy I, then *A* earns 4 and *B* earns —1. To each outcome, there corresponds a double entry. The first of these will be described in the text as 3, 3; the one below it as 4, —1, etc.

Matrix 2 includes an outcome possessing stability in Cournot's sense (the outcome 1, 1 resulting from both participants' using Strategy II). This is the outcome which establishes itself if each participant acts as if the other's choice of strategy were uninfluenced by his own choice of strategy. Starting from (say) 3, 3, there would be a movement toward 1, 1, either via 4, —1 *or* via —1, 4. At 1, 1, neither participant would engage in any further change of strategy. And yet the Cournotesque outcome 1, 1 is *strongly jointly dominated by* another outcome (3, 3, resulting from both participants' using Strategy I).

An outcome or a set of outcomes (alternatively viewed, a strategy or a set of strategies) is said to be strongly jointly dominant if all other outcomes are worse for every one of the participants; if the word "strongly" is omitted, then joint dominance means that all other outcomes are worse for at least one participant without being more favorable for any. In our matrix, 3, 3 is strongly jointly dominant if 4, —1 and —1, 4 are disregarded; and as long as we assume perfect foresight concerning the pay-offs associated with alternative pairs of strategies and assume ability to change strategies instantaneously (without lags), the two outcomes 4, —1 and —1, 4 *should* be disregarded, because neither participant can be made to accept —1 (or, indeed, to accept less than +1, of which he could assure himself by using Strategy II). Even on these assumptions

---

[4] The problem of the "prisoner's dilemma" may be described as follows: Each of two individuals under arrest may choose between the strategy of "confessing" and of "denying." (Say, "deny" is Strategy I of Matrix 2, and "confess" is Strategy II.) It is understood that if both deny, then each will be sentenced to one year; if one confesses and the other denies, then the individual who confesses will be sentenced to three months and the other to ten years; if they both confess, then each will be sentenced to eight years.

of certainty and laglessness, the outcome 3, 3 becomes merely one element in a jointly dominant *set* of outcomes if we wish to allow for the use of mixed strategies—i.e., of randomized mixes of Strategies I and II—because in this event, probabilistic mixes of 3, 3 with 4, −1 and with −1, 4 also will be included in the jointly dominant set. This is illustrated by Figure 8, which shows also that if we should decide to permit side payments (redistributions of the sum of pay-offs by agreement), *then* the jointly dominant set will be made up differently, namely, of 3, 3 and of pay-offs resulting from the redistributions of the maximum available sum (six units). But after demonstrating this, we may just as well limit ourselves to the pure strategies described by the pay-offs shown in Matrix 2; and in our present context, we need not go into the question of side payments either, since we are concerned with the merits and weaknesses of the Cournot point (1, 1), and it should now be clear that 1, 1 remains an inferior (jointly dominated) outcome at any event *as long as we assume certainty of the pay-offs for the strategies and laglessness of strategy changes.* If we limit ourselves to the pure strategy pay-offs shown in Matrix 2, then, on these assumptions of certainty and laglessness which make 4, −1 and −1, 4 inadmissible, the strongly jointly dominant outcome 3, 3 will be established.

FIGURE 8

DOMINANT SETS AND THE COURNOT POINT

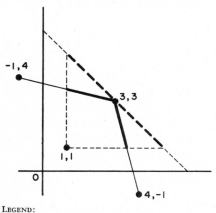

LEGEND:

Abscissa = *A*'s pay-off
Ordinate = *B*'s pay-off

The graph demonstrates the following: (1) Point 3, 3 strongly jointly dominates if the game is limited to pure strategies and no side payments are allowed (note that 4, −1 and −1, 4 are excluded because neither participant needs to accept −1). (2) The set expressed by the heavily drawn section of the fully drawn cornered line jointly dominates all other possibilities if mixed strategies are included but no side payments are allowed. (3) The set expressed by the heavily drawn section of the broken straight line (going through 3, 3) jointly dominates all other possibilities if side payments are allowed; the corresponding strategy is pure, since no mixed strategies are needed to get into the dominant set.

It remains true, of course, that the Cournotesque outcome 1, 1 (resulting from each participant's using Strategy II) has stability in Cournot's sense; in this particular matrix, it *happens to be true* also that the Cournot strategies are the maximin strategies of the participants, although Cournot equilibrium does not *generally* coincide with maximin. But the point is that, on the assumption of certainty and laglessness, the result of the preceding dominance analysis is relevant, and the Cournot-type stability analysis is irrelevant.

We have now arrived at a much more specific formulation of a proposition which a few pages back was stated in a general way, namely, of the proposition that it is unconvincing to derive Cournotesque equilibria simply by arguing that if for some strange reason each participant should believe that the strategy of the other remains uninfluenced by his own choice of strategy, then Cournotesque equilibria will become established and will be stable. In the real world, we do observe Cournotesque tendencies as well as joint maximizing tendencies; but further analysis is needed to explain why the instability (in Cournot's sense) of 3, 3 matters at all—i.e., why, in some circumstances, there actually does develop a tendency toward 1, 1. After all, why should A ever push from 3, 3 into 4, −1 if this will be followed by B's pushing from there into 1, 1? Or why should B ever push from 3, 3 into −1, 4 if this will be followed by A's pushing from there into 1, 1?

To explain this, we shall have to abandon the assumption of certainty and laglessness. We shall have to recognize that if a firm pushes from 3, 3 into 4, −1, or into −1, 4, then it is a matter of subjective-probabilistic appraisals *how long* it will take for the rival to get the duopoly into position 1, 1. Also, even if, for the sake of simplicity, we assume that the pay-offs are guaranteed for all combinations of stratgeies, we should at least leave room for uncertainty as to the length of time for which the validity of the pay-off matrix is effectively guaranteed. Thus the question of *timing* acquires significance, a question that our preceding dominance analysis disregarded.

We shall interpret our matrix in the following way: Strategy I means setting the values of one's own variables at a level such that the joint profit is maximized in the event that the rival sets his variables at the same level. Strategy II means setting the values of one's own variables at the individual profit-maximizing level, given the now-observed values of the rival's variables. Note that limitation of Matrix 2 to these two strategies implies a mutual understanding to the effect that each firm will react to the other's strategy according to an approved or permissible strategy as long as the other also does so. Limitation to two strategies involves, of course, far-reaching oversimplification—more than two strategies could be included in a model of the same general character—but it *is* essential to recognize that the number of strategies from among which oligopolists may freely choose at any time is frequently limited by mutual consent, and that the set of potential strategies frequently excludes the cutthroat strategy (very risky strategy) of incurring losses for the sake of hurting a rival and of thereby eliminating him or bringing him to terms.

Furthermore, it is essential to recognize that Strategy II—the Cournotesque strategy—frequently leads to satisfactory profits for all parties concerned and that among the strategies which possess this property, it lends itself to being regarded as the relatively least co-operative strategy. Indeed, the strategy taken in itself could even be regarded as outright nonco-operative, except for the fact that a degree of mutual understanding expresses itself even here in the limitation to specific kinds of strategy.

If joint maximization were to be assured, then not only would strategies other than I and II have to be excluded by mutual consent, but Strategy II also would have to be excluded. In some cases, it no doubt is excluded; but in other cases, it may be difficult to reach a tacit agreement on the exclusion of Strategy II from the permissible strategies. This is because *now*, or at some future time, each firm may want to assign an appreciable probability to a sufficiently long duration of the transition process from 3, 3 to 1, 1, that is, to a duration which on the way from 3, 3 to 1, 1 would enable it to make a substantial gain in location 4, -1 or in $-1, 4$; *or* each firm may be afraid that a tacit agreement which would limit the permissible strategies to Strategy I would *now*, or at some future time, be violated by the rival firm, since the rival firm might attach an appreciable probability to a sufficiently long duration of the transition process. The time element plays a decisive role in such considerations: The model expressed by Matrix 2 is entirely noncommittal about how long the firms stay in each location during a transition process. Driving the duopoly from 3, 3 to 1, 1 (via 4, -1 or via $-1, 4$) may be profitable, or may at some future time become profitable, for the firm in the driver's seat, even though 3, 3 is more favorable for both than 1, 1. Each firm is aware of this, and this frequently makes it impossible to exclude Strategy II from the permissible strategies.

The profits on the way from 3, 3 to 1, 1 will be transitional, but the duration of the transition is a matter of probabilistic appraisals. So is the duration of the conditions under which any pay-off may be confidently assumed in the event of mutual reliance on Strategy I, and under which any pay-off may be confidently assumed in the event of mutual reliance on Strategy II.

The statement that for these reasons, Strategy II is often included in the permissible strategies is of course not identical with the statement that Strategy II will actually be adopted. But in some cases, it will be adopted. Whether it will or will not—that is, whether 1, 1 or 3, 3 will tend to become established—depends on the *probabilistic appraisals of timing* and of slanting tendencies in various phases of the life history of an industry. These appraisals *may* be such as to result in a tendency toward 1, 1. The basic reason for this is that *if* the transition from higher to lower levels of co-operation promises sufficiently large and sufficiently long-lasting temporary profits to the initiator, then there will develop a tendency toward the least co-operative among the strategies of which it is still true that a descent to that strategy has a good chance of being, on balance, profitable to the firm initiating the transition. On the other hand, if a firm makes a first move toward a higher level of co-operation, then the transition period during which mutual adjustment has not yet been reached will be a period of losses rather than of temporary profits for the initiator.

The reality of Cournotesque tendencies can be explained in models which recognize the fact that in oligopolies the number of permissible strategies is limited and which call attention to the importance of the probabilistic appraisals determining whether the process just described is or is not touched off.

(4) Liquidity versus Risky Returns

In our earlier discussion, it was shown that on plausible assumptions concerning the shapes of utility functions, investors will usually find it attractive to go some way toward diversifying their portfolios. Any attempt to determine the desirable extent of diversification in general terms requires rather complex formulations, but even radically simplified models are useful for illustrating the nature of the problem.

Let us make the assumption that there are only two assets, namely, *cash* and the *security*. The security will yield a definite flow of interest without risk of default, and it is equally likely to bring capital gains of any magnitude as to bring capital losses of the same magnitude. Let us assume also that the utility function of the decision maker shows decreasing marginal utility throughout the relevant region, so that to him the security carries (in relation to cash) the advantage of guaranteed interest, on the one hand, but also the disadvantage of potential capital losses, on the other. These potential losses are actuarially offset by the potentiality of capital gains; but as a result of decreasing marginal utility, the potential losses weigh more heavily in the decision maker's mind than do the potential capital gains. Further, let us assume that the variance about the mean rate of return of the security—or the standard deviation which is the square root of this variance[5]—is an acceptable measure of dispersion, in the sense in which this decision maker regards dispersion as a disadvantage. The last of these assumptions implies either that the utility function is quadratic (in which case, higher moments than the second of the frequency distribution do not matter to this person), or that the specific probability distribution with which the decision maker is faced can be fully described by using the mean and the second moment about it (as is the case if the distribution is normal). The probability distribution to which we are referring is, of course, a *subjective* probability distribution concerning future prices of the security and hence concerning rates of capital gain and loss.

In a first approximation, we shall also assume that the decision maker plans for a fixed holding period of the security, although later we shall relax this particular assumption.

Having made these simplifying assumptions, we may replace the analytical framework used in Chapter 5 by the model which was developed in James Tobin's article, "Liquidity Preference as Behavior Towards Risk" **(52)**. Here, I shall also follow Tobin's algebraic notations with minor changes.

The portfolio of our individual will be described by the proportion of his assets which he decides to invest in the security. The total initial value of his assets is assumed as given; the proportion which he invests in the security is denoted by A_s.

Denote the rate of return of the portfolio by r_p, the rate of guaranteed interest on the security by i_s, and the rate of capital gains on the security by g. Then:

$$r_p = A_s(i_s + g) \quad \dots \dots \dots \dots \dots \dots \quad (1)$$

The "expected value" of g is zero—i.e., $E(g) = 0$—since the probability of realizing any positive g is by assumption actuarially offset by the equal probabilistic expectation of suffering a negative g of the same numerical value. Hence, for the expected value of r_p, we obtain:

$$E(r_p) = A_s i_s \quad \dots \dots \dots \dots \dots \dots \quad (2)$$

We denote the standard deviation (about the mean) of the rate of return of the portfolio as a whole—i.e., of r_p—by σ_p; and we denote the

---

[5] The variance in question is the second moment *about the mean*.

standard deviation of the rate of return of the security by σ_s. We may then write:

$$\sigma_p = A_s \sigma_s$$

or:

$$A_s = \frac{\sigma_p}{\sigma_s} \quad \ldots \ldots \ldots \ldots \ldots \quad (3)$$

From equations 2 and 3, we obtain:

$$E(r_p) = \frac{i_s}{\sigma_s} \sigma_p \quad \ldots \ldots \ldots \ldots \ldots \quad (4)$$

Equation 4 defines a linear market opportunity function. Plot on one axis—say, on the ordinate—$E(r_p)$ and on the other axis (abscissa) σ_p. Then, for a given i_s and a given σ_s—i.e., for given characteristics of the security—equation 4 describes a straight line which is the locus of the available pairs of $E(r_p)$ and σ_p. The decision maker can avail himself of *any one* of these alternative pairs by selecting the value of A_s accordingly, that is, by investing more or less of his assets in the security. The slope of this market opportunity line is $\frac{i_s}{\sigma_s}$. The line itself moves from the point of origin $[E(r_p) = 0, \sigma_p = 0]$, which stands for holding 100 per cent of the assets in cash, to points corresponding to increasingly high $E(r_p)$ *and at the same time* to increasingly high σ_p, i.e., to points standing for increasingly high security-cash ratios.

We have described the market opportunity line measuring σ_p on the abscissa and $E(r_p)$ on the ordinate. Following Tobin's presentation, we may now describe the indifference map of the decision maker in the same system. If the decision maker has monotonically decreasing marginal utility, then the following assumption is justified. In each point of the ordinate, there originates an indifference curve which slopes upward, thereby expressing the fact that a rising σ_p must be compensated by a rising $E(r_p)$ in order not to cause a decline in the preference level. The upward slope of the indifference curve will increase as we move to higher levels of σ_p—that is, the curves will be convex from below—thereby expressing the fact that more and more units of potential gain are needed to compensate for one *additional* unit of potential loss. The resulting family of indifference curves, along with a family of market opportunity lines, is portrayed in Figure 9. Given the characteristics of the security— i.e., given the value of i_s and that of σ_s—only one market opportunity line is valid, since the slope of any such line equals $\frac{i_s}{\sigma_s}$. But the whole family of indifference curves is needed for describing the tastes of a single decision maker.

FIGURE 9

PORTFOLIO SELECTION: PURELY PROBABILISTIC DECISION MAKER

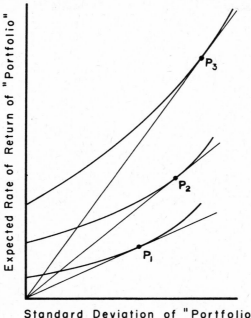

Standard Deviation of "Portfolio"

As we move up along any vertical line originating in a point on the abscissa, the preference level is increasing monotonically. As we move to the right along any horizontal line originating in a point on the ordinate, the preference level is decreasing monotonically. This property of the graph reflects the assumption of monotonically decreasing marginal utility, an assumption by which the possibility of multiple equilibria is excluded. On more general assumptions concerning possible shapes of the decision maker's utility function, the problem of multiple equilibria would have to be recognized, as was the case in Chapter 5 (page 127). Analysis based on these more general assumptions cannot limit itself to the use of indifference functions. The tangency of market opportunity lines with appropriately shaped indifference functions marks a local maximum, and if it cannot be taken for granted that the local maximum which we have found is a unique maximum, then finding the *maximum maximorum* requires comparing the amounts of utility provided at the various local maxima. This the indifference curve technique cannot perform, as, indeed, in Chapter 5, we could not have established our basic propositions with the aid of this technique. On the simplifying assumptions of our present analysis, we are assured of the uniqueness of any maximum which is pointed up by the tangency of a market opportunity line with an indifference curve; and hence, we may fully rely on Tobin's indifference map.

Assume, for the sake of illustration, that the security in which the decision maker may invest is characterized by a value of i_s and a value of σ_s such that our $\frac{i_s}{\sigma_s}$ is measured by the slope of the *lowest* of the three market opportunity lines in our graph. Then P_1 is the decision maker's optimum point. Further, if $\frac{i_s}{\sigma_s}$ were measured by the slope of the *middle* market opportunity line, then the optimum point would be P_2; if $\frac{i_s}{\sigma_s}$ were measured by the slope of the *highest* market opportunity line, then the optimum point would be P_3. Since the distance of each of these points from the axes measures the corresponding $E(r_p)$ and σ_p, respectively, we may, for any security with known i_s and σ_s, obtain A_s—i.e., the invested proportion of the total assets—from equation 2 (page 187).

We have now seen that the tools which Tobin uses for demonstrating these propositions can be developed from a purely probabilistic background if certain simplifying assumptions are made. The question arises whether these tools can be employed even if we formulate semiprobabilistic basic postulates. The answer is in the affirmative, but it needs to be pointed out that slanting inclinations of certain kinds will show in the slopes of the market opportunity lines, while other kinds of slanting inclinations will show in the shapes of the indifference curves.

For the sake of illustration, we shall consider a downward-slanting individual. He will proceed as if the probabilities of any outcome were smaller when he stakes his fortunes on that outcome than when he stakes his fortunes on its complement. This is because all the probabilities in question are interpersonally controversial and are unstable in the decision maker's mind, and the downward-slanting individual is disturbed more by losing on such probabilities than by not gaining on them.

In the model of Figure 9 the stream of *interest* (i_s) is guaranteed, i.e., is not subject to probabilistic appraisal. But the capital gains *are* subject to probabilistic appraisal, and the purely probabilistic apparatus depicted in the graph implies that $E(g) = 0$. The downward-slanting individual differs from a purely probabilistic one in that he underweights the positive ranges and overweights the negative ranges of the possible values of the capital gains. This manifestation of the slanting tendency shows in the slope of the *market opportunity line* rather than the shape of the *indifference curves* of Figure 9. The phenomenon in question is the equivalent of lower yield expectations as a result of the expectation of capital *losses* (as if i_s were lower).

This is all we need to say about the effect of slanting tendencies in the model expressed by Figure 9, as long as we persist in the simplifying assumption that the holding period of the security is fixed in advance (page 187). But what if, in a somewhat modified model, we take account of the fact that the individual assigns various probabilities to the prospect that he may have to sell at various dates, and to the prospect that he may be able to wait for a convenient date of liquidation without a sacrifice of important other objectives? In such a modified model a downward-slanting tendency expresses itself *also* in an inclination to overweight the probability that the security *will have to be sold at a time when its price is low*. I believe that in the real world, this may well be the most important manifestation of the downward-slanting tendency. Hypotheses bearing on the probability distribution of holding period durations are likely to be particularly elusive. A downward-slanting semiprobabilistic individual frequently proceeds as if there existed a high probability of his not being able to wait for a favorable time of liquidation. He slants downward the probability of his being able to choose his date of selling in such a way as not to be harmed by the fluctuations of the security (i.e., by the standard deviation σ_s). If he were selling the security short—or in some other way were acquiring an interest in its *low* price—then he would slant downward the probability of his being able to *buy* the security in such a way as not to be harmed by its fluctuations. Differently expressed, his probability judgments about the chances that the fluctuating security will be high or low in any one period become modified through an act of slanting in view of whether he would be appreciably hurt by a low or by a high price in that period, i.e., by whether we offer him a prize contingent on a high or on a low price of the security in any period we may select. This particular deviation from purely probabilistic norms expresses itself in the shape of the *indifference curves* in Figure 9. This second manifestation of the downward-slanting tendency leads to a *steepening* of the indifference curves. Any given standard deviation (σ_s) becomes more repelling to a downward-slanting individual (less repelling to an upward-slanting one).

Chapter 8

TOWARD ADMITTING
THE SUBJECTIVITY
OF JUDGMENT

The revival of interest in subjective-probabilistic think-ing and in its Bayesian corollary—or rather the emergence of modern equivalents of these—is of very recent origin. This development is quite likely to have a profound influence in many areas of scientific activity. I shall limit myself here to an attempt to appraise the prospective influence of this development with respect to three problems, and I shall do so from the point of view of an economist.

But workers in other fields will no doubt recognize the analogy existing between these problems and the ones they encounter. Indeed, while, in my present efforts, I have been guided mainly by an interest in a broadened version of the economic theory of profit maximization (see Section 3, below), it was unavoidable that I should reach over into other areas as well. Perhaps I should be apologetic about it; but on the other hand, these other areas cannot stay wholly reserved for the specialists who are most at home in them. These areas form a natural meeting ground for investigators with diverse specializations.

(1) Reduction of the Scope of Objectivistic Practices

In Chapter 2, Section 5, it was argued that in some circumstances the Bayesian complexities can be avoided, essentially because frequentist-objectivist procedures can be used to arrive at results no different from those to which Bayesian analysis would lead.

In particular, when a large sample of exchangeable events has been examined, and the likelihood ratios favor very strongly one of the hy-potheses (say, favor very strongly a narrow range around those specific parameter values which describe a hypothesis), we may simply wish to accept the hypothesis which the objective evidence favors as against all others that need to be distinguished in the given context. Under the appro-priate conditions, we should indeed be willing to proceed in this fashion. Sometimes, general familiarity with the nature of a decision problem and crude inspection of the data suggest that the necessary conditions of taking such a short cut without penalty are quite likely to be satisfied. Yet, even if this is so, we should still stay aware of the fact that we are using a short cut in a Bayesian framework, rather than get into the habit of using the short cut in cases where we do not really intend to go along with the implications of this timesaving and effortsaving device.

Avoidance of the Bayesian complexities is justified if we feel thoroughly convinced of the fact that the likelihood ratios, computed from the sample evidence, testify for one hypothesis strongly enough to beat any contrary asymmetries which our prior probabilities may show in favor of another hypothesis, and also to beat any contrary asymmetries which our utility assignments may exhibit in favor of the consequences of acts not supported by the likelihood findings. After giving this matter some thought, we may well decide on continued use of the objectivist procedure, but even if we do so, we should remember that a reasonable decision maker's betting odds on the course of action he takes depend on his prior probabilities and his utility assignments as well as on the sample evidence. This remains true regardless of how large the sample is. On the other hand, it should be recognized that in some decision problems the relevant question merely is whether the odds favor one or the other hypothesis very strongly; and in that event, it matters little whether the odds are one to 100 or one to 1,000.

At any rate, in the situations considered in the present section the decision maker should convince himself at least by an informal Bayesian exercise of whether for the specific purpose at hand he does or does not wish to rely on frequentist-objectivist methods. I believe that in some cases in which it is routine procedure to rely on them, one may well discover that on reflection the implications are not as convincing as they appear to be at first sight. For this reason, reporters of findings who draw conclusions from these should feel under obligation to explain and to justify in essentially Bayesian terms the implications of their objectivistic short cuts, unless it can be said in entirely good conscience that any reasonable person would be willing to go along with these implications. In economics, these cases are rather rare, because various decision makers may have appreciably different prior probabilities, and they may wish to make appreciably different utility assignments to the expected consequences of different courses of action.

Except in analysis the results of which will be used exclusively by the analyst himself, it should be considered a requirement to play into the hands of readers and listeners who may wish to substitute other prior probabilities and other utility assignments for ours (and whose slanting inclinations are likely to be different from those we may have). The spread of Bayesian attitudes may be expected to have a good influence in this regard.

(2) Reduction of Scope of the Rule-of-Thumb Subjectivism Implied in Significance Tests

The brand of rule-of-thumb subjectivism which in special circumstances provides a reasonably adequate check on the suitability of frequentist-objectivist short cuts is the brand we considered in Chapter 2, Sections 5 and 6 (rather than in Chapter 6). It is the brand which is characteristic of the conventional methods of performing tests of significance.

Say that we do *not* feel sufficiently convinced that likelihood ratios favor one hypothesis (i.e., favor the immediate parameter-value neighborhood of one of the hypotheses which are worth distinguishing from each other) *so strongly* as to give us the green light for an objectivistic short cut without further exploration. Our doubts may result* (*a*) from not being sure whether the objective evidence provided by some known sample does or does not point *with sufficiently great force* to the validity of that hypothesis which is relatively best supported by the sample; or (*b*) from having recently obtained from a sample an estimate of a parameter which, viewed superficially, does not clearly confirm our previous expectation based on extensive past experience. In case (*b*), our doubts relate to the possibility that this time we may have sampled a population (collective) the properties of which are different from those of the populations with which we have had experience; hence the suspicion arises that a time-honored hypothesis is not applicable to the present problem. The reasoning in Section 1 suggests that *in either case* the problem is ripe for Bayesian analysis. Instead, it is rather common to use a more mechanical device for checking on the acceptability of the frequentist-objectivist procedure. Note that this is not the same thing as taking for granted that in specific situations, frequentist-objectivist practices provide an acceptable approximation to Bayesian results but, on the contrary, amounts to admitting that a check involving subjectivism is necessary, even though the check here avoids the essential phases of a genuinely Bayesian procedure. The check relies on the rules of thumb with which the present section is concerned.

The rule-of-thumb subjectivism in question involves a somewhat different conception in case (*a*) of the immediately preceding paragraph than in case (*b*). In case (*a*), it typically involves formulating, in addition to the hypothesis which is relatively best supported by the sample, also *another hypothesis*; and the rule prescribes exploring whether given that other hypothesis, the observed sample or something even more unfavorable to that hypothesis is or is not exceedingly unlikely. In such situations the other hypothesis is considered the Null Hypothesis, while the hypothesis which is relatively best supported by the sample is the Alternative Hypothesis. The Null Hypothesis is selected in such a way that, in the event of its validity, the consequences of action based on the hypothesis which is relatively best supported by the sample—action based on the Alternative Hypothesis—would be considered very harmful. If the Null Hypothesis is valid, then the Alternative Hypothesis is *very* misleading. For example, the Null Hypothesis might maintain that the true value of a parameter is zero and that therefore the value estimated from a sample expresses a wholly spurious relationship, which results from sampling error and is about to mislead us. Hence, one wishes to discover whether the Null Hypothesis is or is not *exceedingly poorly* supported by the sample evidence. If it is exceedingly poorly supported— say, if, given the Null Hypothesis, the cumulated conditional probability of the sample evidence and of anything even more unfavorable for the Null Hypothesis is less than 5 per cent or less than 1 per cent, or whatnot —then one proceeds as if the sample evidence did support the Alternative Hypothesis *well enough* to justify use of the frequentist-objectivist short cut to Bayesian results by reliance on this Alternative Hypothesis. In the contrary case—that is, if the Null Hypothesis is not sufficiently unlikely to be valid—the suggested procedure is *not* to rely on the Alternative Hypothesis but to make an effort to formulate further hypotheses—new alternative hypotheses—which might qualify by these standards (or perhaps to fall back wholly on previously formulated hypotheses of a different nature which did qualify). This relates to case (*a*) on page 194.

In case (*b*), it is usual to make the hypothesis which is derived from long past experience the Null Hypothesis,[1] and to conclude that this hypothesis is for some reason inapplicable to a present situation if and only if the parameter value estimated from the present observations falls in a range of values which is so far removed from the true value suggested by the Null Hypothesis that, given the Null Hypothesis, the observation

---

[1] Both in case (*a*) and in case (*b*) the Null Hypothesis is the hypothesis which receives the benefit of the doubt, and the Alternative Hypothesis is the hypothesis which will be considered true only if the data testify strongly against the Null Hypothesis. But in case (*b*) the "Alternative Hypothesis" is not really a *hypothesis*, as we are using the term in this volume, because in case (*b*) the alternative to the Null Hypothesis is formulated as a *denial* of a parameter value rather than as an assignment of parameter values. See p. 66, above.

would be exceedingly unlikely. If the value estimated from the observed data *should* fall in such a range, then here again the advice is to make a strong effort at formulating new hypotheses which will prove acceptable by the standards by which an old hypothesis has failed in relation to the data at hand. If the sample does not testify against the Null Hypothesis strongly enough, then we continue to rely on the latter for the population we have sampled.

More refined variants of such practices have been described, but for the present purpose the foregoing statements give an adequate account of very widely used conventional procedures. What matters here is the idea underlying practices of this kind. I believe I have stated this idea with fairness.

An attempt was made in the final paragraphs of Chapter 2, Section 5, to formulate conditions under which such practices serve a useful purpose. While it would be difficult to provide general guidelines for the interpretation of such conditions of usefulness, it seems to me that these have the following in common: The decision maker feels in these situations that the objectivist short cut to the Bayesian procedure is justified (his prior probabilities and his utility assignments will not modify directives obtained by trusting earlier experiences with frequency ratios or by trusting a present estimate of these in a sample) *unless* he should find that, as concerns his present observations, more than negligible probability attaches to an interpretation of the data which has *very* different implications. If he should find this, then he will give the matter further thought and will try to arrive at a different interpretation of the data. For a long time, practitioners have found frequentist-objectivist methods combined with checks of this sort appealing; and even now, few deny that the combination does fit the needs of many decision makers in specific situations. Yet, it is worth saying again that many decision theorists have recently become critical of these practices, that is, of significance tests falling in the category I have characterized as that of rule-of-thumb subjectivism. To me, it seems that the critics are right in maintaining that such procedures are frequently applied to problems which decision makers could appraise more satisfactorily if the analysis were developed along Bayesian lines.

This is true in circumstances where the reader or listener—the consumer of the analytical product—would like to know *what positive weights he should attach to the validity of a wide range of potentially valid hypotheses* (some of which may, for example, relate to different values of parameters in a *given type* of regression, while others may relate to *different types* of relationships). In these situations the objective is not that of relying on one hypothesis and of disregarding all others, i.e., not that of accepting a hypothesis if another hypothesis seems unlikely enough, nor that of rejecting the first-mentioned hypothesis if the other does seem unlikely enough. Hence the pertinent question is not whether the data do or do not fall in a range of small conditional probability, should a single hypothesis be accepted. Instead of being presented with answers to questions of this sort, the reader or listener would in these circumstances like to know what the likelihood is of the data on various hypotheses, all of which he wants to weight as potentially valid ones; *and* he would like to know how these likelihoods, *along with* his prior-probability judgments, and *along with* his utility assignments to the potential consequences of alternative courses of action, should influence him in supporting action which truly corresponds to his preferences.

Frequently the problem is that of deciding which (if any) of several possible acts is sufficiently well supported by factual evidence, and the task usually calls for appraising the odds on a *good many* hypotheses. Conclusions follow from this concerning desirable criteria for presenting research results even where we are aiming merely at an imperfect counterpart of the neo-Bayesian ideal (as indeed must be the case when the problem becomes essentially one of nonmonetary rewards). Usually it is much more revealing to report likelihood ratios for a given sample and for alternative hypothetical "true values" of parameters, than to report that a significance test was performed successfully or unsuccessfully.

A decision maker to whom research results are communicated can base a reasonable decision on likelihood ratios, but only if he *also* articulates his prior probability appraisals concerning hypotheses, and events, and articulates *also* his utility assignments to the potential consequences of acts (and takes account of his slanting inclinations, unless these are worked into his utility assignments). In situations in which the essential rewards and penalties are nonmonetary it is usually impossible to fit the subjective appraisals into a general theory possessing operational content, but it is nevertheless necessary to rely upon the appraisals in question for deciding what chances should be taken on the basis of the operationally defined likelihood ratios. In cases in which the technical expert presents analysis for the benefit of authorized decision makers, the significant subjective appraisals are those of the latter; but it is undesirable that the expert should conceal *why* he believes that his findings possess interesting traits. Hence he should usually give an indication of how he would combine his own subjective judgments with his research results for some specific purpose. We may add that he can also be helpful to a decision maker who in each particular instance wishes to fit his own subjective judgment into an internally consistent system of subjective judgments, but this last statement has greater importarnce for problems involving pay-offs of monetary character than for problems involving essentially nonmonetary rewards and penalties.

What has just been said is merely an elaboration on our previous proposition, according to which it should be considered a requirement to play into the hands of readers and listeners who want to substitute different subjective probabilities and different utility assignments for ours. Sometimes, it is excusable to disregard this requirement because practically all would agree that if a specific hypothesis passes a significance test, then, for the time being, it is clearly reasonable to proceed *as if* no other constructive hypothesis were conceivable. Also, in some cases, practically all would agree that if the significance test is not passed, then it is clearly reasonable to stay inactive until a hypothesis is found which does pass such a test (or to take action on grounds other than those suggested by the investigation at hand). But cases in which such judgments may legitimately be considered uncontroversial are rarer than is often implied, and the appraisal which in the preceding sentences was attributed to practically all to whom the expert expresses his opinions is often a distinctly subjective appraisal *of the expert himself*. This is true especially in those sciences in which it is impossible to control—use laboratory techniques for keeping at given values—the variables whose changes influence the probabilities of the events with which we are concerned.

Methods of rule-of-thumb subjectivism are not well suited to articulating and to making explicit the subjective judgments of the expert. On the whole, they are apt to obscure these elements and to wrap them into a parcel that has the appearance of scientific objectivism and of impartiality. In view of the fact that groups of experts tend to develop a distinctive outlook of their own, this carries with it one of two dangers, particularly when the problem under investigation bears on issues of public policy.

One of these dangers is that the advising expert, relying on conventional varieties of implicit subjectivism, assumes a more comprehensive decision-making role than that he is supposed to have. This can be quite unconscious, because it results from the use of routinized professional methods; and for a while, it can remain unnoticed. But at any rate, it amounts to the technical expert's exercising part of a decision-making function which should be performed by others, namely, by agents authorized to perform it; and the consequences may even include reduced concern of professional groups with their genuinely analytical or intellectual functions. The other danger is that the authorized decision makers, as well as the public itself, develop a strong reaction against experts who present *indivisible* packages containing subjective judgments of value along with the needed skills. This, in turn, may lead to the neglect of expert advice, and to uninformed decision making, on the part of those whose legitimate role it is to make significant decisions but who lack the technical skills of the expert.

Neither of these two possibilities is at all pleasant to contemplate. Perhaps we have been witnessing alternations of such tendencies. The more usual it becomes to articulate the subjective elements entering into professional analysis, and the easier it is made for others to adapt the analytical product in view of their own subjective judgments, the smaller these dangers will be. This is one of the reasons why the fundamental attitude underlying the Bayesian approach should be welcomed.

(3) *Lessening the Element of Haphazardness in Business Decisions*

The main part of the analysis in this volume was directly or indirectly concerned with profit-seeking decisions. Still, I feel there is need for a few words of summary and appraisal here.

Rational business decisions should be aimed at the maximization of expected utility, except that in our semiprobabilistic view, specific types of nonmonetary rewards and penalties do not lend themselves well to being incorporated into "utility functions." It seems preferable to us to take account of these specific nonmonetary consequences in the weighting system of the individual, along the lines of our Version 1. We have in mind the rewards and penalties associated with reliance on firm versus shaky judgments, or on widely shared judgments versus those which are highly controversial even among the well informed. The rewards and penalties in question are particularly important in situations involving decision making for *groups*. Many decision situations which on first sight do not appear to possess this trait do in fact possess it.

For decision problems outside the business world, it is often necessary—though difficult—to formulate a basic nonmonetary pay-off function; and in such circumstances, it may be preferable to lump together the utilities of the basic nonmonetary rewards with those resulting from the quality of the judgment itself (Version 2). Even in some of these situations the decision maker may find it helpful to proceed along the lines of Version 1, that is, to separate the utility of the basic nonmonetary rewards of the acts he contemplates from the consequences of relying on one or the other type of judgment; and if the latter variety of consequences matters to him, he may sometimes find it easier to make allowances for it by playing safe in his *weighting system*. But I think it is especially true of business decisions, which always involve monetary payoffs, that the Version 1 procedure is advantageous, because it avoids lumping together tangibles with intangibles. Regardless of whether the decision theorist does or does not share my methodological position in this regard—i.e., regardless of whether he thinks along the lines of Version 1 or of Version 2—he should recognize that the investor is entitled to act differently, depending on whether a decision can be based on a widely shared and firm judgment or merely on a vacillating opinion about which people tend to disagree, regardless of how much information they exchange.

Aside from this semiprobabilistic factor for which it is possible to adjust the theory, Bayesian analysis, with its reliance on prior probabilities, on likelihoods derived from factual observations, and on utility assignments, is well suited to decision making in business. This is true not only when the problem at hand possesses technical-statistical content. A problem may be said to possess such content if a reasonably large sample can be drawn from a set of exchangeable events, or from events which (perhaps with some misgivings) are treated as if they were exchangeable because regression analysis or other statistical techniques have been employed to make allowances for changes in "other variables."[2] In Chapter 2, Section 6, it was pointed out that even the distinctly technical methods of making such allowances are usually incomplete enough to leave quite a bit of room for subjective judgments of an informal kind. Hence, as soon as allowances for changing "other variables" have to be made—i.e., if we become concerned with the variety of problems discussed in Section 6, rather than Section 5, of Chapter 2—the analysis moves into the area in which at least *somewhat* subjective (controversial) judgments need to be made not only about the prior probabilities in the initial stage, but *also* about the effect of the subsequently observed data on the probabilities of future events. This is because the correction factors which the decision maker uses to make the future events exchangeable with the already observed events become at least somewhat controversial. At the end of this range, we have many situations in which the decision maker relies com-

---

[2] For the concept of exchangeable events, and for these allowances, see Chapter 2, Section 5; and also Chapter 3, Section 3.

pletely on informal (intuitive) adjustments for the effects of changing variables on the probabilities of prospective events. At this end of the range the appraisal of the effect of factual observations on the probabilities of future events becomes no less subjective than are the prior probabilities, and the problem ceases to possess technical-statistical content. Yet, regardless of how much subjectivity enters into the decision process through these various channels, the Bayesian framework provides useful guidance for achieving internal consistency in combining prior judgments with conclusions derived from factual observations, in accordance with the decision maker's preference system.[3]

It is necessary to keep in mind the whole range which has been described in the immediately preceding paragraph, the range from highly technical to casual methods of estimating the effect of changes in a good many variables on the probabilities of events. Subjective probability judgments are always based on factual props, but individuals differ from one another with respect to the kind of prop on which they find it helpful to rely. In particular, they differ from one another in how useful they find highly formalized statistical techniques as compared to more casually constructed props, in circumstances where it will be necessary to undo some of the precision of highly formalized procedures by hunch-like allowances for the difference between past and future events. While this is a matter of gradations, there exist a good many business problems which clearly do not possess technical-statistical content in the foregoing sense. These problems need to be decided on the basis of experience which no one would try to organize into anything like a statistical sample. But in these contexts, too, a reasonable decision maker should find the principle of weighted utility maximization and the Bayesian principles of internal consistency valuable because these can help him to act more thoughtfully and more in keeping with his genuine preference system. There should be room for further applications of subjective-probabilistic and Bayesian ideas in business practice. Decision making always takes

---

[3] To take a rather extreme illustration, let us assume that I am faced with a man whose native language is French, and that I assign the prior probability 0.9 to the prospect that a person whom I meet in the given circumstances turns out to be a French national and the prior probability 0.1 to his being a Swiss national. Furthermore, I assign the probability 0.2 to the prospect that a Frenchman whom I meet in these circumstances has good reading knowledge of German (by specified standards) and the probability 0.9 to the prospect that a French Swiss has this knowledge. If I then discover that the man does have good reading knowledge of German, I should assign the posterior probability 2/3 to his being a French national and the posterior probability 1/3 to his being a Swiss national. Thereby I comply with the consistency requirement expressed by Bayes's theorem, a requirement which stays valid even though any inference I may wish to draw from this experience with respect to individuals whom I may meet in the future "in similar circumstances" will remain as controversial as is the term "similar circumstances."

202 · *PROBABILITY AND PROFIT*

place under uncertainty, and it is difficult to make sense of the idea of profit maximization without reliance on the theory of subjective probability and utility. After all, the problems discussed in Chapter 7 belong among the best-known standard problems involving the maximization of profits.

This leaves open the question whether methods can be developed for discovering *how* economic decisions are reached in actual fact. The modern theory of subjective probability and utility is expressed in operational terms; but this, of course, does not imply that we can test the probability judgments and the utility functions of top management experimentally. It has proved possible to carry out experiments which have led to interesting conclusions concerning the utility functions, probability judgments, and strategy attitudes of subjects. However, such subjects are invariably tested under conditions that have not enough in common with those under which significant business decisions are reached.

Along different lines, it is possible to explore whether various broad observations about the workings of economic processes—usually observations of a rather casual kind—do or do not lend themselves to being interpreted in terms of subjective-probabilistic ideas. This, too, has an important place in economic analysis, but the method cannot be expected to yield *conclusive* results.

Indeed, it would be too much to hope for conclusive results. But the operational structure of modern decision theory makes it possible also to obtain a kind of verification which, while it does not stand up too well by the criteria of the laboratory sciences, nevertheless deserves emphasis. The theory enables us to ask decision makers questions *in operational form*, and the answers to such questions can presumably be made more similar to experimental observations than answers to questions about general views and feelings. Such quasi-operational methods include interrogation concerning acceptable odds in hypothetical standard process bets and in business ventures. More dependable answers may be expected for hypothetical bets involving monetary pay-offs than for hypothetical commitments associated with basically nonmonetary rewards.

Taken by themselves, none of these methods can decide the question of the empirical realism of modern decision-theoretical ideas. But taken together, they will gradually throw some light on this question. As has been said before, the theory combines normative and positive traits in an intriguing fashion, and it is unlikely that future research will lose sight of either aspect.

Chapter 9

APPENDIX ON
BETTING EXPERIMENTS
WITH YALE STUDENTS

(1) *Preliminary Experiments and Their Shortcomings*

As one of the participants, along with Daniel Ellsberg and Howard Raiffa, of a symposium which appeared in the November, 1961, issue of the *Quarterly Journal of Economics* (**16**), I reported there on some experimental findings in support of the hypothesis of slanting. These experiments—and some similar ones which I undertook—were made each time with no more than about twelve Yale students as subjects, and the experiments had the following property: The subjects had to choose between two options. The first option gave them a prize contingent (in their choice) either on a standard process event with probability 0.5 or on its equiprobable complement; the second option gave them *a somewhat higher prize* contingent (in their choice) either on a nonstandard process event, about which they had merely vague guesses, or on the complement of that same event, in circumstances which made it appear likely to me that most subjects would be roughly indifferent between betting on the nonstandard process event in question or on its complement. A purely probabilistic subject would, of course, have to show a preference for the second option. I found that a varying proportion of the subjects preferred the first option, in spite of the difference between the prizes.

For example, in one experiment, one half (or slightly more) had a preference for the first option when the difference in favor of the second option was 25 cents for prizes that were in the range between $5.00 and $6.00. In some situations the proportion of subjects that gave *this* particular indication of slanting was very small; but any reasonable theory would lead to the expectation that in these situations, little slanting would be observable. These were situations in which I did not succeed in describing to the subjects a nonstandard process event which they considered roughly equiprobable with its complement, so that the degree of slanting would have had to be very great indeed to make the bet on one of the two nonstandard process events less attractive to them than the bet on the standard process event. Also, I found little preference for the first option in cases where the prizes were small (say, $1.00 or less), and where various indications pointed to a risk-loving attitude—i.e., to increasing marginal utility of wealth—in the range under consideration. In general, I have acquired the conviction that tests of this sort should involve several dollars' worth of prizes and that it is desirable to make the subjects put up some of their own money on each of these bets.[1] On one occasion, I resorted also to the device of letting the subjects play partly at the risk, and to the benefit, of fellow students whom they were representing. It is fair to say that on the level of experimentation to which my foregoing remarks relate, I found a good many indications of slanting. A precise description of some of these small experiments is found in the Q.J.E. symposium which I have mentioned.

In the same symposium, Howard Raiffa—whose views I consider purely probabilistic—dissented from my interpretation of these factual observations. It seems legitimate to me to group his critical remarks under two headings.

In the first place, Raiffa argued generally that in matters possessing technical implications, many intelligent individuals make mistakes—just as untrained people find wrong solutions to algebraic problems—and that, therefore, only if the decision situations had first been properly decomposed or explained to the subjects would the results of such experiments be relevant to the problem in which I am interested. Secondly, Raiffa argued that in experiments of the sort I had performed, a rather *specific type* of technical explanation would have been in order. As I said a moment ago, I had found—as had other experimenters also—that many subjects showed an inclination to prefer a smaller amount contingent on their drawing the color of their choice from a "guaranteed regular deck of French cards" to a larger amount contingent on their drawing the color of their choice from an "uncertain deck" (where I am using quotes because the phrase "drawing the color of one's choice from a guaranteed deck" merely stands here for a regular standard process probability of 0.5, and "drawing the color of one's choice from an uncertain deck" stands for ignorance about the chances, with no reason to favor, on bal-

---

[1] It is, of course, possible to pay them wages at a rate which makes it appear very unlikely that the experiment as a whole would cost them money. If one has strong reasons to believe that there is no communication between groups of subjects participating in successive experiments, it may even be acceptable procedure to refund losses on one or the other occasion.

ance, one or the other of the two possible outcomes).[2] Raiffa argued that in such experiments, it is desirable to call the attention of the subjects to the fact that they could *randomize their choices from the uncertain deck*—say, they could flip a fair coin to decide on which color to bet from the uncertain deck. In the experiments on which Raiffa commented, I had engaged in no explanations before letting my subjects make their choices.

Raiffa reported that in experiments he had performed at Harvard—but in which he apparently did *not* actually pay out money or collect stakes—he, too, first found a preference for betting on the guaranteed deck (as defined above), but that *after explanations*—particularly after his demonstration of the existence of *randomization opportunities*—the subjects in question agreed that one should opt for drawing the color of one's choice from the uncertain deck whenever this carries a higher prize than the guaranteed deck.

As the reader knows, I have some misgivings about the randomization argument even for symmetrical bets when the number of trials with which the decision maker is confronted is very small. (To asymmetrical bets the randomization argument simply cannot be made to apply; see Chapter 6, Section 6, and the Appendix to Chapter 6.) Quite aside from this, it is difficult to decide just how much explanation is in order when experts are performing experiments with subjects who, in technical matters, are used to accepting the views of the expert in question. The fact that Raiffa's subjects, who neither risked any money nor could hope to win any, ended up by accepting his views, does not of course establish the validity of the purely probabilistic hypotheses. On the other hand, it is quite true that in experiments of this sort, one is not trying to observe miscalculations.

I do not know whether introducing actual stakes and money prizes should or should not be expected to make a decisive difference in this regard, as long as explanations are given, and interpretations are suggested, by experimenters whom their subjects know to be university professors with a professional interest in the technical problems under consideration. Still, after reading Raiffa's contribution to the Q.J.E. symposium—and before performing the experiment to which I shall turn in the next section—I repeated an earlier experiment of mine, with the following modification: I gave the subjects (Yale students who, how-

---

[2] In the experiments in question, I confronted the subjects with various equivalents of the uncertain deck, including true or false questions about which I hoped they were ignorant and about which their hunches in *one direction* were apt to become neutralized by their hunches *in the other direction*. On another occasion, I formulated to the subjects a stock exchange bet which had these characteristics.

ever, were unacquainted with my views on the matter) a write-up which explained to them briefly the purely probabilistic position—including Raiffa's position on randomization—and explained to them also some of the counterarguments I am presenting in this volume. I *believe* that the write-up had a neutral tone and that the presentation was fair and reasonably clear. Money was at stake in the modified experiment, as was the case also in the original ones. Eight out of twenty students still preferred to bet at somewhat worse odds on what in the modified experiment was the equivalent of the guaranteed deck rather than to bet at somewhat better odds on the equivalent of the uncertain deck.

On the whole, I got to feel somewhat uneasy about experiments which (as Raiffa rightly pointed out) were subject to legitimate criticism if they did *not* involve a large amount of interpretation by an experimenter with definite views about his problem, and which (as I felt) were subject to legitimate criticism *also* if they *did* involve a lot of such interpretation. In an attempt to circumvent this difficulty as well as it seemed possible (the difficulty cannot be wholly circumvented), I undertook the last experiment to be discussed in the present volume. To this I now turn.

(2) *An Experiment Centered on a Schelling Problem*

The subjects in this experiment consisted of sixty undergraduates who were taking a course I have been giving at the University for some time. The experiment was performed rather early in the fall term of 1963. It is safe to assume that at that time the subjects were wholly unaware of the nature of purely probabilistic and of semiprobabilistic approaches to decision problems. While, subsequently, this problem was indeed discussed with them, no mention was made of it beforehand in the class.

I believe that all subjects interpreted the experiment as being aimed at an objective of a different sort, in particular as being a slightly modified version of an experiment which Thomas C. Schelling (47) had performed at Yale. However, my true intention was to pose a problem that had the following characteristics: (*a*) The subjects could have merely vague or shaky appraisals of two nonstandard prospects, namely, the prospect of a specific nonstandard process event and of its complement. (*b*) There existed an a priori presumption that few people would consider the nonstandard process event and its complement equiprobable, so that if a subject strongly asserted that he considered the event more probable than its complement (or vice versa), then this seemed acceptable evidence of his preference for one of the two nonstandard prospects over the other. (*c*) Each subject could choose to bet on one of the following three events: on a nonstandard process event, *or* on the complement of that event, *or* on a standard process event with probability 0.5. The terms were identical for these bets, *so that an individual who selected the third of these bets was presumably slanting down his nonstandard process probabilities*, especially if he gave indications of not being indifferent between the two nonstandard prospects (and of thus finding himself in a situation in which, given equal odds, a purely probabilistic subject would have to prefer the more probable nonstandard prospect to a standard process probability of 0.5). The true purpose of my experiment was to test the subjects on a problem possessing these characteristics. But one of the Schelling experiments served as a particularly useful frame of reference for posing the problem.

Schelling had developed and tested the hypothesis according to which individuals who were not in touch with each other were often capable of tacitly co-ordinating their behavior by concentrating on "focal points" which caught the eye of each participant. In one of his experiments, Schelling asked his subjects to write down a positive number on a piece of paper and to mail it to him; the participants knew that the winners were to be those who wrote down a number which was written down by more subjects than was any other single number. In Schelling's experiment the number one was the winning number. About 40 per cent of his subjects wrote down this particular number (see his *Strategy of Conflict* [**47**], pages 55–56).

In the *first round* of my experiment, on which I am now reporting, I described the nature of this Schelling experiment to my subjects, and I promised them a small prize if they *made a correct guess of the winning number of the original Schelling experiment*.

Immediately after this first round—before the answers to the Schelling question were examined—I gave the same subjects a choice of betting on one of three prospects. The terms were identical on each of these bets: If the subject won, he was to get $4.00; if he lost, he was to lose 50 cents. The following were the three bets from among which they could choose (the standard process bet is listed here first):

A. A bet on drawing from among 10 numbers a number of their choice which had a regular 50 per cent probability of being drawn.[3]

B. A bet on the prediction that in the first round *at least 40 per cent* of the

---

[3] Those opting for A had to indicate which five of the 10 numbers were to be their winning numbers, in the sense that they won $4.00 if they drew one of the five numbers (or lost 50 cents in the contrary case).

subjects had made a correct guess of the winning number of the original Schelling experiment.

C. A bet on the prediction that in the first round *less than 40 per cent* of the subjects had made a correct guess of the winning number of the original Schelling experiment.

While the number of students who participated in the first round was 63, the number of bettors in the *second round* (the bettors on A or on B or on C) was 60. When the terms were communicated to them, a few participants asked questions to clarify details; but I feel confident that before making their choices, practically all subjects did acquire a clear understanding of the terms. As soon as the choices were made—before I examined them—I asked those who had opted for A to indicate in writing whether, if A had not been available, they would have had a preference for B, or a preference for C, or whether they would have felt *indifferent* between B and C. Note that even a purely probabilistic individual *may* well have opted for A, *provided* he regarded B and C as equiprobable. But a purely probabilistic subject who preferred B to C, or C to B, must be assumed to have bet on the preferred of these two alternatives rather than on A. In other words, a bet on A disclosed slanting, unless the subject was indifferent between B and C.

Of the 60 bettors, 36 opted for A; of these 36, *at least five and at most nine* can be interpreted as having declared themselves indifferent between B and C. While in four cases (the difference between nine and five), this is very much a matter of interpretation, I feel I should put the number of "indifferents" (with respect to B versus C) at nine, to make sure that I am not strengthening my argument by a low estimate of the number of indifferents. *Twenty-seven of the 36 A optants stated definitely that if A had not been available, then they would have shown a preference for one over the other of the two remaining bets.*

We now turn from the 36 A optants to those 24 of the 60 bettors who opted for either B or C.

Of the 60 bettors, 20 opted for C, and four opted for B. The C optants were winners, and the B optants losers, because in the first round, only 14 of 63 students (i.e., 22 per cent) had made the correct guess that the number one was the winning number of the Schelling experiment.[4]

I suggest the conclusion that at least 27 subjects—45 per cent of the 60 bettors—were slanting down their nonstandard process probabili-

---

[4] While in my experiment, too, the number one was the guess of more participants than was any other single number, the degree of concentration on the number one was smaller in this experiment than in Schelling's. In the original Schelling experiment, about 40 per cent of the subjects wrote down this number (a fact which I did not communicate to my subjects).

ties. I mean the 27 who opted for A even though they expressed a clear-cut preference for B over C, or for C over B. Even those readers who might feel somewhat skeptical about mere expressions of preference— i.e., statements of preference for B over C, or vice versa, by subjects who in fact had opted for A—should, I think, readily admit that it would be wholly unreasonable to attribute to anything like 36 out of 60 subjects (i.e., to all A optants) a judgment of indifference between B and C. A high proportion of the 36 A optants undoubtedly did have a preference for B over C; or vice versa; and a purely probabilistic attitude would therefore have led them to opt for the preferred of *these two* alternatives (rather than for A). But, I think, in this case quite a bit of confidence may be placed in the expressions of preference, which suggest specifically that at least 27 of the 36 A optants were slanting down their subjective probabilities concerning the proportion of correct answers to the Schelling question.

Moreover, in one respect the terms were sufficiently transparent to minimize the danger of confusion. Intelligent individuals who prefer B to C, or vice versa, and on reflection nevertheless opt for A, may be assumed to know that they are placing a particular kind of vague guess (a nonstandard process probability) at a discount relative to the firm numbers probability 0.5. I suggest that at least 45 per cent of the 60 bettors proved to be deliberate downward-slanters.

One final remark: A considerable majority of the subjects foresaw correctly that C was a better bet than B. The proportion of these who guessed right on this was particularly high among those who trusted their guesses sufficiently to bet on them (i.e., among the *non-A* optants). The non-A optants numbered 24, and 20 of these (five sixths of the 24) opted for C. The proportion of individuals who deemed C a better bet than B was lower, but still distinctly high, among those who opted for A and thus proved unwilling to bet on C or on B. Among the A optants, 18 expressed in a clear-cut way that, in their view, C was preferable to B; and nine that, in their view, B was preferable to C (that is to say, two thirds guessed correctly).

BIBLIOGRAPHICAL
COMMENTARIES

I

Several bibliographies of very high quality are available in the area of subjective probability and "operational" utility. I should like to refer the reader particularly to the bibliographies included in the works listed in Section II as items **45**, **46**, **33**, **30**, and **14**. Other works which the reader will find listed in Section II also contain very good bibliographies. In spite of this, I concluded that a useful purpose may be served by preparing the bibliographical commentaries that follow here.

In the first approximation, I might describe this bibliography as including the works to which, or to whose authors, direct reference is made in the book. This description is, by and large, adequate; but it needs to be corrected to some extent. It should be corrected for certain "pluses" and, in a sense, for "minuses," too. As for the pluses, I included some contributions to which, or to whose authors, direct reference merely *would have been made* in the book if I had not felt that my quota of long footnotes and of appendices was already exhausted. I included these works in spite of not having referred to them in the text because in my thinking they occupied more room than did my general background readings. As for the minuses, I believe I have not omitted from the bibliography any works to which I referred specifically in the book; but in a few cases, I omitted the works of authors whose names were mentioned in the book merely briefly and in a very general context.

I also omitted from the bibliography publications of my own, although the reasoning in some sections of this volume is an elaboration on views expressed in earlier writings, particularly in my *Competition among the Few* (originally published by Alfred A. Knopf in 1949; reprinted recently with a new introduction and some corrections by Kelley and Millman, New York, 1959). Item **16** is a symposium in which I participated, and this fact *is* mentioned in the description of the item.

The length of my remarks under the bibliographical items varies greatly. This is because in some cases my discussion in the volume itself relates to most aspects of a work which bear at all closely on our subject matter, and a further discussion of the work in these commentaries would have led into topics of a somewhat different character. In other cases the commentaries are much longer because parts of a contribution would have lent themselves well to presentation in a long footnote or in an appendix. For the reason indicated a moment ago, it seemed preferable to present a write-up in these commentaries, some items of which relate to more works than one.

In general, a contribution which was printed as an item in a collection is listed *only* as such—i.e., is not listed separately—although, in the case of reprinted essays, the data pertaining to the original publication are mentioned when the item is described as part of the collection. Thus, in general, duplication of listings was avoided. There are two exceptions. Ramsey's essay is listed and discussed separately as item **43**, and it appears also in item **30**, where it is merely briefly mentioned. The reason for this is that the introductory remarks to the presentation in item **43** may be of interest to some readers, and they would seem to fit a separate item better than the third essay of the collection listed as item **30**. There is also another exception. Item **19** was entered separately, even though the entry merely gives the title of de Finetti's contribution in question and then refers to the collection listed as item **30**. This is because the reader might have been confused by finding under this author's name items **17** and **18**, with no mention of **19**. This author is mentioned frequently in our volume, and in most cases with item **19** in mind.

Before asking the reader to turn to Section II, I should like to express my thanks for the valuable help I got from Mr. Charles K. Derber, a student of Yale College, in preparing this bibliography and the commentaries.

II

(1) ALCHIAN, ARMEN. "The Meaning of Utility Measurement," *American Economic Review*, March, 1953, pp. 26–50.

This article provides an introduction to some of the basic theories and methods of utility measurement. It briefly summarizes the development from the Hicksian indifference curve analysis, which assumes ordinal utility, to the contributions of von Neumann and Morgenstern, Friedman and Savage, and Marschak, which reintroduce the assumption of cardinal utility. The bulk of the article is concerned with purposes and methods of utility measurement. Alchian explains how the basic axioms of von Neumann and Morgenstern enable one to predict individual choice according to maximization of expected utility. It is explained also that in welfare economics the assumption of cardinal utility has not proved more useful than the assumption of ordinality.

(2) ALLAIS, MAURICE. "Le comportement de l'homme rationnel devant le risque: Critique des postulas et axioms de l'école americaine," *Econometrica*, October, 1953, pp. 503–46.

The author expresses a criticism of the axiomatic premises of modern operational utility theory. The best-known part of the article is that containing the Allais paradox. A choice situation is described in which intelligent and thoughtful persons are said to be inclined to violate the utility axioms. Allais arrived at this conclusion by discussing the matter with individuals and asking them to answer his questions. Here is the problem:

Imagine, first, that you may choose between Option I and Option II:

Option I: 500,000 monetary units (let us here call them dollars) with probability 1.

Option II: $2.5 million with probability 0.1, and $500,000 with probability 0.89, and the *status quo* with probability 0.01 (only one of the three possibilities will materialize).

Imagine, next, that you may choose between Option III and Option IV:

Option III: $500,000 with probability 0.11, and the *status quo* with probability 0.89 (only one possibility will materialize).

Option IV: $2.5 million with probability 0.1, and the *status quo* with probability 0.9 (only one possibility will materialize).

Many thoughtful decision makers are said to express themselves in favor of I in preference to II, and yet express themselves in favor of IV in preference to III. I think the easiest way to show that, in terms of the utility axioms, this involves a contradiction is to point out the following: A preference for I over II implies that a rise from a $500,000 gain to a $2.5-million gain is *worth less* than the equivalent of a fall from a $500,000 gain to the *status quo*, even if the rise is weighted ten times as heavily as the fall. (Note that in II the rise, as compared to I, carries probability 0.1 and the fall merely probability 0.01.) A preference for IV as against III implies, on the other hand, that a rise from a $500,000 gain to a $2.5-million gain is *worth more* than the equivalent of a fall from $500,000 to the *status quo*, when the rise is weighted by probability 0.1 and the fall by probability 0.01.

Adherents of modern utility theory have argued that while at first they too might be inclined to choose I in preference to II, and IV in preference to III, they would on reflection make the two choices consistent with one another. We may add that in this regard the semiprobabilistic view should not lead to different conclusions than the purely probabilistic, since Allais' probabilities may be thought of as standard process probabilities. If one prefers I to II, one *should* also prefer III to IV; if one prefers IV to III, one *should* also prefer II to I, though it may take a few minutes to figure out a problem of this sort. Many individuals say that, given enough time to understand the problem, they would in fact act in this fashion. What proportion of decision makers would actually do so cannot be decided by asking acquaintances to answer questions under nonexperimental conditions and with no money at stake.

Allais' analysis ties in with our observations *passim* on the difficulties arising from irrationalities, imperfections, and the partly normative, partly positive character of modern utility theory, though Allais would no doubt take the position that these difficulties are more damaging to the theory than we would admit.

(3) ARROW, KENNETH J. "Alternative Approaches to the Theory of Choice in Risk-Taking Situations," *Econometrica*, October, 1951. Published also in Cowles Commission Papers, New Series No. 51, 1952. 37 pp.

The author surveys the important theories of choice under uncertainty developed by economists, mathematicians, and statisticians. The article is divided as follows: (1) discussion of different ways of describing uncertain consequences by (*a*) those who describe uncertain consequences exclusively in terms of probability distributions and (*b*) those who use some other principle to replace or supplement the foregoing; (2) discussion of different ways of ordering consequences, particularly (*a*) in theories of behavior held by those using probability statements to describe uncertainty, i.e., Ramsey and von Neumann–Morgenstern, and (*b*) in theories of behavior held by those who use other statements to describe uncertainty.

While this is a survey article, the author interjects interesting evaluations and appraisals.

(**4**) BAYES, THOMAS. *An Essay toward Solving a Problem in the Doctrine of Chance.* Originally published, with Richard Price's foreword and discussion, in *Philosophical Transactions of the Royal Society*, 1763. 48 pp. Now available as the first of the papers in W. Edwards Deming (ed.), *Facsimiles of Two Papers by Bayes*, with a commentary by Edward C. Molina (Washington, D.C.: Graduate School, U. S. Department of Agriculture, n.d.).

See particularly our Chapter 1, Section 4; and Chapter 2, Section 4.

(**5**) BERNOULLI, DANIEL. "Exposition of a New Theory on the Measurement of Risk," translated by Louise Sommer, *Econometrica*, January, 1954, pp. 175–92. Latin original: "Specimen theoriae novae de mensura sortis," *Commentarii academiae scientiarum imperialis Petropolitanae* for 1730–31 (published in 1738). German translation by Alfred Pringsheim: *Versuch einer neuen Theorie der Wertbestimmung von Glücksfällen* (Leipzig: Duncker Humblot, 1896).

Author referred to in our Chapters 2 and 3; *op. cit.* discussed in Appendix to Chapter 3. In the particular sense explained in our volume, modern utility theory may be said to have originated in this contribution. But the historical line of development is not easy to follow.

In the Appendix to Chapter 3, we discussed the role of Daniel Bernoulli's older cousin, Nicolas, in inspiring *op. cit.* (this cousin should not be confused with Daniel's brother, Nicolas, a mathematician who died young, at the time when the two brothers were staying together in St. Petersburg). In our volume, we mentioned also Daniel's uncle, Jacques Bernoulli (1654–1705), whom it may not be too arbitrary to call the founder of mathematical probability theory. In his posthumously published *Ars Conjectandi* (1713), he derived the binomial probabilities from the probabilities of elementary events and demonstrated that with an unlimited increase in the number of trials the probability of the observed success ratio's falling in a specified range around the probability of the elementary event tends to unity, regardless of how small we make the specified range (Law of Large Numbers, as described in our Chapter 2, Section 2).

(6) BÖHM-BAWERK, EUGEN VON. *Kapital und Kapitalzins*. 2 vols. 1st ed. Innsbruck: Wagner'sche Buchhandlung, 1884–89. English translation by William Smart, *The Pure Theory of Capital* (New York–London: Macmillan Co., 1891).

Author referred to in our Chapter 4, Section 2, as stressing the importance for interest theory of the concept of *pure* time preference, not *merely* the importance of that kind of time preference which is shown by individuals who expect to be better endowed with goods in the future than they are in the present. Thus, pure time preference—the "pure" variety of a preference for present over future goods—is not a result of diminishing marginal utility of income, but of the lesser valuation of the identical aggregate quantity of goods if they become available in the future than if they become available immediately. Both kinds of time preference play a role also in Irving Fisher's analysis (item **20**, below).

(7) CARNAP, RUDOLF. *Logical Foundations of Probability*. Chicago: University of Chicago Press, 1950. 607 pp.

Although Carnap's purpose is to construct a system of inductive logic, a large part of this book consists of the study of the philosophical foundations of probability theory. Carnap's principal contribution is an examination of the differences between those who view probability as an objective logical relation between propositions, such as Keynes and Jeffreys, and those who view probability as relative frequency, such as Mises and Reichenbach. Carnap claims that the disagreements between the two schools rest on misunderstanding, in that both are unaware of being concerned with different concepts. Carnap calls the first of these two concepts probability$_1$ and the second probability$_2$. The first concept is essentially that of the reasonable degree of belief, given specific evidence; in Carnap's terminology, this becomes the degree of confirmation of one proposition by another (say, of a proposition expressing a hypothesis by a proposition expressing the evidence). For the alleged "objectivity" of this, see the Introduction to the present volume. The difference between probability$_1$ and probability$_2$ becomes bridged to some extent by statements such as: *"Thus the common probability$_1$ value of several hypotheses can be interpreted as the estimate of the relative frequency of truth among them"* (p. 72, Carnap's italics).

(8) COURNOT, AUGUSTIN. *Researches into the Mathematical Principles of the Theory of Wealth*. Translated by Nathaniel T. Bacon. New York: Macmillan Co., 1927. 171 pp. Contains also an essay on Cournot, notes on his mathematical economics, and a Bibliography of mathematical economics, by Irving Fisher. French original was published in 1838 as *Récherches sur les principes mathématiques de la théorie des richesses.*

Cournot presented a mathematical treatment of basic problems of economic theory very much earlier than the period in which a systematic use of mathematical tools for this purpose became usual at all, even among a minority of professional economists. Consequently, his contribution remained unnoticed for a long time. Cournot was concerned mainly with price theory, though not exclusively with this area. He formulated continuous demand functions and cost functions; and on the assumption of profit maximization, he established the equilibrium prices and outputs by using first and second derivatives for finding maxima. Thus the concepts of marginal revenue and marginal cost enter here importantly, though these words were not used until much later. Cournot gives solutions for monopoly, oligopoly (which he calls *competition*), and perfect competition (his *unlimited competition*); the third of these is derived from the second by an unlimited increase in the number of rivals. The effect of taxes—mainly of indirect taxes—on monopoly equilibrium also receives attention. The last two chapters discuss problems involving the concept of social income. For the crucial assumption of Cournot's oligopoly theory, see our Chapter 7, Section 3.

(9) DAVIDSON, DONALD, and MARSCHAK, JACOB. *Experimental Tests of a Stochastic Decision Theory.* Cowles Foundation Paper No. 137. New Haven, 1959. Reprinted from C. West Churchman and Philborn Ratoosh (eds.), *Measurement: Definitions and Theories* (New York: John Wiley & Sons, Inc., 1959), pp. 233–69.

This paper is concerned with the principle of expected utility maximization on the assumption that preferences express themselves in its being *more probable* that the preferred alternative will be chosen rather than the less preferred one. That is to say, the preferences discussed in the paper are not "absolute" but are reflected by probabilities of choice. Hence the resulting theory of choice is stochastic.

With reference to a contribution by Stephen Vail, weak stochastic transitivity is defined by the requirement that if the probability of a subject's preferring a over b is greater than 0.5, and the probability of his preferring b over c is greater than 0.5, then the probability of his preferring a over c should also be greater than 0.5; strong stochastic transitivity is defined by the requirement that if the probability of a subject's preferring a over b is greater than 0.5, and the probability of his preferring b over c is greater than 0.5, then the probability of his preferring a over c should exceed the greater of the two foregoing probabilities. With a self-evident *mutatis mutandis* clause, these requirements apply also to the relationship between a and c in cases where the relationship between a and b, or that between b and c, or both these relationships, are relationships of indifference rather than of preference. A person is said to have a utility function provided the following is true: The probability of his preferring a over b exceeds the probability of his preferring b over c *if and only if*, to him, the difference between the utility of a and b is greater than the difference between the utility of b and c (again with the appropriate *mutatis mutandis* clause for indifference, that is, for equal probabilities). Assuming that greater probability of preference expresses itself in greater frequencies of choosing the preferred item, it then becomes testable whether a person is a maximizer of expected utility. Experiments were performed with seventeen Stanford students as subjects. The results indicate the acceptability of the hypothesis of weak transitivity of alternatives and of utility intervals for all subjects and of the hypothesis of strong transitivity for the great majority.

The article ties in with our statements on the difficulties of testing indifference, particularly with statements in our Chapter 1, Section 2, and Chapter 3, Section 7.

(10) DAVIDSON, DONALD, and SUPPES, PATRICK, in co-operation with SIEGEL, SIDNEY. *Decision Making: An Experimental Approach.* Stanford: Stanford University Press, 1957. 121 pp.

Authors referred to in our Chapter 3, Section 11. A general discussion is presented here of the operational theory of utility and of subjective probability, and a detailed account is given of experiments undertaken with Stanford students as subjects to measure their subjective probabilities and their utility functions. We may add to what was said in our *loc. cit.* that the authors found that "objective" equiprobability (of, say, red and black or of even and odd) frequently does not lead to behavior disclosing *subjective* equiprobability. Colors, numbers, etc., tend to acquire emotive content. Hence, in the Davidson-Suppes-Siegel experiments, nonsense syllables (*ZEJ* and *ZOJ*, *QUG* and *QUJ*, *XEQ* and *WUH*) were employed instead; i.e., three sides of a guaranteed fair die were labeled with one nonsense syllable, and the three other sides with another. The authors selected these specific labels with reference to an article on the association value of nonsense syllables by A. J. Glaze, in the 1928 volume of the *Journal of Genetic Psychology.* Their choices were successful: Objective coincided here with subjective equiprobability. My own experience with Yale students suggests to me that color bias and the like have played a negligible role in my experiments, but no definite conclusions can be formulated about this problem in general; and the volume under consideration is worth reading on this point, too. The reader may be interested also in Davidson and Suppes' application of linear programming techniques to the solution of the inequalities resulting from the preferences of subjects for certain options over others.

(11) DOLBEAR, FRANK T. "Individual Choice under Uncertainty." Ph.D. dissertation. Yale University, 1963. Published in *Yale Economic Essays,* Fall, 1963.

Referred to in our Chapter 3, Section 7. Dolbear constructs in his thesis a model of choice which attempts to cope with the empirical finding that individuals do not behave in a manner perfectly consistent with the von Neumann–Morgenstern axioms. His model is designed to permit random deviations from the expected utility maximization demanded by the von Neumann–Morgenstern axioms, and he assumes that the probability of such a deviation is a function of the difference between the expected utility of alternative options. He formulates a mathematical relationship which expresses the probability of one option's being chosen in preference to another, as a function of the difference in expected utility; and he presents the results of experiments which suggest that as a tool of prediction, this function is superior to several alternatives with which one is tempted to compare it.

(12) EARLEY, JAMES S. "Recent Developments in Cost Accounting and the 'Marginal Analysis,'" *Journal of Political Economy*, June, 1955, pp. 227–42.

This author's views—on which see our Chapter 7, Section 2—have developed under the influence of his intensive study of management accounting practices. There exists a considerable body of writings on these, and the author has been able to benefit also from co-operation with Albert J. Bergfeld, senior associate of Stevenson, Jordan, and Harrison, Inc., New York. The main thesis of the article is that more recently the analytical tools and decision methods suggested to management by their experts have become similar in essential ways to the tools and methods suggested by marginalist theories of profit maximization. Earley's terminology implies that in interpreting marginalism, he does not place the emphasis on continuity assumptions and on the solution of maximization problems with the aid of derivatives (hence, he refers to linear programming as a method broadly supporting his claim, though this is not the method with which Earley is concerned here). Earley seems right in drawing the distinction between marginalism and the contrary not by such criteria but according as profit maximization is suggested, or a rule of thumb in the nature of "average cost plus adequate profit margin" is proposed. The conventional textbook illustration is obviously an idealization, and maximization with reliance on continuity assumptions for all variables (including input ratios) is an oversimplification; business practices do, of course, have to take account of situations where the possible values of variables are at some distance from each other, and this in itself does not violate the spirit of marginalism, as long as approximations to profit maximization are sought.

The management accounting and advising practices discussed by Earley involve reliance on somewhat sophisticated variants of break-even charts for the various operations of multiproduct firms. The contribution of each operation to the profits of the firm can be read from these charts, on the assumption of constant average variable costs and of given product prices, and for various amounts of fixed costs which are allocated to the operations, with the proviso that wherever fixed costs are separable, the costs caused by the operation itself be assigned. Insufficient profitability suggests various adjustments in the profit-maximizing direction for the firm as a whole; it is said, however, that price adjustments do not belong among those most readily made. Nevertheless, the behavior of firms following such practices cannot simply be described by the sweeping formula called "average cost pricing."

In a subsequent article, "Marginal Policies of Excellently Managed Companies," *American Economic Review*, March, 1956, pp. 44–70, Earley published the results of a careful questionnaire study which points to the use of marginalist methods (in his sense) of a high proportion of the firms included in the survey.

(13) EDGEWORTH, F. Y. *Mathematical Psychics.* London: C. K. Paul & Co., 1881. 150 pp. Reprinted by the London School of Economics and Political Science, 1932.

Author referred to in our Chapter 3, Section 6. Using an analytical framework which includes neoclassical cardinal utility functions of the intuitive-introspective ("nonoperational") kind, Edgeworth introduced in this essay the concept of indifference functions. These have logical validity even in a system postulating cardinal utility. For example, by cutting through a three-dimensional utility surface, where the quantity of one commodity is measured along one axis, that of another commodity along the second axis, and utility is meaesured cardinally along the third axis, indifference curves can be obtained for the two commodities. It is *possible* to dispense with the cardinal measurability assumption and to build a theory of choice exclusively on tools, such as indifference functions, which imply merely ordinal utility (and which are operational even if the cardinal utility concept implied in the utility surface is not). But the development, along ordinal lines, of a consistently operational theory of choice for certain—i.e., for nonprobabilistic—prospects came much later (see item **24**, below); and full development of the operational concept of cardinal utility for probabilistic choice came even later (see item **38**, below). Edgeworth introduced indifference curves but did not dispense with the original nonoperational concept of cardinal utility. This may be regarded as the Jevons-Menger-Walras-Marshall concept of utility. See also items **20** and **39**, below.

(14) EDWARDS, WARD. "The Theory of Decision Making," *Psychological Bulletin*, July, 1954, pp. 380–417.

This is a comprehensive review of the theoretical literature dealing with decision making by mathematicians, economists, and psychologists over the past thirty years. Five areas of theory are considered: the theory of riskless choices, application of the theory of riskless choices to welfare economics, the theory of risky choices, the transitivity of choices, and the theory of games and decision making. In each area a description is given of the pioneer studies, the important criticisms and follow-ups of these studies, and the kinds of experiments undertaken to test the theories. A Bibliography containing more than two hundred items is appended to the article.

(15) EDWARDS, WARD. "Probability-Preferences among Bets with Differing Expected Values," *American Journal of Psychology*, January, 1954, pp. 56–67; and "Reliability of Probability-Preferences," *ibid.*, pp. 68–95.

The first of these two articles is a description of an experiment undertaken as a sequel to one dealing with probability preferences among bets with constant expected values. In his initial experiment, Edwards found that his subjects preferred certain bets to others of equal expected value, in circumstances suggesting that the subjects had a preference for numerical probabilities of certain magnitudes, and hence for given numerical probabilities compounded in specific ways rather than in others. In his next experiment, Edwards offered choices among bets differing slightly in expected value. He found that bets with higher expected values were not consistently chosen and related this to probability preferences manifested in the initial experiment. He argues that expected value and probability preferences are both determinants of choices among bets and that the smaller the difference becomes between expected values, the more important becomes probability preference as a determinant. In the second article the same conclusion is suggested after description of a series of further experiments also other variables.

(16) ELLSBERG, DANIEL; FELLNER, WILLIAM; and RAIFFA, HOWARD. "Symposium: Decisions under Uncertainty," *Quarterly Journal of Economics*, November, 1961, pp. 643–94.

Referred to in our Chapter 9.

Ellsberg's contribution criticizes the foundations of the purely probabilistic position, that is, the Savage axioms. The criticism is based mainly on observations of the behavior of individuals who were answering questions concerning the choices they would make if money prizes were set on various outcomes of risky processes. He suggests that it might be realistic to use a decision rule which combines the rule of subjective-probabilistic maximization with another rule. The latter involves maximization on the assumption that favorable events have the lowest probability which in the given circumstances they may subsequently turn out to have had. The author describes a method of weighting the two principles.

The present writer's contribution to the symposium contains an early version of the views expressed in this book. Raiffa, in his contribution, expressed himself in favor of the Savage axioms as normative guides. He also reported that subjects who were initially inclined to violate the Savage axioms (in "experiments" in which no money was at stake) came around to behavior consistent with the axioms when he called their attention to randomization possibilities. In view of our discussion in Chapter 6, Section 6, and in the Appendix to Chapter 6, it should be pointed out that all the hypothetical bets on which Raiffa is reporting here were "symmetrical." See also Harry V. Roberts' observations on the symposium and Daniel Ellsberg's reply in *Quarterly Journal of Economics*, August, 1962; K. R. W. Brewer's observations, *ibid.*, February, 1963; and the present writer's note, *ibid.*, November, 1963.

Earlier, at a conference held at the Carnegie Institute of Technology in 1955, Nicholas Georgescu-Roegen presented a paper which expressed the idea that probability judgments of different types are not strictly comparable. Generally speaking, the presentation suggested the same kind of noncomparability which is assumed by two of the contributors to the foregoing symposium. The papers read before this conference were published in 1958 by the Committee on Business Enterprise Research of the

Social Science Research Council as *Expectations, Uncertainty and Business Behavior* (ed. Mary Jean Bowman).

(17) FINETTI, BRUNO DE. "Sul divario tra valutazioni di probabilità per operazioni assicurative nei due sensi," published in Dott. A. Guiffrè (ed.), *Studi Sulle Assicurazioni* (Milano, 1963), pp. 531–68.

Relates to problem discussed in our Introduction, Section 4.

See also Jacques Dreze's earlier discussion of the same problem in *Economie Appliquée*, January–March issue, 1961 (pp. 55–70).

(18) FINETTI, BRUNO DE. "Probability: Philosophy and Interpretation," an article for the *International Encyclopedia of the Social Sciences*. Available at the present writing in mimeographed form.

Distinctions are drawn between three versions of the objectivistic and three versions of the subjectivistic view, and a discussion is presented of all of these.

(19) FINETTI, BRUNO DE. See item **30**, below, for the contribution which we mainly had in mind when speaking of the Ramsey–de Finetti–Savage line of development ("Prévision: Ses lois logiques, ses sources subjectives").

(20) FISHER, IRVING. *The Theory of Interest as Determined by the Impatience to Spend Money and the Opportunity to Invest It.* New York: Macmillan Co., 1930. 556 pp.

This is a revised version of the same author's *Rate of Interest*, published in 1907. Author referred to in our Chapter 3, Section 6. He defines indifference curves for individuals who are comparing the advantages of present with those of future income. It may be said of Fisher, as it was of Edgeworth (item **13**), that in spite of his having used indifference functions, he did not dispense with the neoclassical cardinal utility function. By describing in another contribution a method of utility measurement for choices among *certain*—i.e., nonprobabilistic—prospects, Fisher did *attempt* to make the cardinal utility concept operational; but as was pointed out in our *loc. cit.*, such attempts could not be successful for *certain* prospects because the Independence Axiom is not valid for simultaneously available goods (and to have the decision maker become faced with mutually exclusive prospects, it was necessary to develop a probabilistic theory of choice à la Ramsey–von Neumann–Morgenstern).

(21) FRIEDMAN, MILTON, and SAVAGE, L. J. "The Utility Analysis of Choices Involving Risk," in American Economic Association, *Readings in Price Theory* (Chicago: Richard D. Irwin, Inc., 1952), pp. 57–96. Reprinted from *Journal of Political Economy*, April, 1948, pp. 279–304.

Referred to in our Chapter 3, Section 12. The article is devoted primarily to the description of a von Neumann–Morgenstern utility function capable of accounting for types of behavior which have been generally observed. The authors describe the shape of the utility function of an individual who will pay a premium to avoid risk (as in the purchase of insurance) and at the same time will accept bets which are worse than actuarially fair (as in the purchase of lottery tickets). A utility function convex from above up to some income, then concave over a stretch, then again convex, is shown to be compatible with the mode of behavior just described, and with other types of behavior generally observed. Maximization of expected utility is postulated.

(22) GOOD, I. J. *Probability and the Weighing of Evidence.* London: Charles Griffin & Co., 1950. 119 pp.

In his opening chapter, Good proposes four measures by which to classify all probability theories, as follows:

1. The theory may or may not depend on a system of axioms.
2. Probability may or may not be "objective," in the sense that it may or may not be assumed to exist independently of the views of particular individuals.
3. The theory may be frequentist, or it may emphasize degrees of belief.
4. Probability may or may not be associated with numbers.

According to these measures, the theory that Good develops in the following chapters can be described as (1) axiomatic; (2) subjective, i.e., viewing probability as dependent on the views of individuals; (3) emphasizing degree of belief, i.e., nonfrequentist; and (4) primarily nonnumerical. Although Good uses terminology associated with Keynes and Jeffreys, he emphasizes the similarities between his theory and that of Bernard O. Koopman. This is because Keynes—and perhaps Jeffreys, too—expressed objectivistic views in the foregoing sense of the word (see the Introduction to our volume). Also, Jeffreys' theory is numerical, while Good wishes to recognize that individuals may be incapable of a judgment finer than one maintaining that the probability of an event to them is greater or smaller than that of another event (so-called "qualitative probability").

(23) GRAYSON, C. JACKSON. *Decisions under Uncertainty.* Boston: Harvard Business School, 1960. 402 pp.

The first section of Grayson's book is a description of how specific oil industry operators, with whom he maintained close contact while working on his study, make decisions about drilling. The second section is an examination of the feasibility of using utility theory to rationalize the decision-making process described in the first section. Rational decsions involve the arrangement of events and actions into a pay-off table in which a consequence (in monetary terms) is assigned to each act. The second step consists of the derivation of the utility function of the decision maker in view of the probability with which the project promises each pay-off. The decision maker then chooses that act which maximizes his expected utility. Grayson actually derives the utility functions of several operators based on answers to his questions concerning the willingness or unwillingness of the decision makers to accept the risk of drilling under various specified conditions which describe alternative (hypothetical) deals. Not all operators showed consistent utlity functions by the von Neumann–Morgenstern–Savage standards, and not all who showed inconsistencies felt (after proper explanations) that it was a requirement of reasonable behavior to adjust their hypothetical decisions so as to eliminate the inconsistencies. But Grayson found that in many cases the application of utility theory was considered a convincing and useful guide for the decision maker, and that it disclosed differences between the preference systems of various operators quite effectively.

(24) HICKS, J. R. *Value and Capital*. Oxford: Clarendon Press, 1938. 331 pp.

Author referred to in Chapter 3, Section 6, in connection with the ordinal concept of utility. This ordinal approach is presented in Part I of the book and in its Appendix. In articles published in the 1934 volume of *Economica*, Hicks and R. G. D. Allen developed the essentials of this analysis. They used indifference functions not simply as legitimate tools in a framework including cardinal utility functions, as had earlier writers (items **13, 20, 39**); but they relied exclusively on concepts—such as indifference functions—which are valid in a purely ordinal framework. Their system can be made "operational," while the neoclassical cardinal utility function was intuitive-introspective, i.e., lacked operational content. At about the same time, a concept of cardinal utility started developing which does have operational character (see item **41**, and particularly item **36**, below).

(25) HIRSHLEIFER, JACK. "The Bayesian Approach to Statistical Decision: An Exposition," *Journal of Business*, October, 1961, pp. 471–89.

This very helpful article begins with a brief and lucid general discussion of the difference between the Bayesian approach and the procedure which leads to significance tests based on rule-of-thumb subjectivism (to use our terminology). The latter procedure is often, but misleadingly, called "classical," mainly because in the present century such procedures became "conventional." The author goes along with this widely used terminology, though he clearly is an adherent of the Bayesian approach. The main part of the article illustrates the difference between the two methods with reference to a specific decision problem. On the basis of a sample of fifty units— and hence permitting fifty observations—a buyer needs to decide whether to accept delivery of, or to turn down, a shipment consisting of many units; he is to reach this decision given the fact that he considers it advantageous to accept delivery, rather than to turn down the shipment, *if and only if* the true ratio of defectives in the shipment as a whole is no more than 4 per cent. While the author calls his article merely "an exposition," it also contains observations of his own which bear on essentials.

(26) JEFFREYS, HAROLD. *Theory of Probability*. 3d ed. Oxford: Clarendon Press, 1961. 447 pp.

The theory developed in this book—the first edition of which was published in 1939—is well described by Good (see item **22**, above) as axiomatic; objectivistic by Good's criterion No. 2; nonfrequentist; and numerical. Jeffreys' work contains one of the significant early modern contributions to the theory of numerical probability interpreted as reasonable degree of belief. Two statements may be added here. In my opinion, Jeffreys' claim to the "objective" character of his concept of probability is a considerably qualified claim, and I am inclined to give this claim less emphasis than do some of his interpreters (see Jeffreys, *op. cit.*, pp. 405 ff.; and Good, above; and the Introduction to our volume). Secondly, I should like to call attention to the particularly effective way in which Jeffreys demonstrates the circularity of the frequentist definition of probability. It is only *almost always* true— i.e., true with unitary *probability*—that heads with an ideally unbiased coin tend to a relative frequency of 0.5. Hence, if the relative frequency of 0.5 is used for *defining* probability, then in such a definition one resorts to the concept of probability to define the concept of probability. On the other hand, we do not get involved in this vicious circle if we say that the more one gets convinced of a coin's being unbiased, the more reasonable it becomes to assign to heads the degree of belief 0.5 (see Jeffreys, pp. 62 ff).

(27) KEYNES, JOHN MAYNARD (Lord Keynes). *A Treatise on Probability.* London: Macmillan & Co., 1921. 466 pp.

Keynes's study is based on the conception of probability as a degree of rational belief. According to Keynes, probability expresses a relation between an unknown and a known set of propositions. It is always possible to deduce the unknown from the known proposition with a degree of certainty ranging from perfect impossibility to perfect certainty. The degree of rational belief represents the confidence which it is legitimate to place in the argument relating the known and unknown sets of propositions. A degree of rational belief must always be interpreted with reference to some given body of evidence. When so interpreted, it exists objectively. For the meaning of "objectivity" in this sense, see the comments on Good's work (item **22**, above), and also the Introduction to the present volume.

In Chapter III, Keynes deals with the question of whether all probabilities are numerically measurable. He concludes that it is not possible to quantify all probabilities because of the necessity, in evaluating certain probabilities, of considering multiple dimensions which cannot be weighted according to a common standard. Keynes attempts to clarify his argument in the following words:

> But the closest analogy is that of similarity. When we say of three objects A, B, and C that B is more like A than C is, we mean, not that there is any respect in which B is in itself quantitatively greater than C, but that, if the three objects are placed in an order of similarity, B is nearer to A than C is. There are also, as in the case of probability, different orders of similarity. For instance, a book bound in blue morocco is more like a book bound in red morocco than if it were bound in blue calf; and a book bound in red calf is more like the book in red morocco than if it were in blue calf. But there may be no comparison between the degree of similarity which exists between books bound in red morocco and blue morocco, and that which exists between books bound in red morocco and red calf. This illustration deserves special attention,

as the analogy between orders of similarity and probability is so great that its appre-
hension will greatly assist that of the ideas I wish to convey.

In Keynes's view, it is sometimes impossible even to determine
whether one conclusion is more or less probable than another conclusion.
There are many dimensions to consider in determining the probability of
such conclusions, and it is not possible to ascertain the weight that should
be accorded to each dimension. Therefore the relative probability of such
conclusions cannot be placed on a numerical scale.

(28) KEYNES, JOHN MAYNARD (Lord Keynes). *The General Theory of Employment, Interest and Money.* London–New York: Macmillan Co.,
1936, 403 pp.

Referred to in our Chapter 5, Section 2, in connection with the proposition that if at full employment the amount of planned investment tends to
be insufficient to match the planned savings of the public, then—effective
demand being insufficient for full employment—the economy tends to underemployment equilibrium. If we wish to employ the now usual concepts
of national accounting, we should substitute in the foregoing sentence the
words "planned investment plus government expenditures on goods and
services" for "planned investment," and the words "planned savings plus
net tax payments" for "planned savings." For the proposition that this theory
of underemployment equilibrium implies disregarding the Pigou-Patinkin
effect (which it is legitimate to do only if downward rigidity of the money-
wage and price level is assumed), see items **39** and **41**, below.

(29) KNIGHT, FRANK H. *Risk, Uncertainty and Profit.* Boston–New York:
Houghton Mifflin Co., 1921. 381 pp. Reprinted by the London School of
Economics and Political Science, 1933.

Views of the author on the distinction between risk and uncertainty
discussed in our Chapter 1, Section 4. This book contains a significant analysis of profit theory and its history.

(30) KYBURG, HENRY E., JR., and SMOKLER, HOWARD E. (eds.). *Studies in
Subjective Probability.* New York: John Wiley & Sons, Inc., 1964.
203 pp.

Six important items are reprinted in this volume; pieces written in a
foreign language were first translated into English. The editors wrote a very
useful introduction to the volume. The following are the six pieces.

John Venn, "The Subjective Side of Probability." This is taken from
chapter vi of Venn's *Logic of Chance* (1888), with some deletions.

Émile Borel, "Apropos of a Treatise on Probability." Reprinted from
the *Revue philosophique* (1924); concerned with Keynes's book on probability (item **27**), and critical of his views.

Frank Plumpton Ramsey, "Truth and Probability." See item **43**,
below.

Bruno de Finetti, "Foresight: Its Logical Laws, Its Subjective

Sources." This is a translation of the author's famous essay, "Prévision: Ses lois logiques, ses sources subjectives," from the *Annales de l'Institut Henri Poincaré*, Vol. VII, 1937. The essay is one of the important links in the Ramsey–de Finetti–Savage chain of development. However, the analysis makes no use as yet of utility functions, and hence part of the reasoning is acceptable by today's standards only if linear utility functions are assumed. This is because de Finetti's 1937 contribution to the theory of subjective probability preceded the von Neumann–Morgenstern book by several years, and the author was unacquainted with Ramsey's work. De Finetti explains here his concept of exchangeable events (in the original, he called them equivalent events; but in the present edition, he changes the terminology to "exchangeable," a term first suggested by R. M. Fréchet).

Bernard O. Koopman, "The Bases of Probability." Reprinted from the *Bulletin of the American Mathematical Society* (1940); originally an address delivered before a meeting of the American Mathematical Society. The author is axiomatizing a concept of probability which differs from that used in our analysis, and does not fit directly into the Ramsey–de Finetti–Savage framework, either. See, for example, Savage (item **45**, below, p. 39), where it is pointed out that in Koopman's conception a logical certainty always has a greater probability than an event which has unitary probability without being a logical certainty, though the same numerical probability attaches to the two. For the problem which Savage has in mind, we refer to our page 17, above; and to Axiom I on page 164 of the Koopman reprint now considered. It should be noted that Koopman's axioms relate to a *qualitative* (ordinal) concept of probability which is conceived of as a formal-logical relation between propositions, namely, the relation "not more probable than" and "not less probable than." A further assumption is then made to obtain *numerical* probabilities, which Koopman calls "(unfaithful) representations of relations belonging to the more far-reaching logical theory," and he says explicitly that "numerical probability gives but a blurred rendering of the ultimate logical relations between probability and certainty." In a frequentist context the concept of probability acquires empirical importance because scientists find it convincing to treat the limit values on which relative frequencies appear to converge as numerical probabilities.

Leonard J. Savage, "The Foundations of Statistics Reconsidered." Reprinted from Volume I of the *Proceedings of the Fourth Berkeley Symposium on Mathematics and Probability* (1961). In the author's words, this essay "particularly emphasizes the paths which some of us have followed to a position that may be called Bayesian or neo-Bayesian." The essay summarizes with great clarity the essentials of the Bayesian development.

The editors of the volume have prepared an excellent Bibliography. Separate bibliographies are appended to de Finetti's paper and to that of Savage.

(31) LAPLACE, PIERRE SIMON (Marquis de). *Théorie analytique des probabilités.* 1st ed., 1812, 3d ed.: Paris: Mme Ve Courcier, 1820. 506 pp. and supplements.

Referred to in our volume particularly in Chapter 1, Section 4, and in Chapter 2, Sections 1, 4, and 5, in connection with Laplace's "Bayesian" views. Item **32**, below, was included in the third edition of *op. cit.*

(32) LAPLACE, PIERRE SIMON (Marquis de). *Essai philosophique sur les probabilités.* 1st ed., 1814. From 1820 on, printed as Introduction to item **31**.

Contains the essentials of Laplace's views, as discussed in our volume. For a qualification to the acceptability of these views, see our Chapter 2, Section 1. Translated as *A Philosophical Essay on Probabilities*, with an introduction by E. T. Bell; translators, Frederick Wilson Truscott and Frederick Lincoln Emory (New York: Dover Publications, Inc., 1952; 196 pp.).

(33) LUCE, R. DUNCAN, and RAIFFA, HOWARD. *Games and Decisions.* New York: John Wiley & Sons, Inc., 1957. London: Chapman and Hall, 1957. 509 pp.

Referred to in our Chapter 7, Section 3. The subtitle of this important and widely used book calls it an "introduction and critical survey," but it is written on an advanced level. The book is concerned with utility theory, the theory of games, and the theory of subjective probability. Economic problems involving the principles of games of strategy receive the most attention. An extensive and very useful Bibliography is appended.

(34) MARKOWITZ, HARRY M. *Portfolio Selection: Efficient Diversification of Investments.* Cowles Foundation Monograph No. 16. New York: John Wiley & Sons, Inc., 1959. 344 pp.

This book is concerned with the principles governing the rational individual's selection of a portfolio. The work expands the analysis of efficient sets which Markowitz originally presented in a brief article in the March, 1952, issue of the *Journal of Finance* (reprinted as Cowles Commission Paper No. 60). The efficient set of portfolios, from which the individual will select a particular portfolio on the basis of his willingness to give up expected return for reduction of risk, is defined in terms of expected returns and variance. The definition of the efficient set corresponds to the principles expressed in our Chapter 5, Section 4, since risk aversion is assumed. In particular, it is demonstrated that when the individual's utility function is quadratic, the portfolio which maximizes the individual's expected utility will be an element of the efficient set as here defined. In a brief chapter dealing with subjective probability, based on the writings of Ramsey and Savage, Markowitz assumes that rational individuals will behave on the basis of personal probabilities exactly as they do on the basis of objective probabilities, i.e., they will conform to the expected utility maxim. Referred to in our *loc. cit.*, and *passim*.

(35) MARSHALL, ALFRED. *Principles of Economics.* 1st ed. London-New York: Macmillan Co., 1890. 8th ed., 1920. 754 pp.

Author referred to particularly in our Chapter 3, Section 6, in connection with the cardinal measurability of the utility of goods that have a very small weight in the budget of the consumer. The proposition is developed for choices among *certain* prospects (not among probabilistically appraised ones). Book III of *op. cit.* contains an outstanding presentation of his neo-classical utility theory.

(36) MISES, RICHARD VON. *Probability, Statistics and Truth.* 2d rev. English ed. prepared by Hilda Geiringer (New York: Macmillan Co., 1957; 244 pp.). 1st German ed.: *Wahrscheinlichkeit, Statistik und Wahrheit* (Vienna: Julius Springer, 1928).

Author refers to a 1919 publication of his as expressing the essentials of his position for the first time. In our volume, his views are discussed particularly in Chapter 2, Sections 2 and 3, and also *passim*.

(37) MOSTELLER, FREDERICK, and NOGEE, PHILIP. "An Empirical Measurement of Utility," *Journal of Political Economy*, October, 1951, pp. 371–404.

Referred to in our Chapter 3, Section 6. The authors describe gambling experiments which they performed to determine the utility of money curves for a small group of Harvard undergraduates and of Massachusetts national guardsmen. In addition to constructing a utility curve for each individual by discovering a set of indifference offers among bets, they attempt to predict future behavior toward risk on the basis of these curves, and to test their predictions. The authors discuss their assumptions and theoretical framework, the experimental methodology, and weaknesses of the experiment; and they give an appraisal of their results. A subject is assumed to have a preference for an act over another act if he chooses the first act in more than 50 per cent of the cases in which he is given a choice. For a different approach to discovering "preference," see item **11**, above.

(38) NEUMANN, JOHN VON, and MORGENSTERN, OSKAR. *The Theory of Games and Economic Behavior.* Princeton: Princeton University Press, 1944. 625 pp.

Referred to extensively in our volume in connection with the operational concept of cardinal utility. For the main characteristics of the axiomatic system underlying this concept, see our Chapter 3, Section 5; in *op. cit.*, see pp. 26–27 or, more generally, pp. 15–31; and see the Appendix of the second edition of the work (1947). We referred to the theory presented in *op. cit.* also in connection with the existence of a saddle point in the two-person zero-sum game, when mixed strategies are used. See our Chapter 6, Section 3.

(39) PARETO, VILFREDO. *Manuale di economia politica.* Milano: Società Editrice Libraria, 1906. 579 pp. French translation of latter by Alfred Bonnet: *Manuel d'économie politique* (Paris: V. Giard et E. Brière, 1909; 695

pp.). Cf. also Pareto's earlier book, *Cours d'économie politique* (2 vols.; Lausanne: F. Rouge; and Paris: Pichon, 1896–97).

Author referred to in our Chapter 3, Section 6, in connection with shift from the neoclassical (intuitive-introspective) concept of cardinal utility to the employment of tools with merely "ordinal" implications, a line of development which became completed with item **24**, above. The role of Pareto's work in this development is not strictly comparable to items **13** and **20**, above, because as his work was progressing, he became increasingly convinced of the advantages of relying on indifference functions and thus avoiding the measurability implications of the neoclassical utility functions. He did not, however, undertake the general reconstruction which was presented in Hicks's and Allen's work.

(**40**) PATINKIN, DON C. *Money, Interest and Prices.* Evanston, Ill.: Row, Peterson & Co., 1956. 510 pp. Second, revised edition about to be published.

Author referred to in our Chapter 4, Section 2, and in Chapter 5, Section 2, in connection with the proposition that in the event of unlimited flexibility of the general level of money wages *and* of prices (not of *real* wages), a tendency toward underutilization because of insufficient effective demand could not become realized. The decline in money wages and of prices would always increase the real value of the already existing liquid assets sufficiently to induce the amount of spending on goods and services which is required for full utilization. This is a proposition in macroeconomics, i.e., it disregards problems arising from the specalization of resources and from imperfect mobility (as did the classical Say's Law, which, however, was stated very imprecisely). Also, the stability problem cannot be settled by any simple generalization, as is shown by Patinkin. But at any rate, it seems safe to conclude that Keynesian underemployment equilibrium presupposes a rigid money-wage and price level (i.e., the absence of any downward flexibility). One may conclude also that a logically consistent "classical system" can be built on the assumption of unlimited flexibility, and presumably on further assumptions assuring the stability of equilibrium.

Patinkin called the favorable effect, on commodity demand, of an increase in the real value of the money stock (which results from falling money wages and prices) the *real-balance effect*. In our Chapters 4 and 5, we call it the Pigou-Patinkin effect. The effect which Pigou had explained in an earlier article develops in a model which is not identical with that of Patinkin; but our reasoning is concerned merely with the bare essentials of these effects, and on the level of these essentials it is permissible to omit the distinction. See also item **41**, below.

(**41**) PIGOU, A. C. "The Classical Stationary State," *Economic Journal*, December, 1943, pp. 343–51.

Author referred to in our Chapter 4, Section 2, and Chapter 5, Section 2. See foregoing reference to Patinkin.

The Pigou effect, as explained in this article, is deduced in a model in which we postulate (for the sake of argument) that there would be *stationary* equilibrium at *less than full-employment* if money wages and prices did not decline. But on the assumption of perfect money-wage and price flexibility, money wages and prices do decline, and thus the real value of the money stock increases. The demand for liquidity becomes saturated, and the amount of consumption expenditure rises to the level required for the stationary state at *full employment*. Pigou's argument was developed in response to Alvin H. Hansen, who argued that while the classical economists were right in maintaining that without technological progress, diminishing returns would gradually put an end to net investment and would lead into the stationary state, they were wrong in taking it for granted that in the stationary state there would be enough consumption expenditure to assure full employment (i.e., that a unitary average propensity to consume would establish itself *at full employment*). Pigou answered here that on the flexibility assumptions of classical reasoning the classics were entitled to their conclusions (although we may add that in the classical writings, one does not find an acceptable demonstration of this proposition, which nevertheless is valid). It follows that the Pigou effect, literally interpreted, relates to an economy in which, by postulate, there is no net investment, and hence the rise in the real value of the money stock induces merely additional consumption spending. Patinkin's model includes net investment, and his real-balance effect increases expenditures in general (item **40**, above).

(**42**) POLYA, GEORGE. *Patterns of Plausible Inference*, Vol. II of *Mathematics and Plausible Reasoning*. Princeton: Princeton University Press, 1954. 190 pp.

Genuinely probabilistic reasoning is distinguished from plausible inference. The latter may be based on pieces of evidence that are not comparable and, even where they are comparable, need not lead to numerical degrees of belief (but may merely result in the decision maker's attaching *more* or *less* credibility to one or the other event or proposition). Various interesting rules of plausible reasoning are suggested for these cases of merely qualitative appraisal. Some of these might be termed qualitative analogies to the theorems of quantitative or numerical conditional probability (i.e., to theorems which do, of course, involve quantitative judgments). The following is a particularly simple illustration of a set of rules which relate to qualitative appraisals: "If A implies B, and B is found true, then the credibility of A increases." I have chosen here a rather trivial illustration. Polya's suggestions include some propositions of appreciably greater complexity.

(**43**) RAMSEY, FRANK PLUMPTON. *The Foundations of Mathematics and Other Logical Essays*. Edited in 1930 by R. B. Braithwaite after the author's death, with a Preface by G. E. Moore. (Edition available to present author: New York: Humanities Press, 1950; 292 pp.)

Ramsey died in January, 1930, at the age of 26 years. He was a fellow of Kings College in Cambridge and lecturer in mathematics. This posthumously published volume contains some articles that had already been published and some pieces that had not been. The piece bearing most closely on our subject belongs in the second of these two groups. This is the essay on "Truth and Probability" (pp. 156–98), written in 1926. A large portion of the essay had, however, been read by the author to the Moral Science Club at Cambridge. See also item **29**, above.

The essay presents an operational theory of choice based on the concept of subjective probability and on the postulate of expected utility maximization. Ramsey limits his theory to ethically neutral propositions (about the occurrences of events). He also distinguishes between the utility of payoffs, on the one hand, and "eagerness or reluctance to bet," on the other, attributing the latter to the enjoyment or dislike of excitement. But in his analysis, this latter distinction is not operational, since the enjoyment or dislike of betting may show also in what we call standard processes (hence the phenomenon is inseparable from utility). In Chapter 3, Section 11, above, we discussed Ramsey's suggestions concerning the operational definition—and hence the "measurement"—of utility, and also of probability (in the sense of degree of belief). We may add that Ramsey's orientation was "axiomatic." Yet while he derived his statements from axioms, some of these are very near to the level on which a derived statement itself is located; i.e., some are formulated with a specific *ad hoc* application in mind, and thus postulates of a more elementary character become merged into one (are not formulated separately). This is avoided in the von Neumann–Morgenstern system, which, for example, does not postulate directly the maximization of expected utility but lets this develop as a by-product of the acceptance of more elementary axioms. However, Ramsey's essay precedes *The Theory of Games* by almost two decades, and it would be difficult to overstate its originality and its quality.

(44) RICHTER, MARCEL K. "Cardinal Utility, Portfolio Selection and Taxation," *Review of Economic Studies*, June, 1960, pp. 152–66.

Referred to in our Chapter 5, Section 4, in connection with the conditions that need to be satisfied for the mean-variance approach to be satisfactory in terms of utility theory.

(45) SAVAGE, LEONARD J. *The Foundations of Statistics.* New York: John Wiley & Sons, Inc., 1954. London: Chapman and Hall, 1954. 294 pp.

The most complete, unified presentation of what we called the purely probabilistic theory. Its most significant original contribution consists of the formulation of seven postulates about the ordering of "acts" and of the demonstration that individuals obeying these postulates display a behavior from which it is possible to read their numerical subjective probabilities and their utility functions. The book appraises also other decision theories (mostly critically), and it contains analyses of various problems in statistical theory. The Bibliography is exceedingly useful. See particularly our Chapter 6, Section 9; but the book and its author are referred to throughout the volume.

(46) SAVAGE, L. J.; BARTLETT, M. S.; BARNARD, G. A.; COX, D. R.; PEARSON, E. S.; and SMITH, C. A. B. *The Foundations of Statistical Inference.* London: Methuen & Co., 1962. New York: John Wiley & Sons, Inc., 1962. 112 pp.

Papers presented by these authors at a conference in London (1959). The opening paper by Savage develops an argument for rethinking basic problems of statistical theory in terms of Bayesian principles, recognizing the role of subjective prior probabilities. Most other contributors expressed preference for not formalizing subjective hunches as "probabilities" (but Smith should be interpreted differently). The volume contains also the observations of either other statisticians at the conference, and a good Bibliography.

(47) SCHELLING, THOMAS C. *Strategy of Conflict.* Cambridge: Harvard University Press, 1960. 303 pp.

Schelling's study presents an original analysis of basic concepts and analytical techniques useful in a consideration of conflict situations. He is concerned mainly with a special group of conflict situations, i.e., those in which the actors have a varying degree of mutual interest and thus must co-ordinate their behavior. Exploration of essential characteristics of non-zero-sum games is the author's primary intent. In the first part of the book the reader will find Schelling's well-known essay on bargaining, reprinted from the *American Economic Review*, June, 1956. This essay develops the hypothesis that bargaining advantages may be acquired by getting oneself into a position in which it can be maintained with *credibility*—which usually means truthfully—that acceptance of relatively unfavorable bargains has become practically impossible. The book contains many further valuable contributions. For a problem bearing on our analysis, see our Chapter 9.

(48) SCHLAIFER, ROBERT. *Probability and Statistics for Business Decisions: An Introduction to Managerial Economics under Uncertainty.* New York–Toronto–London: McGraw-Hill Book Co., Inc., 1959. 732 pp.

An outstanding textbook on, and a general survey of, Bayesian decision theory. Discusses the basic probabilistic processes which play a central role in frequentist approaches (Bernoulli process, binomial and Pascal probabilities, Poisson process, etc.). Uses the results in a Bayesian framework, with considerable emphasis on prior probabilities. Is subjectivistic in its basic orientation; but Part V (about sixty pages) deals briefly with some "objectivist" methods, particularly with significance tests and confidence intervals.

Howard Raiffa and Robert Schlaifer's *Applied Statistical Decision Theory* (Cambridge: Graduate School of Business Administration, Harvard University, 1961. 353 pp.) contains a more technical analysis of statistical problems bearing on Bayesian decision making.

(49) SHACKLE, G. L. S. *Decision, Order and Time in Human Affairs.* Cambridge: Cambridge University Press, 1961. 302 pp.

The latest and most complete presentation of this author's position. He suggests an alternative to the probabilistic and the semiprobabilistic position in decision theory. The author's views are nonprobabilistic for decisions concerned with sets of events not satisfying the frequentist criteria. For decisions of this sort—e.g., typical investment decisions—Shackle postulates that different potential outcomes are associated with different degrees of potential surprise, in the mind of the decision maker, and that his mind becomes focused mainly on the potentiality of a favorable and of an unfavorable outcome carrying relatively high degrees of surprise; the degrees of these surprises and the decision maker's inclinations as to how to weigh them against one another then lead to a ranking of his preferences.

(**50**) SHUBIK, MARTIN. *Strategy and Market Structure.* New York: John Wiley & Sons, Inc., 1959. 387 pp.

Referred to in our Chapter 7, Section 3. The purpose of this volume is, in the author's words, "to explore the nature of oligopolistic competition by using the methods of game theory." The bulk of the work is devoted to the description of monopolistic, duopolistic, and oligopolistic markets in terms of game theory principles. The first half of the book presents the essentials of game theory and constructs game models for nonco-operative markets. In the second half of his work, Shubik describes a new set of games called games of economic survival and proceeds to develop a dynamic theory of oligopoly.

(**51**) SMITH, CEDRIC A. B. "Consistency in Statistical Inference and Decision," *Journal of the Royal Statistical Society*, Series B, Vol. XXIII, No. 1, 1961, pp. 1–37.

Technical exposition of ideas which have some essential traits in common with those expressed by the present writer in item **16**, above, and in our present volume. Smith assumes that in situations in which probability judgments are controversial, many individuals are in the habit of assigning to prospects an upper pignic probability and a lower pignic probability (pignus = bet). By the least favorable odds which they are willing to accept, such individuals disclose their *lower* probability assignment to the event *on* which they place a bet and their *upper* probability assignment to the event *against* which they bet. Their pignic probability assignments are said to lie between such lower and upper bounds. For a rather exceptional type of person who is defined as "self-assured," the upper and lower probabilities generally coincide; and with respect to the special class of bets involving well-established frequency probabilities, all reasonable individuals are assumed to be "self-assured" (especially when they face a long series of trials). I have placed here a somewhat one-sided emphasis on sections of the article which bring out the similarities between Smith's modified Bayesian views and those presented in this volume. Discussion papers appended to the article include that of G. A. Barnard (who is generally skeptical about decision theories postulating rational "maximization of utility"); of D. R. Cox, I. J.

Good, D. V. Lindley, D. J. Finney, P. Armitage, M. C. Pike, and D. F. Kerridge; and of F. J. Anscombe, who calls attention to the inapplicability of Bayesian views to decision problems involving hypotheses that do not specify parameter values properly (or where doubt exists as to whether all relevant hypotheses have been specified). For this latter problem, see also our Introduction; our Chapter 2, Sections 4 and 5; and our Chapter 8, Section 2.

(52) TOBIN, JAMES. "Liquidity Preference as Behavior Towards Risk," *Review of Economic Studies*, February, 1958, pp. 65–86.

The purpose of this article is to provide a new explanation for the relationship between the demand for cash and for securities, on the one hand, and the interest rate and standard deviation of yields, on the other. Along with Markowitz's contributions, this article has inspired much new research on the problem of portfolio selection. Tobin assumes that the investor, when deciding how much of his cash to invest in a security with guaranteed interest yield:

1. Estimates subjective probability distributions of capital gains and losses.
2. Evaluates prospective increases in wealth in terms of a cardinal utility function.
3. Ranks preferences according to expected utility.

He shows how the demand for cash of the risk averter—here an individual with a quadratic utility function–depends on the interest rate.

Tobin also deals with the effects of monetary and fiscal policy on the individual's demand for cash and for securities. He shows that, given the utility functions assumed in the analysis, a tax levied on interest income and capital gains with complete loss offset will lead to a reduction in the demand for cash at given rates of interest. See also our Chapter 7, Section 4.

An earlier piece of analysis based on the idea that investors, guided by their indifference functions, choose from among projects that for any given expected mean return possess a standard deviation no greater than any other project with the same mean, and for any given standard deviation possess a mean no smaller than any other project with the same standard deviation, is found in Chapter 15 of Friedrich and Vera Lutz, *The Theory of Investment of the Firm* (Princeton, N.J.: Princeton University Press, 1951, 253 pp.).

INDEX

A

Acts
defined, 11
preference ordering of, 159–65
Addition rule (for probabilities), 73–74
Alchian, Armen, 211
Allais, Maurice, 211
Allais-paradox, 211–12
Allen, R. G. D., 84, 86, 222, 228
"Almost always" convergence in probability
theory, explained, 17, 225
Alternative Hypothesis, 61–63, 65–67, 195–
97
Anscombe, F. J., 233
Armitage, P., 233
Arrow, Kenneth J., 30, 212–13
Average cost pricing, 173, 177-80, 217
Average revenue, 178
Average total cost, 178–79
Average variable cost, 178–79
Axiomatic foundations of probability and of
utility, 73–75, 81–84, 92, 159–65, 227

B

Bacon, Nathaniel T., 214
Barnard, G. A., 231, 232
Bartlett, M. S., 231
Bayes, Thomas, 1, 25, 26, 39, 48, 49, 213
Bayes's theorem, 50, 53, 57, 74, 78–79, 201
Bayesian theory, 26–27, 49–70, 196–99, 200–
202, 222, 231
Bergfeld, Albert J., 217
Bernoulli, Daniel, 25, 84, 101, 102, 104, 105,
213
Bernoulli, Jacques, 25, 39, 44, 213
Bernoulli, Nicolas (older cousin of Daniel),
101–3, 108, 213
Bernoulli, Nicolas (brother of Daniel), 213
Bernoulli process, 42
Bet acceptance boundary, 87–88
Binomial distribution, 42–43
Binomial theorem, 42
Böhm-Bawerk, Eugen von, 117, 214
Borel, Émile, 224
Bowman, Mary Jean, 220
Brewer, K. R. W., 9, 219

C

Capital gains, 138, 187
Carnap, Rudolf, 214
Central Limit Theorem, 43
Churchman, West C., 215
Coherence, in the decision-theoretical sense,
150, 151, 169
Compensating variation (Hicksian), 86
Complement, the logical concept of, defined,
73
Complementarity, 82, 86, 161, 220
Compound events, 68, 172
Consistency requirements of semiprobabilis-
tic behavior, 36, 146–55
Constant column axiom, 82
Consumer
outlay, 65, 85, 86, 129, 229
surplus (Marshallian), 85, 124, 137
Continuous probability distributions, 43, 55,
121–23, 175
Corrected probabilities, 155–59
Costs, 173, 178–80, 217
Cournot, Augustin, 180–81, 214–15
Cournotesque results (in oligopoly), 180–86
Covariance, 134
Cox, D. R., 231, 232
Cramer, Gabriel, 84, 101, 104–6, 108

D

Davidson, Donald, 94, 215–16
Decision weights, defined, 11
Decisions, defined, 11
Demand
curve, 174, 176
elasticity, 178
Deming, W. Edwards, 213
Derber, Charles K., 211
Diversification, 114–15, 130–37, 187–91,
226, 233
Dolbear, Frank T., 87, 216–17
Dominance, in the game—theoretical sense,
182
Drèze, Jacques, 220
Duopoly; see Oligopoly

E

Earley, James S., 177, 217

235

V

W

Z

*This book has been set in 12 and 10 point Inter-
type Garamond, leaded 1 point. Chapter numbers
and titles are in 18 point Futura Medium. The
size of the type page is 27 by 45½ picas.*